ROB 2

Contributions to the History of Geology

Volume 1
American Mineralological Journal
. . . to Elucidate the Mineralogy and Geology of the United States
Conducted by Archibald Bruce
With an introduction by John C. Greene
Foreword by George W. White
Volume 1 (all published) 270 p. + index. New York 1810-1814

Volume 2
C. F. Volney
View of the Soil and Climate of the United States of America
Translated, with occasional remarks by C. B. Brown
With an introduction by George W. White
XXVIII, 446 p. + 2 maps + 2 plates. Philadelphia 1804

Volume 3
Monthly American Journal of Geology and Natural History
Conducted by G. W. Featherstonhaugh
With an introduction by George W. White
Volume 1 (all published) 576 p. Philadelphia 1831-1832

Volume 4
Nicolaus Steno 1638-1686
The Prodromus of Nicolaus Steno's Dissertation concerning a Solid Body enclosed by Process of Nature within a Solid
An English version with an introduction and
explanatory notes by John Garrett Winter
With a foreword by William H. Hobbs
With an introduction by George W. White
University of Michigan, Humanistic Studies. Vol. XI, part 2. 1916 and 1930

Volume 5
James Hutton
System of the Earth, 1785; Theory of the Earth, 1788; Observations on Granite, 1794; together with Playfair's Biography of Hutton.
With an introduction by Victor A. Eyles
With a foreword by George W. White

Volume 6
David Thomas
Travels through the Western Country in the Summer of 1816
With an introduction by John W. Wells
With a foreword by George W. White

CONTRIBUTIONS
TO THE
HISTORY OF GEOLOGY

Edited by

George W. White
Research Professor of Geology
University of Illinois

Volume 6

TRAVELS THROUGH
THE WESTERN COUNTRY

IN

THE SUMMER OF 1816

by

DAVID THOMAS

(Facsimile of the 1819 Edition)

Introduction by

JOHN W. WELLS
Cornell University

Foreword by

GEORGE W. WHITE
University of Illinois

Notes on Thomas's Geological Observations
by

JOHN W. WELLS AND GEORGE W. WHITE

HAFNER PUBLISHING COMPANY
1970

CONTENTS

NOTE

This facsimile has been reproduced by photo offset. The printing and paper of the original edition of 1819 is of such poor quality and has deteriorated to such an extent, that, although several copies were used, some pages appear to be smudged. This was unavoidable, even though the best modern methods of reproduction were used.

HAFNER PUBLISHING COMPANY

Editor's Foreword

by

GEORGE W. WHITE

David Thomas's Travels through the Western Country has long been a prized book of Americana. It is an important source of scientific and agricultural information about the then new states, which were just being settled, and a mine of information about the original aspect of the country, its plants and animals, which Thomas described in scientific terms and related to bedrock, soil and drainage. The book has never been reprinted, although excerpts have been reprinted in certain anthologies. A part of his account of the Pennsylvania portion of his observations has been published by Harpster (1938, p. 267-274) and a more extensive selection of his observations in Indiana by Lindley (1916, p. 42-135).*

Thomas's book is included in this series of reprints of geological works because it is one of the earliest, not only to describe, but also to speculate on the origin of many of the geological features in western New York, northwestern Pennsylvania, Ohio and Indiana. Other travelers such as Thaddeus Harris, Christian Schultz, and Thomas Ashe, after reaching Pittsburgh, had made their way to the West by way of the Ohio River, but Thomas traveled entirely by land, observing and reporting on regions and features which had not previously been observed by anyone of scientific ability.

Among the noteworthy observations and speculations of David Thomas were those on morphology of rivers; character of beach sands, both recent and consolidated in sandstone; origin of coal and reasons for differences between bituminous and anthracite coal; scepticism of "universal formations" of Werner; appearance and causes of caverns in limestone terrain; and the economic value

*References are to publications listed in the Bibliography.

ix

of many of the mineral resources he observed. His descriptions of some of the strata he saw are so good that they can be regarded as the first notice of formations which now carry "official" names.

In addition to geological observations, Thomas made penetrating comments on Indian mounds, climate and weather, health and diseases, the state of agriculture and soil productivity, and comparative times and rates for freight haulage. His interest in origin of the original inhabitants of North America is shown by his very long note on this subject.

Dr. John W. Wells, Professor of Geology at Cornell University, who has provided the Introduction, has long been an admirer of David Thomas and has investigated the history of Thomas and his family. He has an intimate acquaintance with the territory Thomas traversed in New York and much of that in Pennsylvania and Ohio, through his earlier academic locations at the University of Pittsburgh and at the Ohio State University. Professor Wells has tracked down Thomas's extensive references to contemporary literature and assembled them in the Bibliography.

Thomas's route is shown on a map here included. We are indebted to Mr. Leslie Lewis, geologic cartographer, for constructing this map. The physiographic diagram for Indiana, which shows the rock units and regions Thomas crossed and described so well, has been made available for reproduction through the courtesy of Dr. John B. Patton, State Geologist of Indiana.

The facsimile reproduction of each page has been enlarged by twenty per cent in order to make the original small print somewhat more readable. As Thomas's original text does not indicate those places for which he provided notes, these are shown in the present reprinting by a "T" and the number of the page on which Thomas's note is located. Notes for this edition by Professor Wells and the Editor are indicated by a number on the margin at the appropriate place. These follow Thomas's text.

Introduction

by

JOHN W. WELLS

In 1805 a young Pennsylvania Quaker came to Cayuga County in central New York and settled on a 400 acre tract of choice land east of the hamlet of Levanna, near Aurora, on the east shore of Cayuga Lake. He had previously visited this region in 1790 when he and his cousin Joseph Richardson rode on horseback from Providence, Pennsylvania. Richardson shortly after settled near Levanna and cleared land afterwards acquired by David Thomas, who was an uncommon type of settler. He was born June 5, 1776, the son of a Quaker and received a good education. After his marriage in 1801 he moved to "Elklands" ("Beach Woods") in Lycoming County, Pennsylvania (now Camp Brule Lake, Sullivan County) where he settled on several hundred acres, but after four years he found that in spite of good land and fine scenery he was too far from markets and the "various facilities of civilization" and moved to central New York where he lived for nearly 50 years on his farm "Great Field."* In 1853 he moved to nearby Union Springs, taking a large part of his collection of rare plants and where he died November 5, 1859, aged 83. "IIis life was unsullied and his death marked by that positive serenity and composure well befitting the character of a Christian gentleman" (J. J. Thomas, 1888, p. 53).

While David Thomas was primarily a successful agriculturalist and especially a horticulturist, his interests and labors ranged far beyond the soil. He was a strong member of the local gathering of the Society of Friends and at the Separation in 1828 he remained with the Orthodox group. He was an opponent of slavery and

---

*"Great Field," about a mile east of Levanna, is now derelict, only the overgrown foundations of the house remain, and traces of David Thomas linger only in a huge arborvitae and masses of snowdrops every spring.

wrote on the subject. A reader of poetry, as evidenced by the many apt quotations in the Travels, and while living on the borders of Elk Lake he found time to write at least two poems, *The Wilderness* and *The Wild Duck*. According to Emily Howland (1882), in her history of the Quakers in Cayuga County, he opened a school near Poplar Ridge, east of his farm. He had considerable medical knowledge that stood his family and neighbors in good stead amongst the malarial fevers and "cold plagues" of those early days; he insisted that his assistants on the Erie Canal drink only boiled water, and his writings show him to have been keenly aware of many of the causes of ill health then so common in the back country.

After developing a sustaining farm by 1810 he began to collect native and exotic plants in his gardens. He was the pioneer nurseryman in western New York, and by 1830 he had the most extensive and valuable collection of fruit trees west of the Hudson. Not only did he continually improve his stock and sell plants and scions widely, but he also studied intensively their cultivation and wrote on horticulture in general as a constant correspondent and mainstay of such early agricultural periodicals as Luther Tucker's *The Genesee Farmer** (founded 1830), *The Cultivator* (established 1834, forerunner of *The Country Gentleman*), and as early as 1819 when Solomon Southwick began to publish his short-lived but lively *Ploughboy* in Albany, there appeared in its columns David Thomas's presidential address at the annual meeting of the Agriculture Society of Cayuga County in which he analyzed the effects of weeds on crop production and recommended that no premium be given to any cultivator who permitted these nuisances to grow in his fields. U. P. Hedrick, in his *History of Agriculture in New York* (1933, p. 60-61) regarded Thomas as "one of the great pomological writers of the country." Thomas's only contribution to formal plant taxonomy was his description in 1831 of a new species of elm, *Ulmus racemosa* (cork, hickory or cliff elm).

---

*The first six volumes contained some 800 articles and notices by Thomas. His son, John Jacob Thomas (1811-1895), a well-known and prolific writer on horticultural subjects, edited amongst others *The New Genesee Farmer and Garden Journal* and the *Illustrated Annual Register for Rural Affairs and Cultivation Almanac*. Another son, Joseph (1811-1891) was a distinguished orientalist and lexicographer.

And to him we owe one of the best contemporary accounts of the mode of construction of the famous cobblestone houses of western New York, published in the *New Genesee Farmer* in 1841.

Thomas had probably met DeWitt Clinton when the latter travelled through central New York in 1810 as a member of a commission appointed by the state to investigate possible routes for a canal from tidewater to Lake Erie, and when the *Travels* was published in 1819 Clinton subscribed for 12 copies. He is said to have remarked "the man who wrote that book will make an excellent canal engineer." Governor Clinton recognized capable, practical men and had long had his eye on Thomas when he appointed him chief engineer on the western section of the Erie Canal in 1820. Thomas now appears not as an upstate farmer, but as an engineer and surveyor who turned to this task as successfully as any of the other amateur builders of the famous ditch. When questions arose as to the correctness of his levels between Rochester and Lockport he had his assistants run two lines the 60 miles to Lockport and back. The result was a difference of only ⅔ of an inch from Thomas's level. Later, when great dispute arose whether Black Rock or Buffalo should be the western terminus of the canal, Thomas was involved in a protracted wrangle amongst various interests that was finally settled in favor of the site (Buffalo) he had argued for from the beginning. He was also chief engineer in 1825-26 for the short canal linking Seneca and Cayuga Lakes, and for the Welland Canal in the first year of its construction.

On May 21, 1816, David Thomas and his friend Jonathan Swan, an Aurora Quaker merchant and inventor, left on a journey to explore the Wabash lands in the New Purchase. With the close of the last Indian war in 1811 and the admission of Indiana to statehood in 1816 immigration to the former territory was rapidly increasing. Their route took them for two months across western New York to Buffalo, along the shore of Lake Erie into Pennsylvania where they turned south through Meadville to Pittsburgh, where they remained ten days examining the budding industries and coal mines. Thence they travelled slowly across Ohio by way of Warrenton, Zanesville, Greenfield, and Cincinnati where they crossed the Ohio briefly into Kentucky, then into Indiana at Rising Sun and across the southern part of the state through Madison, New Lexington, Salem, and Washington, to Vincennes. From

xiii

Vincennes they made several excursions up the Wabash valley as far as Fort Harrison, 3 miles north of Terre Haute ("Tar Holt") and the vicinity of Spring Creek, where Thomas's diary ends on July 14.

On his return from the Wabash, Thomas evidently decided to publish his record of the outward part of the journey, and during the next two years added many footnotes, 133 pages of "Additional Notices of the Western Country" and more "Additional Notes" before the *Travels* was published in 1819. The diary is an honest, matter-of-fact and copious day-to-day account of the weather, road conditions, state of agriculture, the soils, rocks, minerals, fossils, prehistoric remains, plants—his strong botanical interests show in his frequent lists of plants and comparisons with the flora of Scipio*—character and types of people. Although presumably a sober-minded Quaker he could not refrain from quoting poetry on occasion and observes (p. 146) that a "just medium between cool reserve and colloquial freedom, in recording travels, is a *desideratum.*" He would not have agreed with the reviewer of Darby's *Tour* in the *American Magazine and Critical Review* (vol. 4, April, 1819, p. 402) that "it is not enough that a tourist merely write good sense, and favour us with valuable information. He must adorn his subject with the graces and embellishments of style: variegated with incident and anecdote, to prevent monotony. . . ."

Thomas's *Travels* must have appealed to pioneer-minded, restless settlers of central New York, not as one of the hope-inspiring "Emigrant's Guides" of the time, but as a factual account of conditions good and bad as he saw them. Today one reads the *Travels* not from the viewpoint of a prospective settler, but as a picture of the times and for its glimpses of natural history as seen through the eyes of an experienced botanist-horticulturist and self-taught geologist.

*At this time (1816) Thomas's farm was in the township of Scipio, subsequently reduced so that after 1823 it was in the town of Ledyard.

TRAVELS

THROUGH

THE WESTERN COUNTRY

IN

THE SUMMER OF 1816.

INCLUDING

NOTICES

OF THE

NATURAL HISTORY,   ANTIQUITIES,
TOPOGRAPHY,   AGRICULTURE,
COMMERCE   AND   MANUFACTURES:

WITH A MAP OF THE WABASH COUNTRY,

NOW SETTLING.

——◆——

BY DAVID THOMAS.

——◆——

AUBURN, (N. Y.)

PRINTED BY DAVID RUMSEY.
···········
1819.

ADVERTISEMENT.

——◆❖◆——

THE journey, to which the following pages relate was undertaken with a view to explore the *Wabash Lands* in the *New Purchase;* and performed in company with JONATHAN SWAN, Merchant, of *Aurora*, to whose observations I have often been indebted. The intermediate country was an object of less attention.

Believing that in a transient visit, many important facts would escape our notice, I applied to several intelligent persons residing near that river, and now acknowledge with gratitude the liberal assistance of MO_SES HOGGATT, *Honey creek Prairie*, JOSEPH RICHARD-SON, *York*, (Illinois) JOHN D. HAY and JAMES B. BENNETT of *Vincennes*. Many of those interesting remarks will be found in the *Additional Notices*.

I am also indebted to JAMES BENNETT of *Junius*, Seneca county, (N. Y.) for every assistance which a sojournment of several months in that vicinity, enabled him to afford. By his unwearied attention, many defi_ciencies have been supplied; and sketches of the state of commerce and the progress of improvement will be brought down to the 2d mo. 1818.

The *Map* has been drawn from the best materials.
Three different drafts were procured, and the situations
of places have been carefully marked. It will be perceived that the late surveys prove the course of the
Wabash river, &c. on former maps, to be erroneous.

DIARY

OF A

JOURNEY

Through the western parts of New-York and Pennsylvania; the northern projection of Virginia; the southern parts of Ohio; the northern parts of Kentucky, and the interior and western parts of Indiana.

———

5 *mo.* 21.—WE left home. If such sensations as we experience in the moment of departure, were interwoven with existence, an enterprize like this could never be undertaken. Happily, by the law of our nature, the reverse is decreed, and a change to scenery less endeared to us, gradually restored the mind to its former tone.

The season has been unusually cold, and vegetation proportionally retarded. The petals of the peach, and of the May duke cherry have fallen, while the apple, the pear, and the red cherry are in bloom. The leaves of the beech and of the maple are green, but not fully expanded. This note will be useful in comparing climates.

The first part of our intended route, is, northward from *Aurora*,* down the lake to *Cayuga Bridge*; and thence, westward, through *Canandaigua, Batavia* and *Buffalo*, to *Erie* in Pennsylvania.

The *aluminous schist,* or clay slate, which forms, or supports the subsoil in the southern parts of our county, and which constitutes the shore of this lake wherever it is precipitous, crumbles when exposed to the at-

* This village is situate on the lake shore, 12 miles south of Cayuga bridge. It consists of about 50 houses, an incorporated academy, a female boarding school, 2 stores of merchandize, and a post-office.

mosphere. In some places, indeed, its reduction is
complete, and in the sides of the road, we saw fine
dark earth under stiff yellow loam mixed with gravel.
In this process, water appears to be the chief agent.
Where small springs, after soaking the banks of slate,
break forth, parcels of tough clay are found surrounded
by the rock; and in level lands, where this substance
has been slightly sheltered by later alluvions, and has
received the surplus water of the adjoining grounds, every trace of petrification, to the depth of twelve or fifteen inches, has disappeared.

The colour of this earth is variable, and the paler
kinds have been much used as substitutes for lime, in
white-washing.

1   This rock is found both to the east and to the west,
and is situate immediately south of THE GREAT LIME-
STONE LEDGE which forms the *dam* of the *Cayuga*
and of all its parallel lakes. Like all clay slates, it is
an alluvial deposition, and abounds with the distinct
remains of many species of shell fish, which, in places,
are so numerous as to constitute no inconsiderable part.
Hence it effervesces with acids, and is in strictness a
marl. Mixed with the soil that covers it, the mass
parts more easily before the plough, and doubtless, on
some soils, it might be profitably employed as a manure.

One mile north of *Levana,** a rock, of firmer texture,
projects from the bank, in horizontal strata, and differs
from the slate in containing a larger portion of lime.
The hardness appears to depend on the proportion of
this earth.

To the north, within two miles of these banks, limestone of considerable purity, and in regular masses, is
found in abundance. This is the *Great Ledge.* Though
no particular inequality of surface indicates its southern boundary, yet, at *Long Point,* where these rocks
first appear on the shore, the lake suddenly diminishes

---

* The site of this decayed village is uncommonly beautiful;
but the progress of improvement was incidentally checked at an
early period, and no effectual means have since been employed
for its revival.

in depth; and in the severer *frosts of winter, the ice, which only covers the shallow parts, by extending across from that point in a north-west direction, conspicuously marks out its border.

The bottom of Cayuga Lake, to the south of this line, is below the surface of Lake Ontario; and were this *Ledge* removed, an inlet of that vast basin would be formed, of sufficient depth, for vessels of the greatest burden.

The village of *Union Springs,* six miles north of Aurora, derives its name from two fountains, fifty rods apart, with streams sufficient for mills. The lake road passes near them on the east, and forms the principal street. There are twenty dwelling houses; three stores of merchandize, and a post-office. It was first regularly laid out into lots in the year 1813.

We were detained half an hour at this village, by a thunder shower from the south-west. I believe no instance of these storms from the north-west is known, except when the atmosphere has been previously loaded with vapour. The latter wind is destitute of sensible moisture. Frequently, however, it condenses the exhalations from our lakes, and of those which have been wafted hither from other points of the compass. Rains, from that quarter, result from such retrogade movements, and a clear sky generally attends the calm that succeeds.

Salt and sulphur springs rise adjacent to this village, but none of these are deemed valuable for mineral properties, and would scarcely merit notice, except as characteristics of the *Limestone Ledge. Plaster,* of the cockscomb kind, though white or transparent, is found plentifully on the beach after high winds, it having been washed by the waves from the bank where it lay embedded; and, by digging, it may be procured at a considerable distance from the shore. The rose-colour of the French cockscombs is ascribed to iron.

---

* It is only in the severest frosts of winter, that the lake freezes over at Levana. This is a very rare occurrence.

3   About one mile north of this spot, lies the first of the celebrated *plaster quarries,* from which the Susquehanna country has received such large supplies. This fossil, unlike that from France or Nova Scotia, is a dark grey, and when ground assumes a dull ash colour.   Some spe-

T   cimens contain chrystallized sulphur of a fine transpa-
243   rent yellow, and at *Thompson's quarry,*two miles north-north-east, the quantity of this mineral is so great as to trickle down, when fires are kindled near the plaster. The strata of these rocks are nearly horizontal.

East-Cayuga, six miles below Union Springs,has some good buildings, but Improvement has not advanced rapidly, although the *Great Western Turnpike* forms the principal street.   This village is chiefly situate on the western slope of a ridge, from which considerable quantities of plaster have been taken.   The rock, however, is very unequal in quality.   In quarrying, the impure parts were not rejected with sufficient attention; and though some of a good quality might be procured at this place, it is so sunk in reputation as to be no longer found in market.

T   From *Cayuga Bridge,* which is three hundred and
247   sixteen rods in length, we have a fine prospect of the lake.   The irregularity of its shores adds much to its beauty.   From this spot it extends south-south-east
4   about thirty-five miles, but the south half of that distance is hidden by hills.

West-Cayuga is embellished by the *Toll-House,* through which all who cross the bridge must necessarily pass.   This village consists of fifteen or twenty houses, but improvements are nearly at a stand.

We were pleased to observe, that the directors of the great western turnpike were repairing this road, by covering it with broken stone.*   For fifteen years past, in

---

* This remark has now become stale, for these attempts have long since terminated.   The teamster, who has worked his way 1 rough mud to the toll-gate which he finds closed against him,

rainy weather, it has been literally a bed of mortar, and even now we mean to be sparing of our commendations. Considering the great number of light waggons that stop at their toll-gates, we think a covering of earth or gravel, might be afforded to reduce the incessant jolting.

We crossed the *Outlet* of the *Seneca Lake* nearly two and a half miles west of Cayuga-Bridge. Rapids, in the stream at this place, render the navigation difficult, and *Locks* have been commenced; but excellent mill seats are numerous, and some are finely improved.

Here we met an Indian man and woman. Her load was so bulky, that to support it, she held up both hands to her head, and yet on the top was laid a rifle, while her *lord* stepped on before her, unincumbered. It reminded me of *Marius's* mules. The lot of woman has always been hard where mere animal force is the chief object of admiration, and this applies to all savages.

The road from *Seneca Falls*, westwardly, is near the river. The surface is irregular, in places low and wet, and the arable lands are harder and less productive than those a few miles to the south.

The new buildings, which have been erected at *Seneca Falls*, and on the north side of the outlet near the *Scauyz*, within two years, excited my surprise on account of the numbers; and presented a striking contrast to the stationary aspect of *East* and *West-Cayuga*. Here we find mills; and the influence of these in gathering villagers, has often been remarked. In this country, *log* buildings are commonly restricted, with much propriety of taste, to the first openings of the wilderness; *stone* is seldom placed in walls above the cellar; *brick* is more frequently employed; but *frame* houses well painted, chiefly form the dwellings of our citizens, and more especially constitute villages. The

will make a sad response to this commendation; and the drivers of light carriages have small cause to complain of rough pavements. The demand of the gate keeper is amply sufficient to prove this road under the care of an incorporated company.

former of these two, called *Seneca,* is at the intersection
of the *Northern Turnpike,* two and a half miles from
Cayuga-Bridge; and the latter, which now has assumed
the name of *Waterloo,** is three miles further west.

We travelled 19 miles.

5 *mo.* 22.—APPROACHING the north end of the Seneca Lake, we found the surface of the land chiefly to
consist of swamps and of sand-banks.   This tract comprises all the west of *Junius,* and the east part of *Phelpstown,* which lie to the north.   This land is evidently a
deposition of more recent date from the *Limestone Ledge,*
much of which lies buried ; for we observe that quarries of this stone, and the marly soil that attends it,
are found, wherever the channels of the brooks are deepened into chasms, and frequently between the ridges
of sand.

Much of the revolutions of this globe must lie forever
beyond our research ; but the mind contemplates with
eagerness the traces of a period when matter was obedient to impulses which have ceased to exist.   Whether
we indulge in conjecture respecting the cause, or refrain,
at least two facts appear certain :—that the summits of
our mountains have been swept by a *deluge,* and that
much of the surface of this country owes its form to that
extraordinary movement.   Though the *schistus formation,* noticed yesterday, is generally covered by foreign
materials, the greatest violence of that flood was ex-
erted on the district that borders the south shore of
Lake Ontario.   Hills of earth, pebbles, and rounded
stones were arranged by the same surges, which, sweeping out basins for the narrow lake and the morass, have
given to that region, features, peculiar and astonishing.

5   The parallelism of these ridges is nearly preserved,
and the average variation is about ten degrees to the
left of the meridian.   As this determines *the line of
the current,* it becomes an interesting enquiry to ascertain which way it flowed.   Though the country declines

---

* This has since become the capital of Seneca County.

to the north, it appears that this deluge had an opposite direction.

The principal facts that support this opinion, are, that DETACHED PARTS OF EVERY ROCKY STRATUM WHICH IS UNCOVERED, FROM THE SHORE OF LAKE ONTARIO TO THE NORTH BOUNDS OF GENOA, ARE SCATTERED TO THE SOUTH OF THESE RANGES; and that SELDOM, IF EVER, HAVE ANY SUCH FRAGMENTS BEEN FOUND TO THE NORTH. An enumeration is subjoined.

1. The lowest visible stratum of this district, and which is discoverable in places along the margin of the lake, is a *red sand stone, (amygdaloid?)* Detached rocks, on the gravel hills in that vicinity, are numerous, and some are found in the southern parts of Cayuga county.

2. A range of *limestone entirely composed of shells,* appears about three miles to the south. It is an incumbent stratum. On the east side of *Great Sodus Bay,* the chrystals are remarkably fine, and it is classed as a marble. I have observed some on the hills, above the quarries, but the fragments are not widely scattered.

3. Small pieces of the *Williamson ochre,* which is manufactured for paint, have been taken from a mixed mass of earth and gravel, in Scipio.

4. South of the Ridge Road, *impure limestone* projects from the ground. Great quantities of this rock, in fragments, are found on the adjacent hills to the south, along the road from *Palmyra* to *Pultneyville,* and I have seen some near the Seneca River, north of Cayuga.

5. *Sandstone* and *Blue Limestone,*[*] both containing marine shells, appear above ground in Aurelius in regular quarries, and detached pieces, with the exact character of each, are abundantly scattered over our fields in Scipio. To the south,[†] no similar strata have

[*] These rocks are further characterized by containing nodules of flint.

[†] Some beds of limestone, of a different colour, are found near the line between Scipio and Genoa. In the deep valley through which *Salmon-Creek* flows at *Ludlowville,* we also find limestone with shells, but the quantity at either place, scarcely deserves this notice.

been discovered, and I have never seen a single fragment to the north.

6. Detached pieces of *Slate* have been found in Scipio, buried amongst gravel. We believe no vestige of the rock has been found to the north, on the *Limestone Ledge.*

T
247
In addition to this view of our native rocks, *granite* and *gneis* also abound on the surface. Every geologist will admit that these are foreign species, and it is a curious fact, that none are contained in the mountains to the south.

It also merits notice, that *mica slate* has not been discovered in any part of our county, though the mountains to the south contain much of that substance.

Mica, yellow, purplish, and black—is common, both in coarse-grained granite, and in stratified rocks. I have never observed it, of these colours, among the mountains.

As more strongly marking the difference between these rocks, and those which are *native,* to the south, I have seen no fair specimen of *argentine mica* in our county.

These vast beds of alluvial sand are south of the coarser depositions of gravel and rounded stones. Now, a decrease of velocity in the current from the north, would produce such phenomena; and a reflux, loaded with

T
261
earth and gravel, on striking the waves of Ontario, probably deposited the *Ridge Road.*

We observed the leaves of the oaks, which are interspersed among pines, just bursting from the buds; but on the shores of the Cayuga we had seen them considerably expanded. This difference, we refer principally to a *double sun;* for, notwithstanding the occasional chillness of the lake breeze, the temperature is greatly increased, along the shores, by reflection from the water, as the comparative state of vegetation annually demonstrates.

The morning was obscured by a dense fog.* This is

* The appearance of fog, at its commencement, and during its

a rare object in the west of Scipio, where it scarcely appears once a year. Perhaps we ought to ascribe this infrequency, to the regular ascent of land from the lake, as the soil, by receiving every breath of air, acquires a corresponding temperature.

Geneva, one of the principal villages of the western district, is situate on a hill side at the northeast corner of the *Seneca Lake*, of which it commands a pleasing prospect. It is the centre of commerce for the surrounding country ; and will derive much advantage from the *Lock navigation* at Seneca Falls. The Canandaigua outlet, eight or ten miles to the north, has laid bare immense beds of plaster, and considerable quantities have been brought hither on its way to Susquehanna. This trade, however, has declined since the restoration of peace with Great Britain.

Our road now led westwardly sixteen miles to *Canandaigua*, through a delightful country ; and the numerous fruit trees, in blossom, rendered the views particularly pleasing. It is composed of parallel ridges, declining to the north, the summits nearly of an equal height, and the sides, sloping, to discharge the superfluous water of rainy seasons. Sugar maple and bass-wood constitute the principal timber of the woodlands. This road passes near the southern limits of the *Limestone Ledge*, as, in some places, we observed the slate rock.

Four miles east of Canandaigua, we had a view of that beautiful village, which is situate at the northwest corner of the lake of that name. It is a place of consi-

increase, is highly interesting to the student of nature. It is well known that this phenomenon is an exhalation, which is condensed by the cold air as it rises, and thus becomes visible. Though we have been occasionally immersed in it, yet, during twelve years residence in the western part of Scipio, I have never seen it produced, as in other places, by the chill air of the evening. Sometimes it attends the first descent of cold winds, near the termination of a thaw, or in times of protracted rains, and it appears, in every case, to have moved hither from a distance.

derable business.   Here the *Ontario bank*, and a branch
of the *Utica bank*, are established.   It is also the seat of
justice for Ontario county.   The street is spacious, and
many of the houses elegant.

At this village, the great western turnpike ends.

The country, spreading westward, to *East-Bloomfield*,
is pleasant, and the improvements, on many of the
farms, are excellent; but the ridges are more elevated,
and, as a tract of land, we consider it inferior to that
embraced by the last sixteen miles.

East-Bloomfield consists of twelve or fifteen houses,
situate on an irregular line of hills, declining from the
S. S. E. and commands an extensive prospect to the
north.   Westward, the surface is extremely uneven, but
no material difference of soil is either observed or expected.   The marl, from the *Limestone Ledge*, appears to form
a part of the alluvion, which overwhelmed this tract, as
well as the district to the eastward; neither ought we
to forget of how much less value our country would
have been, had that flood passed in a contrary direction,
and brought along the barren soil of the mountains.

32 miles.

5 mo. 23.—The morning was rainy, cold, and uncomfortable, with wind from the north.   Such winds sometimes occur in Scipio, though rarely.   There, the north
wind is no indication of fair weather; and by it, our
deepest snows have been borne, along.   These have
happened in spring, at which time it has been most
prevalent.

6   In this neighborhood the Phelpstown plaster is used
in considerable quantities, and from its effects on veg-
T   etation, we cannot assign it any inferiority on a compar-
265 ison with the imported kinds.

I remark, that all the quarries of this stone, in the
state of New-York, are confined to the *Limestone Ledge;*
and though discoveries, in other parts, have been announced, such have uniformly proved to be fallacious.   It has
been found eastward at Canaseraga, and westward at

Grand River in Upper Canada. In the intermediate
country it is abundant. From *Carver's** description of 7
certain rocks near the Mississippi, which accord with
some of the characters of this stone, it is probable that
this ledge continues westward to that river.

West-Bloomfield, five miles from East-Bloomfield, is
a considerable village, though inferior to Geneva or Canandaigua. It is situate chiefly on the sides of this road.

I learn that *aluminous schist*, or *clay slate*, as at Cayuga 8
and Seneca, forms the banks of the *Honeoye Lake*, twelve
miles south of this place; and limestone is found within two miles to the north; but the south border of the
Great Ledge is probably irregular, and a glance, at the
country, is insufficient to determine its position. Indeed, so much is it buried in places, that the inattentive
traveller may distrust its reality. The outlets of our
lakes, however, will set all cavils of this kind aside,
and to me it is an object of much interest:—it contains
inexhaustible stores of fertility for our southern hills,
and stands unrivalled in the sublimity of its scenery
at Niagara.

As we approach the Genesee River, *oak* and *chesnut*,
appear on the hills; but in the moist, rich lands to the
eastward, the latter is very rare. Fences, of considerable extent have been made from *white cedar* which is
procured in the swamps. It is not that of West-Jersey,
(Cupressus thyoides,) which it greatly resembles in the
grain of the wood, but the *Thuya occidentalis.* These
Genera with the *Pinus,*† the *Taxus,* and *Juniperus,* constitute a natural assemblage of plants, which, in our land,

---

* *"A little way* from the mouth of the river St. Pierre, on the
north side of it, stands a hill, one part of which, that towards the
Mississippi, is composed entirely of *white stone of the same soft
nature,* as I have before described; for such indeed is all the stone
of this country But what appears remarkable, is, that the colour
of it is as white as the driven snow The outer part was *crum-
bled by the wind* and weather, into heaps of sand, of which a
beautiful composition might be made." CARVER'S TRAVELS.

† The larch will form one exception.

seldom intrude on soils well adapted to the labours of man ; but retiring to the swamp, the sandy waste, the precipice, the hill, and the mountain, give verdure to the wintry landscape.

We observed with regret, that the road was bordered by many detached patches of the poisonous hemlock, *(Cicuta maculata.)* This is a dangerous plant, and much industry is required to exterminate it. It is a naturalized foreigner. How this vegetable, and the hemlock* of our forests, so dissimilar in appearance, habits and qualities, should have acquired the same name, is a cause of wonder ; but it exemplifies the confusion and absurdities that prevail among many of the common English names of our plants.

Genesee River, at the ferry on this road, is about twelve rods wide. Though a deep boatable stream, it is interrupted by falls, and in many places may be forded in summer. The flats here are chiefly on the west bank, nearly one and a half miles wide, and very fertile. This tract is an Indian Reservation. A large pasture, in which many horses were feeding, was enclosed by good fence, but disfigured by bushes. Westward, we saw the Indian habitations, six or eight log buildings, covered with bark or puncheons.

Gradually ascending from the flats, we passed into a plain, which probably in former times had been annually ravaged by fires.† This is indicated by the underbrush. We also infer, from the stunted white oaks which are scattered over this district, and from the foundations of the country being limestone, that the rock is near the surface, and very compact. Though the soil is chiefly sand and gravel, yet wheat, rye, and clover might be cultivated with success. With the exception of two

---

* *Pinus 'canadensis.*

† This plain resembles many tracts of woodland which enclose *Prairies* in the western country. The vast bodies of limestone, that become visible at Caledonia, together with the appearances noticed in the text, strongly support what I have suggested of the cause of these wastes.

or three families, this tract is uninhabited; extends more
than five miles in a westwardly direction, and terminates at *Caledonia* village.

This collection of twelve or fifteen houses, is situate
twenty rods south-easterly from a spring, which now
turns a grist-mill, saw-mill, and carding-machines. A
great bed of limestone surrounds the mill pond. This
change of scenery commences at a small declivity, and
the gravel totally disappears.

Stunted oaks continue two miles westward ; and lime
rocks occupy so much of the surface, that it is difficult
to find a space of six acres capable of being well ploughed. The soil, however, is black and fertile,–a mixture of
decomposing rock and vegetable matter,–and would
form excellent sheep pastures.

At the end of that distance, beech and maple become
the principal timber. Silicious sand and gravel cover
much of the calcareous rock, which, however, appears
regularly stratified in the channel of *Allen's Creek*, sev-
en miles from Caledonia. This creek is remarkable
for its falls, and for the numerous mills which are turned by its current.

The district between this stream and Churchill's, is
embellished by new farms ; but though the soil is good,
and the country beautiful, the rocks render cultivation
difficult. Water is also a scarce article.

About noon, the clouds disappeared, and the latter
part of the day, though cool, was pleasant. The *features* of a country must be nearly the same in all weather ; but the *colouring*, to be beautiful, requires a bright
sky, and an unclouded mind.

The east line of the *Holland Purchase* passes near
the west end of Marvin's house, six miles east of Batavia.

Lodged at *Churchill's* a large, handsome house, well
furnished.

36 miles.

5 mo. 24.—AT this place, a fine spring supplies them with water. It is indeed a treasure. At an inn, one and a half miles westward, we are told it can only be procured from a well eighty feet deep.

Yesterday, in some places, we had observed impure lime rocks of a dull ash colour, in blocks six or eight feet high, the strata of which were horizontal; but half a mile west of Churchill's, a rock of this kind appears to the right, in the shape of a round table of ten feet diameter, and seven or eight feet in height. The sides, apparently, have been broken away by the hammer and wedge, to which it owes much of its singularity.

Depositions that form strata are irregular. We cannot believe, however, that the materials which compose these, were poured down on one spot, while the adjoining waters were limpid; and the horizontal position would be conclusive against that conjecture. The geologist, therefore, may ask what has become of the strata that once surrounded these piles? A deluge, such as I have traced in many parts of this route, would sweep off the friable earth, and the country to the eastward demonstrates, that large masses of this kind of rock have been removed entire.

As we advanced towards Batavia, small ponds appeared on both sides of the road; and from the great quantities of vegetable matter, which putrify in summer, we suspect that intermittents prevail in the neighbourhood. But the first of these ponds, containing two acres, has a clean shore, and is consequently innoxious.

Batavia, the capital of Genesee county, forty miles from Buffalo, contains forty houses, situate on both sides of the main street, which the road enters obliquely. At the end of this street (for the road turns again to the left) the arsenal, built of stone, two stories high, apears on a knoll to great advantage; and on a retrospective view, we find the opposite end of the street closed by the court-house, a building of unusual magnitude. The former edifice is guarded by a detachment of soldiers.

At this village we came to the *Tonnewanta Creek*, a heavy mill stream; and as its course is westwardly, we travelled on its banks. These are not more than four or five feet high, and the land being level on both sides, this water resembles a canal. The land, indeed, is too level to be pleasing; and the north side of the road, throughout a distance of several miles, is border-ed by cedar swamps, while hemlock and beech occupy the firm ground. This is chiefly sand; and it is remark-able that hemlock, by decaying on such soils, imparts a yellow tinge which continues for ages. In some cases, this colouring matter has been mistaken for ochre.

Though, in places, the surface is diversified by considerable ridges, the same timber is abundant for eighteen miles.

Six miles west of Batavia, I observed the clay slate. **10** As the origin of this stone is from depositions, and comparatively of a recent date, the manner in which the mass was split into prisms, becomes a curious sub-ject of enquiry. The fissures in sand rocks, granite, &c. are generally irregular and crooked. These we ascribe to earthquakes. But in Scipio, where this schist abounds, the sectional planes continue for consid-erable distances, crossing each other nearly at right an-gles, and the sides of the blocks are as smooth as pol-ished marble. We cannot conceive any motion, to which this globe is subject, that would produce such results.

Twenty-two miles east of Buffalo, limestone occu- **11** pies much of the surface; not in detached fragments, as in the southern parts of our county, but apparently resting in its native bed. Beech and hemlock disap-pear, and shrubby white oaks become the principal tim-ber. These are not more advanced in vegetation than those were which we noticed in Junius; and from the lapse of time, the season evidently is later as we ap-proach Lake Erie.

Eighteen miles from Buffalo, the prospect suddenly becomes extensive to the west, and I looked with eager-ness for the lake; but thick clouds, which darkened

the horizon, rendered it impossible to distinguish distant objects.   On reaching the brow of the declivity, a
breeze struck us, so damp and chill that instantly we
stopt, and put on our great coats. Doubtless, this change
of temperature should be ascribed to the lake.

12   Near this place, the surface of the land becomes remarkably smooth and even, but a large proportion is too
rocky to be arable.   The stunted oaks continue.

At "*Eleven-mile-Creek,*" the soil is better, the timber more thrifty, and we had some pleasing prospects of
farms along the road toward Buffalo.

                                    39 miles.

5 mo. 25.—RAIN began last evening, and much fell
through the night.   This morning was so cold that we
shivered in a winter dress, with great coats and gloves.
The peach tree is opening into full bloom, but very few
blossoms of the red cherry are expanded.   On the lake
shore, the ice disappeared only five days ago. Vegetation
is at least two weeks later than at Cayuga; for the elm,
the beech, and the sugar maple, have no leaves, and the
last is only in blossom.

Buffalo, the seat of justice for Niagara county, is
hidden by an intervening ridge, till we are almost within the street.   Here we obtained the first view of the
lake ; but the misty coldness of the morning rendered
the prospect indifferent.   The Canada shore, four miles
north-westwardly from Buffalo, is a continuation of the
Lime-stone Ledge, and appears broken into hills.
This village consists of more than one hundred houses ; many are frame, several of brick, and a considerable number are large and elegant. These have been principally built during the last season, on the site of the
old village, which was burnt down by the British and
Indians, near the close of the year 1813.   The black
sills of former buildings still remain, and in him, who
looks on man as his brother, it must excite painful reflections.

At this place, a ship navigation commences of more

than one thousand miles in length. The term of "IN-
LAND SEAS" may be used here with much propriety;
and, from its general excellence, the soil that surrounds
them, must one day support a vast population. Give
their commerce an outlet to the ocean, and these
shores will rival in prosperity those of the Mediterranean. It is true, the climate is not so delightful, but its
influence is not less productive and salubrious.

Provisions have long commanded high prices in the
vicinity of this lake, and there appears to be no obstacle to the industrious farmer's acquiring wealth. At
this village, wheat is now selling at $2 a bushel, corn
(maize) at $1 50, and potatoes at $1 *a* 1 50.

Our course, a few miles east of Buffalo, had been to
the south-west; but now we turned south-eastwardly,
and went up the *creek* of that name, a fine smooth
stream, fifteen or twenty rods wide, one mile to the
ferry. On both sides, the soil is a cold yellow clay,
timbered with shrubby beech.

The manner of conducting business, at this ferry,
merits severe reprehension. In jumping from the
wharf, into the boat, our horses were in danger of breaking their legs and necks; and on landing on the opposite shore, we were compelled to climb a causeway of
large logs, over which, for a considerable distance, the
waggon was kept bouncing, and the horses in continual
jeopardy. Whether the proprietor has been licensed to
exact money from the traveller in this manner, or not,
merits an enquiry.

Having turned to the westward, we soon arrived on
the beach. Every object now conspired to assure us,
that the waves had recently overwhelmed this desolate
shore. Pieces of timber lay across the narrow track
which winded to avoid obstacles of greater magnitude;
the sand or gravel, piled high round the trees and bushes,
was so loose as to cover the felloes; and the surges had
uncovered the miry clay that forms the general founda-
tion, in which one waggon had become fixed by
passing near the water. Backward, from the lake,

lies an extensive swamp; and no ground, fit for the foot
of man, is discernible.

Three miles from the ferry, we had the satisfaction
to tread, once more, on solid earth. I was told that
wells are dug through slate, and the first bluff, in going up the lake, is of this substance. It therefore appears that this vast basin, and those of all the smaller
lakes, to the eastward, for one hundred and fifty miles,
have been formed in this crumbling rock.

At *Eighteen-mile-Creek,* much of the shore was cov-
13 ered by handsome limestone, suitable for buildings, with
square edges, as if just from the quarry, and I was interested in searching for the origin. From a remnant
of this stratum, it appears, that these rocks once over-
laid the crumbling slate; and as the latter was broken
away by the waves, the incumbent blocks were precipitated, in succession, on the beach.

Similar strata, containing animal remains, are found
on the eastern shore of Cayuga, in the sides of precipices, and in the beds of streams. These strata are now
supported, and once were covered by the slate.

Amazing quantities of young fishes appeared in the
lake, near the shore, but we did not ascertain the species. A neighbour told the ferryman, in our presence,
that up this creek, at least fifty bushels had died in one
pond, in consequence of the decrease of water.

The water, round the bluffs, being too deep to admit
a passage with safety, soon after crossing this stream, in
a ferry-boat, we were compelled to leave the beach.
The road that leads to the uplands is unusually steep,
and the showers, which fell to-day, had rendered it slippery. This difficulty, however, was soon surmounted;
but the continual wading through mud and water, which
ensued on gaining the summit, required more patience.
The reflection, however, that every step assisted to remove us from this land, and that nothing should again
lead us hither, was a powerful stimulus to exertion.

At *Lay*'s, we overtook our much valued friend J.
RIDGWAY, whom we had expected to find at Buffalo.
In ascending the steep hills at Eighteen mile creek,
the harness broke, and his waggon was only saved from
destruction by his twitching the shafts as the horse left
them, which turned it sideways. Through the woods
he had procured the assistance of an ox team.

We proceeded three and a half miles further on the
beach.

The slate on this part of the shore is nearly black,
and, excepting the thinness of the lamina, greatly resembles coal.* When heated, it even flames. Between the
leaves, a coat of yellowish matter is found which
some have believed to be copper ; and indeed many of
these plates are variegated like the peacock's tail.

5 *mo.* 26.—The diligence, with which we travel,
has often been a cause of regret; and to write, under
such circumstances, greatly increases the fatigue. " To
snatch, not take" must be the motto to these remarks.

Pebbles, in great variety, decorate this shore. A
large proportion are from primitive rocks, and beautifully coloured. Many of these might be cut for watch
seals; but when dried, the brightness, that marked them
in the ebb of the waves, is diminished.

A bark canoe had drifted ashore. It appears that
the bark had been taken from the birch tree in one
piece of equal length. It was then doubled like a sheet
of paper, and the folds, at each end, permanently connected by sewing. On opening and spreading the longitudinal edges, with light timbers, a sharp taper to
the stem and stern is preserved. For light boats, we
equally admire the simplicity and excellence of this
construction.

* Springs of *Petroleum* are found a few miles south-east of this
place. As that fluid is identified with one of the component
parts of pit coal, it is a rational belief, that this valuable fuel will
be discovered, at no distant period of time, in that vicinity.

The Canada shore, of which we had some fine views, yesterday, seems to recede from us. To the south-west, the prospect is only bounded by the clouds. This bank of the lake is very sinuous, and whenever we leave the beach, the road is distressingly bad. This often occurs, as many of the bluffs* or precipices project into deep water. Round these, however, we are assured that the old road passed, three or four years ago, and the 15 periodical rising and falling of this lake is frequently mentioned.

Not presuming to decide on this popular opinion, with such an imperfect knowledge of the facts, I only suggest, that obstructions in the channel of the Niagara river; a breach in some of the *dams* of the upper lakes; and extraordinary seasons of rain or snow, may, singly or combined, raise the water on those shores. A reverse of these circumstances may also lay them dry; but I am not prepared to believe, that this phenomenon has any connexion with a regular periodical influence.

16　　　Ferruginous sand empurples many parts of the shore. Though finer than the silecious sand, it settles first to the bottom, when agitated in water, on account of its greater specific gravity. It is obedient to the magnet, and, in this way, is easily separated from other mixtures. It is used for writing. It appears to be derived from granite, by trituration; as the *micaceous parts* of these rocks, when reduced by the hammer, furnish an excellent sand for the same purpose, and may be readily selected by the magnet.

Several plants, which were new to me, appeared on the beach; but our bookstores could furnish nothing valuable in this department of science. The disappointment would cause much regret, if our circumstances would accord with the calm pursuits of the botan-

T
266 * It is said that the waters of this lake are now slowly subsiding My friend J. Ridgway's, was the first of thirteen waggons, which passed round these bluffs in the last season (1817) in safety. This company was the first that had effected a passage in several years.

ist ; but we are hastening from a land of scarcity, and of consequent extortion.

We have had several opportunities of observing the curvature of the earth. The Canada shore, that could not be seen from the beach, became plainly visible from the bluffs; few of which are elevated one hundred feet above the level of the lake.

After breakfast, we entered the *five mile woods.* This tract of clay, situate on the clay slate that extends to the lake, in bluffs of different altitudes, is excavated by waggons into innumerable basins. These receive, not only the frequent shower, but also the soakings of higher ground. This clay is so compact as to prevent leakage ; and a thick shade of beech, in places interspersed with hemlock, retards evaporation. Every few rods of this *emphatical distance* was measured

" With splash, with scramble and with bound ;"

and when these sloughs, continually deepened by wheels which roll out loaded with mud, deject the waggoner, he goes to work, cuts a new road* or lays a causeway. Indeed, we observe with regret, that no repairs are made by other hands. Yet, even the labour of one man, well applied, for three or four days, would effect great improvements; as many of the worst ponds are near precipices, and might be drained in a few minutes. The same neglect appears in every part of this road from Buffalo-Creek ; but much of that distance is beach. We are aware of the difficulties and inconveniences to which new settlers are subject, but all these are insufficient to excuse the inhabitants for this breach of duty as citizens. It is even a prevalent opinion, pro-

* In consequence of such attempts to avoid the sloughs, these roads have multiplied to a degree of which we can furnish no correct idea, for we judged it most prudent to keep near the shore; but wherever the ground would admit, the intersections are remarkably numerous as far eastward as we could discover. Some have affirmed, that the breadth of this space is not less than a mile ; but doubtless this is an exaggeration. The statement, that some travellers have been bewildered, and were wading in an opposite direction, we think is very probable.

bably founded on such shameful negligence, and on extortionate demands for assistance rendered, that they are averse to all improvement of this road; and like the wretches who inhabit dangerous coasts, delight in the miseries of the unfortunate.

After six hours of danger, difficulty, and extreme fatigue, and partaking largely of the soil which flew in every direction, we arrived at *Mack's* on the southwest side of Cattaraugus Creek.

I have seen much of swamps, and of mountains, but never any road so vile as this, which the traveller would do well to take a circuit of twenty or thirty miles to avoid. It is a disgrace to the state; to the Holland company whose lands adjoin it, and to the county in which it lies.

17   On the beach, backward, a few miles towards Buffalo, appeared a most singular kind of fossil. It is of limestone about ten inches thick, and five feet diameter, composed of ridges, lying nearly in concentric circles. The outermost ridge is diminished in thickness, but very smooth, resembling the curves of the large hard *Boletus,* so common in our forests. I observed in a few instances two of these to be connected, and the stones appear double-headed.

In all these rocks, there are cracks, generally one inch wide at the centre, apparently filled with red ochre, intermixed with black and white chrystals. These extend within two inches of the circumference, and taper as they recede from the centre.

This fossil is confined to one stratum, which is three feet above the lake, where I first observed it, and declines, south-westwardly, till it disappears in the waves. The angle with the plane of the horizon is nearly one third of a degree; and the other strata, along the shore, dip in the same direction.

Oblate spheroids* resembling a grindstone, formed of stratified lime-rock, were also seen on the beach. These

* In some places, such stones, though rounder, are very numerous in the slate rocks of Scipio.

appear to have been rounded by rolling, and are fixed
in the slate which is bent or arched over them. This
singular fact evinces, that the present barrier of the
lake was once a morass, which settled as it became compacted round the stone.

Blocks of granite and of limestone of many tons
weight are numerous along this shore, and reminded
me of a similar appearance at Cayuga.

Pyrites are found in some strata of the precipices,
and, by their metallic brilliancy, excite much attention.

The flats on Cattaraugus Creek, exhibit the most
luxuriant vegetation. The broad leaved leek *(Allium
canadense)* grows here in profusion ; and the leaves of
this plant may be seen eight inches long, exclusive of
the footstalk, and three inches wide in the middle.
The bulbs form the lower frustum of a cone, and some
are one inch diameter, and one and a half inches long.
The black walnut also grows to a great size. It is rare
along the road to the eastward.

The *Cattaraugus Reservation*, lies on the north-east
side of the creek, extending twelve miles along it, and
in places six miles in width. The Seneca Indians,
who inhabit this tract, are much respected by their
neighbours for honesty and sobriety. We were assured
that drunkenness is excluded from their habitations.
In times of scarcity,* they deal out corn in proportion
to the necessities of the *whites,* and some of them having much to sell, have become rich. I observed both

---

* Corn, (maize,) the chief support of these tribes, was injured by frost in the autumn of 1816, and assistance, from the white
people, became necessary. The culture of different crops is very important ; for, in proportion to the number, the danger of
famine decreases. This arises from the difference of temperature, and of moisture, that different plants require. Thus, wheat
succeeds best in dry seasons ; oats and potatoes with frequent
showers ; hot weather is most congenial to corn, but most injurious to buckwheat. These notices will explain the paradox, that
our most extraordinary crops have been produced in seasons
commonly deemed unfavorable ; and the wheat harvest of 1816
may be cited as an example.

men and women to go with their heads uncovered, in rain and in sunshine.

After a short stay at Mack's, we continued our journey, though rain from the north-east continued. I had noticed the *sand hills*, along the shores of the lake; and had been unable to explain how such could be thrown by the waves, twenty feet higher than the adjoining land to the eastward. While passing over Cattaraugus flats, we observed one of these hills which is remarkably elevated, and at once determined to examine it. We found very fine sand, the surface extremely irregular, like snow drifts, and an altitude of not less than fifty feet above the lake. On gaining the summit, we were instantly satisfied, that the winds had whirled it up to that height. I had observed, with surprise, that these banks were confined to the vicinity of creeks, and that the shore in other parts, though not more than ten feet high, exhibited the naked slate. We therefore infer, that the creeks have supplied the sand.

Near this place we left the dreary shores of Lake Erie, having seen nothing inviting to the cultivator in thirty miles. The timber is generally shrubby; and much of the land too wet and level for the production of grain. It is also clayey; for though it rests on slate, similar to that in Scipio, the fine varieties of soil which cover that rock to the eastward, are not observable. We were told, however, that on receding from the lake, the country rises into ridges, and assumes a more pleasing aspect.

This part of the lake is shallow. Much of the bottom is slate, which may be seen, outward, to a considerable distance; and we were assured, that even one mile from the shore its depth is only a few feet.

Lodged at *Walnut Creek*, having travelled 12 miles.

5 mo. 27.—This morning, I mistook the dark rough surface of the lake, which appeared obscurely through the trees, for a ploughed field, but the sun breaking

through the clouds, while we sat at breakfast, I started
to see that field all in motion with the rolling of waves.

*Walnut Creek** is properly named, and I have not
seen, in any place, so many large trees of this kind.
Half a mile from Howard's, we passed one, which is
computed to be nine feet in diameter, and it is probably
so, if measured eighteen inches from the ground. The
trunk is stately, though tapering.

The influence of the *Lake breeze*, in retarding vegetation, at this season, yesterday was rendered most
strikingly visible. On the shore, the trees were leaf-
less, but in the thick woods, backward from the bluffs,
the beeches were green. It will be recollected, that
wind pressing along the surface of water, on striking
a bold shore, whirls over it in high arches; and a station
on it, which at first view might be deemed the most exposed, is, in reality, the most sheltered; for, air like water has its eddies.

We are told, that *the road from this place to Erie,*   18
(60 miles) is nearly parallel to the beach, but lies back
from it two or three miles, and in all that distance we
shall have no view of the lake. We find, that it is cut
out on a broad ridge, the sides of which slope very gradually.

A few miles from Walnut Creek, I observed the
trees, whose names follow, growing together, and which
I notice as a very singular occurrence in our forests:

* It is said, that an excellent harbour, for twenty or thirty vessels, is formed by the estuary of this stream. A village has been
laid out, and from the scarcity of good harbours on the coast, it
is expected to flourish.
No islands appear in the eastern part of Lake Erie; and when
we consider that the surges by " beetling the rocks," are enlarg-
ing their borders, the reason will be obvious. Islands, in large
waters, can only withstand the tempestuous violence of the
waves, when protected by rocks harder than clay slate.

Juglans nigra	black walnut
Juglans cinerea	butternut
Juglans squamosa	shell bark
Quercus rubra	red oak
Quercus alba	white oak
Pinus canadensis	hemlock
Pinus strobus	white pine
Castanea vesca	chestnut
Fagus ferruginea	beech
Liriodendrum tulipifera	whitewood or poplar
Carpinus americana?	iron wood
Prunus virginiana	wild cherry
Acer saccharinum	sugar maple
Acer rubrum	soft maple
Betula nigra	birch
Sambucus pubescens	Canadian elder
Ulmus americana	elm
Magnolia acuminata	cucumber tree
Fraxinus alba	white ash

The soil of this ridge is a loam, containing gravel, evidently rounded by rolling in water. These pebbles appear to be formed of *micaceous schistus,* or mica slate.

Thus we have left in succession the calcareous soil of the *Limestone Ledge,* and the clay of the uplands along Lake Erie.

As this ridge has been thickly timbered, it is difficult to drive fast, on account of stumps and trees in the road. It is the first ridge that we have noticed lying N. E. and S. W. but we are told, that such are numerous in the south-eastern part of the state of Ohio.*

* No such ridges are found in that part of Ohio, except for short distances,—THE HILLS THERE HAVING NO DETERMINATE COURSE. It is much less surprising, however, that this mistake should have been made by an unlettered traveller, to whom the ranges of hills, and the course of rivers, are objects of indifference, than that so many draughtsmen should trace mountains from Virginia and Kentucky, across the Ohio River. We indulge the fancy of him who sketches a landscape, but in a map we look for sober truth. Here every flourish of the pencil leads to error.

At *Robard's*, twelve miles from Cattaraugus, I saw *mica slate*. It was brought from a quarry one mile **19** south-east of this road.

This stone belongs to the class, called by geologists, *primitive*, and which owes its formation to that period, when *"darkness was on the face of the deep."* It exhibits no vestige of organic life. Generally it rests on granite; and we can scarcely doubt of its having been derived from that rock, which is properly deemed the *nucleus* of the earth. The latter, indeed, contains all its elements, and the minute particles of the mica evince a chafing or trituration. Like the clay slate, this schistus is foliated. It differs, however, not only in its chrystallization, and in containing mica, but also in its curvilineal surface. This figure, with some variations, is assumed by these strata, whether depressed in vallies, elevated on mountains, or separated by oceans; and conjecture is bewildered in searching for a rational theory of this singular appearance.

Canadaway,* (now Fredonia,) a village of thirty houses, is situate on the banks of a small creek of that name, 45 miles from Buffalo, the same distance from Erie, and three miles from the lake. We should judge that three fourths of the houses were erected within the last year.

We have frequently observed with pleasure and surprise, the rapid improvements of these new districts. From the appearance of the stumps, we presume that even a large proportion of the fields between Caledonia and Buffalo, have been recently cleared; and five

* *Dunkirk Bay* is situate two miles east of the mouth of Canadaway creek. It is a semicircular cove. A rocky bar extends across the entrance, but the harbour within is deep, and sufficiently capacious for an immense commerce. The preparations for business, at this place, indicate an unusual appropriation of Capital; and a pier for the improvement of the harbour, 300 feet in length, is nearly completed. It is expected that a new and direct road to Canandaigua will become the great thoroughfare of western emigration.

years ago, this road, which is still more remote, must have been through the wilderness. Considering how many of our countrymen, who had lived as tenants or as labourers, were thus advancing to independence, we viewed this rapid reduction of the forest with much satisfaction.

20   This ridge, with the exception of a few places, is handsomely level for a road; and being gravelly, affords the best materials for one, that we have seen on the journey. Along it, scarcely a stone is to be found, and the brooks lay bare no strata of rocks.

Near Canadaway, a hill or ridge of considerable elevation, distant two or three miles, appeared on our left, and parallel to the ridge on which we travelled.

Westwardly, five miles from this village the streams uncover mica slate, at the depth of a few feet. Many fragments are scattered over the surface. Of these, all that I saw, exhibit the curvilineal form, and probably were raised by the roots of trees from the strata underneath. The whole mass of soil appears to be derived from the decomposition of this rock; and though it is not so favorable to grass as more tenacious lands, yet it parts easily before the plough, and winter grain has a very promising appearance. Good husbandry, however, will be necessary to prolong its fertility. The timber is tall, fine, and in great variety; and in some places, we saw unusual quantities of chestnut.

Proceeding on our journey, we bore a little to the left of the small ridges, crossing them diagonally. The hill, on our left, continues at the same distance.

Williams's, 22 miles.

5 *mo.* 28.—We are told by our landlord, who is an intelligent man, that iron ore has been discovered twelve miles south of his house; but the mine is not yet sufficiently explored. Fourteen hundred acres are reserved by the agents of the Holland Company.

We breakfasted at a new tavern, seven miles further

westward. The man is a Pennsylvanian, who lived ten years in Canada, and left that country about six weeks ago. Since the late war, we observe a material change in the current of emigration; and be the cause what it may, citizens of the United States seem generally disposed to keep on this side of the great lakes. His farm, which is considerably improved, cost him $20 an acre.

" *The Four Corners*," in Portland,* [now URBANNA,] one mile to the south-west, is a new village, situate on the portage road to Chautauque Lake, and two miles from Lake Erie. It is so much easier to collect a living from the crowd, than from the forest, that at the intersection of two great roads, it is reasonable to expect an increase of numbers and consequence.

The *Chautauque Lake* lies beyond the hill which we noticed on our left, and is seven miles from this place. It is, doubtless, much above the level of Lake Erie. A remarkable difference of climate has been observed on the shores of these waters; and while bare ground, and pleasant sunshine, prevailed at the latter, the former was wrapt in the drapery of winter.

It has been remarked, that the navigable waters which flow southwardly to the Atlantic, range, comparatively close, along the borders of our lakes. Thus, the *Susquehanna*, after a long course, and having swelled to a considerable river, passes within thirty miles of the Cayuga; and the *Owego*, a creek which may be easily rendered navigable, might diminish the portage more than two-thirds of that distance. The boatable waters of the Seneca and *Chemung*, approach within fourteen miles of each other, and at this place [*Chautauque*] the land carriage is reduced to nine miles; but the height of land is considerable. Advancing westward, the approximation continues, and the ridge declines, till the

T
267

---

* From a cleft in a rock, near the lake, a stream of hydrogenous gas issues, which is fired by the flame of a candle, &c. An attempt to obtain this air, in a pure state, by means of an arched curb, would not be very expensive, and if crowned with success, this *fountain* would prove a treasure.

21

rivers finally interlock, and admit between them, in high water, a free passage to large boats.

The *Chautauque Outlet,** though a navigable branch of the Allegany, is not the principal thoroughfare to the Ohio. This commences further eastward, at Olean,† 130 miles from Cayuga Bridge. That part of the road, which leads over the hills to the valley of the Ohio, is extremely rough ; and though the state has made liberal appropriations, and much labour has been applied, it is still a cause of dread to the emigrant.

I have never seen the black snake-root *(Actæa race-mosa)* in the country eastward of Cattaraugus. From that place, along this road, it is abundant.

We were detained, three hours, by a cold rain, six miles from "the Four Corners." The stranger, who feels the house that shelters him, a prison, will scarcely rejoice, with the farmer, at the interruption of showers. With him, as with Ossian, the hieroglyphic of beauty is a sunbeam.

The hill, on our left, nearly preserves its parallelism with the shore of the lake, till we almost reached " *Twenty-mile Creek,*" where it seems discontinued. The sides of this stream exhibit mica slate in horizontal strata, from the water upwards, more than fifty feet, to the top of the bank. This rock is decomposing, and forms the principal part of the soil.

Here we crossed the State line, and passed into *Pennsylvania.*

The " *Holland Purchase,*" of which this line is also the western boundary, is part of the tract ceded to *Massachusetts,* on a compromise of the claims of that state, whose charter covered all the lands directly westward to the Pacific Ocean. This cession extended only to the private right of soil.

---

* The mill-dams on this stream are *locked.* It is navigable for boats of twenty tons burden.
† Pronounced O-le-ann.

The population and prosperity of this country appear to have exceeded all calculation, and thirty years ago, (will posterity believe it?) this land was valued at less than six cents an acre. Such property, at that time, it would seem, was considered a burden to the state, and to dispose of it, on any terms, an act of patriotism. Neither was this view confined to one government; other states felt the same *mania*, and to sell land before it was in market, (or in demand for actual settlement,) was the fashion.

Though business is now managed differently, I feel no disposition to censure the rulers of that age, for not seeing what *time*, or rather a flash of *genius* across our path, has since unfolded. Neither do I feel such disposition, when apparently, they mistook the dictates of common sense. Common sense is much more confined in its operation than we often believe, and common habit might be used as a more definite term. The state of the Arts in different nations will demonstrate this proposition; and, notwithstanding the pride of genius, no man has yet seen so much that posterity may not wonder at the narrow limits of his vision. Even while FRANKLIN presided at the helm of government in Pennsylvania, the privilege, granted in land-warrants, for the purchaser to choose his own bounds,—that source of injurious and disgraceful controversy,—was not extinguished. Well may we look with amazement on *the past;* and certainly our views of *the future* are more elevated than man has taken in any former period.

In this quarter, the soil possesses considerable tenacity; for, the reduction of much of the slate, appears to have been very complete. Bricks are manufactured, and one handsome brick house, near the road, evinces a commendable spirit of improvement.

Having travelled 24 miles, and much of the latter part of that distance, through rain, we reached Gibsonville; and had the satisfaction, at sunset, to see clear sky in the west. 22

Provisions, of every kind, are scarce, and we expect nothing better till we leave these shores far behind.

5 mo. 29.—GIBSONVILLE is a *town* of ten or twelve houses, adjacent to a mill. The hill on our left again appears, distant three miles.

Last night was cold. This morning was very frosty, and ice covered the water one-fourth of an inch thick. We had a brisk breeze from the north-east, which indicates a considerable change of climate, as we cannot recollect a similar occurrence at Cayuga. We heard the roaring of the lake very distinctly at the distance of two miles.

We found, to-day as well as yesterday, that great coats were comfortable. The state of vegetation compares well with that of Cayuga when we left it; and though eight days have elapsed, much of that time has been cold. Peach, cherry, and apple trees, grow very thriftily throughout the whole extent of country that we have traversed; and the variation of temperature appears small, except near Buffalo, were the air is chilled by the ice that is driven on that shore.*

The black walnut, which is almost unknown in our county, is here plentifully scattered over the land. Great quantities of oak and chestnut, which have been

---

* It is well known, that latitude is an uncertain indication of climate; but it is questionable if all the causes, that produce those irregularities, have been enumerated? The elevation of land, however, is the most remarkable. The effects of prevailing winds, on the temperature, have also been noticed; but, until lately, the influence of rivers appears to have been overlooked : except in summer, such as flow from other latitudes affect the neighboring districts. Thus the sugar cane succeeds further to the north at a distance from the Mississippi than on its banks; because the sources of that stream are in frozen mountains, and its whole volume is collected in colder countries. The Ohio, after receiving warm currents from the borders of Carolina, becomes the line where sleighing terminates on the south; and an advancement of one month, in the progress of vegetation, might have been expected, if the waters of this lake had arrived from a champaign country in southern climates.

deadened by girdling, now cover the fields; and a stranger to the prospect of luxuriant crops of wheat in such
situations, remarked how well it grew in the woods.

This tract of country, called the *" Triangle,"* lies T
north of the 42d degree of latitude, and belonged to **268**
the state of New-York. For the purpose of accommodating Pennsylvania with a port on Lake Erie, connected with a valuable consideration, a transfer of both soil
and jurisdiction was completed. We learn that many
of the titles to these lands are disputed ; and the
emigrant, who may intend to purchase, should be
circumspect.

Eight miles from Erie, I observed the Pawpaw *(An-
nona triloba.)* I have not discovered it in any part of
the state of New York.

We had lately remarked, that the land appeared better as we advanced ; and, near this place, we entered on
a large tract, uncommonly excellent. Black walnut,
hemlock, chestnut, butternut, white oak, poplar or white
wood, red oak, cucumber tree and black snake root, all
grow together. We think no wild land ever appeared
more inviting to the cultivator ; but we suspect, that on
our right and left, it is low, wet, and of an inferior quality. The latter is a pleasant soil to cultivate, and produces fine crops of clover, wheat and Indian corn. It
ought to be noted, however, that the fields, when neglected, become encumbered with sorrel *(Rumex ace-
tosella ;)* and that this fertility should be ascribed more
to vegetable matter than to a proper mixture of elementary earths. No traces of marl or limestone are
discovered.

The deep green leaves of the sugar maple are now
fully expanded. As a shade tree, in beauty, it excels
all the trees of our forests.

One mile from *Erie*, the road turns north, to that

town. Here we had a glimpse of the blue rolling of the lake, which appears like a hill, almost sunk in the horizon. On walking to the shore, in bright sunshine, the vastness of the prospect unfolded ; wave rolled beyond wave in countless progression, and the bewildering idea of immensity rushed on the mind.

The bay is bounded on the north and west by a low island, which till lately,* was a peninsula, whence the old name of *Presque Isle,*† by the French. This formed nearly the arch of a circle ; and a point of land down the lake, which projects along the same curve line, renders it probable, that the bay was once enclosed and constituted a pond, or a marsh. Vessels appear to be exposed to the wind, but completely sheltered from the violence of the waves.

Near the spot where the waves broke through the late peninsula, a fine quarry of mica slate has been opened, and the stone were procured there for Brown's tavern, a large two story house. These have a pleasing argentine appearance, and exhibit the curvilineal form.

Erie, consisting of 150 houses, is situate on a small plain. It is embellished by the court house for Erie county, an elegant brick building. Though from the construction, and from the want of paint, some of the dwellings have a shabby cast, yet it is a place of considerable trade, and must eventually be populous.

Great quantities of red cedar *(Juniperus virginiana)* have grown on "the *Peninsula*." It is said to produce the bayberry *(Myrica cerifera.)*

I had observed in several places, on the road towards Erie, small patches of granite, scattered on the surface;

* The surges have broken through the bank of clay near the shore.

† Almost an Isle.

but no limestone among them, as at Scipio. I now learn, that the latter is plenty on the S. E. shore of lake Erie, but it is not found above the beach. This evinces that these two kinds of stone were not brought hither by the same deluge. Probably, the limestone floated on ice from the Canada shore ; and, doubtless, the granite was deposited by an overwhelming flood at another peri- od.

In the afternoon, we departed for Waterford on our route to Pittsburgh. The turnpike, between that place and Erie, extends fourteen miles. From Cattaraugus, as I have noted, we travelled parallel to the ridges ; but now we turned south-eastwardly, and crossed them at right angles. From their summits, which rise one above another like the seats of an amphitheatre, for nearly eight miles on this road, we had prospects of the lake.

The soil on these acclivities is wet, more tenacious than the lands on the ridges towards Cattaraugus, and almost destitute of stones. It is unfavorable to the production of wheat and corn ; but when the indigen- ous plants are completely subdued, the grasses flourish ; and oats,—which, like the potatoe, loves the cooling breeze, and the frequent shower of the mountain,—pro- duces an abundant crop. Vast quantities of chestnut continue to border our way.

We took lodgings near the summit of this great ridge. To the simple traveller it is an object of small interest, because it presents no serious obstruction to his progress ; but the naturalist, who reflects on the vast distance that its waters diverge, will view it with no or- dinary feelings.

5 *mo.* 30.—A SEVERE frost attended this morning. From this place, the descent of the road is very per- ceptible, but much less than the angle of altitude from Erie to the summit of the ridge.

We breakfasted in *Waterford.* The site of this pleasant town, of fifty houses, was included by a state reservation ; and the lots were laid out under a law for

that purpose. It stands at the head of navigation, on
24 the north-west bank of *Le Bœuf*, a fine creek, and the
first tributary of the Mississippi that we had seen.
Like most of the brooks that originate in pine swamps,
the water is nearly of a lye colour; and though this is a
blemish on its scenery, the idea vanishes on contempla-
ting the utility of this stream. It is scarcely two rods
wide, yet the depth is sufficient for boats of the greatest burden, and it forms the grand thoroughfare of commerce from *Pittsburgh* to *Erie.* Several thousand barrels of flour have passed up this season; and on the
turnpike we met waggon after waggon, loaded with
this necessary article, which was destined chiefly for
Detroit and *Mackinaw.**

The facility with which merchandize may be taken
from lake Erie, down these waters, is obvious; and in
the present state of things, it is probable, that the transportation from New York to Pittsburgh, will not exceed
that from Philadelphia; yet the merchants even at Erie
are largely supplied from the last named city, though
the carriage is eleven dollars per cwt. If sloops of fifty
tons burden could pass direct from New York to lake
Erie, the whole complexion of the western world
would be changed.†

* *Michilimackinac* is quite a task for both tongue and ears; and,
in this instance, I see no impropriety in adapting the orthography
to the established pronunciation. *Ty,* the popular name for *Ti-
conderoga,* by omitting four-fifths of it, is certainly exceptionable.

† The following statement was furnished by an intelligent friend
who has lately returned from the western country. From this, it
appears, that the merchants in Ohio are beginning to take advantage of the superior facilities for commerce, which are offered by
the state of New-York:—

In the last season (1817) a merchant at Newark, Licking county, purchased goods in New-York,—sent them from Albany to Buffalo in waggons,—had them landed from a sloop at Huron, and carried by land 105 miles, to his place of residence. The expence
was less than from Philadelphia.

A merchant, at Worthington, in Franklin county, on Whet-
stone River, has also procured goods in the last season by the
same route.

The delays, and the discouragements, that have continually attended every step towards the commencement of of the Great Western Canal, impart gloom and grief to the philanthropist. With equal despondency he must consider, how much of the wealth and energy of nations is exhausted in gratifying the savage passions, and how little is contributed to the cause of benevolence, and ameliorating the condition of our race.

W. Smith, for whom I had a letter, received us with much civility; and his friendly services are gratefully remembered.

Vegetation is much less advanced than at Erie. The buds of the white oak are still closed. The country round Waterford is rather low, and I suspect unfriendly to the peach.

The block-house which was built at this place during WAYNE's Indian war, is still standing, apparently in good repair. Things have greatly changed since that time. The friends of humanity must rejoice that no hostile Indian would now shew himself within hundreds of miles, and every day is extending these limits.

After a delay of three or four hours, we proceeded on our journey to Pittsburgh, crossing land chiefly low and level for three miles, when we came to *French Creek*, a fine deep stream, fifteen rods wide, which we crossed on a bridge. About eighty rods below, it forms a junction with Le Bœuf.

We now passed, in succession, over flats inclining to clay, and injured by excess of moisture from the rising grounds; and over the points of hills, of moderate ascent, which may be cultivated to the tops.

About the same time, one of a company who trade at the Indian Village on Huron River, took his furs and peltry to Philadelphia; and as it afforded a better market for these articles than New-York, he *laid in* his goods at that city,—freighted them to Albany,—had them carried by land to Buffalo,—and received them by water at Huron. He had chosen the most favorable season, and stated that the whole expence was only $6 per cwt.

The timber is various : groves of oak, of white pine, of beech and sugar maple, and of birch and hemlock, are interspersed. These, though contiguous, rarely exhibit much intermixture; yet I perceived no essential difference of soil, except what is dependant on the degrees of moisture.

At *Polock's*, a decent inn, five miles south-east of Waterford, we were told, that for his new stone house, he burnt a sufficiency of lime from muscle shells, which he procured in French Creek. In two days with some assistance he collected forty bushels. We have observed no limestone since we left Erie,—a distance which I have never traversed before without making the discovery.

Hicks's, near the bridge, 17 miles.

5 *mo.* 31.—Our morning ride was through a diversified country ; but eight miles above Meadville, the hills retire to a greater distance, and admit of extensive farms on the flats. Groves of pine, or of hemlock, here terminate. Generally, the current of this creek is gentle, though there are rapids, six miles above Meadville, from which the water is led to a mill.—Here I first noticed the *Houstonia cerulea.* It is not a native of the lake country, nor of soils generally so fertile.—Thorns of great magnitude abound on these flats, and recalled to mind the quaint language of Wordsworth,

> There is a thorn so very old,
> In truth you'd find it hard to say
> How it could ever have been young ;
> It is so old and grey.

Meadville, forty miles from Erie, is situate on the east bank of French creek. It is a *county town* composed of several streets, and consists of one hundred and fifty houses. The land is too flat to be pleasing. The streets are also narrow, and the proper formation has been neglected. An eastern population which is pouring into this place, may however soon remedy the latter evil ; but the former is incurable ; and it is the more to be regretted, as the health and convenience of the inhabitants will be sensibly affected by the narrow views of the original proprietor. At present, we think the appointment of scavengers would be useful. Though there are many decent frame houses, and some of them evidently occupied by persons of taste, yet neatness appears less prevalent than at Waterford and Erie. The practice of erecting houses of hewn logs, and *plastering the chinks with clay,* which is so common in the newly settled parts of Pennsylvania, obtains even here, and gives a solitary aspect to the dwellings. We believe that such are equally expensive as those of frame or brick, but much less durable, commodious and pleasant.

The agent of the Population Company, a native of Holland, has an elegant seat adjacent to this place, which forms a remarkable contrast to such buildings, and imparts a cast of cheerfulness to the country around it.

The hills, or upland, round Meadville, support detached blocks of granite; which, like those before described, were dropped here by some extraordinary effort of Nature. The soil has less sand and more clay than that toward Waterford; and may properly be called hard and gravelly. It is moderately fertile, but better for wheat than for Indian corn; and we know of no district of our country, that has flourished where corn yields a scanty crop. The timber is chiefly oak, of a small diameter and stunted growth, the buds of which are just opening.

25

Meadville is about 16 miles from *the Ohio line.*

24 miles.

6 *mo.* 1.—Dᴜʀɪɴɢ the three last days, the weather has been fine; but, this morning, the clouds rolled on heavily to the eastward, and portentously to those who have neither home nor shelter.

Eleven miles below Meadville, I observed sandstone in detached rocks. The granite, for some miles back has been increasing in quantity.

French *Creek* should be called a *River*. Its sources are in the same neighborhood as those of " *Twenty-mile Creek*," which joins Lake Erie; and the practicability of connecting these streams, has been suggested. Estimates of the descent of water, however, in both, are wanting; and we make the general remark, that those which run northwardly have greater falls. The apparent depression of the dividing ridge at Twenty-mile Creek, may, notwithstanding, favour such a lock navigation, which, if practicable and executed, would greatly advance the prosperity of this country.

We had crossed over French Creek to the east side, three miles below Waterford; to its west bank, at Polock's; to its east bank, at Hicks's; and now, fourteen miles below Meadville, we were ferried over, and saw it for the last time,—having traversed its banks about forty miles.

26 Near this ferry, I noticed the commencement of a district totally different in its formation, from that which we had just traversed. There, *mica slate*, it appears, is the only *native* stone; and both the soil and subsoil derive their origin from its decomposition and intermixture. Here the change is complete; and sand, and sand rock, piled into hills, embosom *coal, limestone,* and *iron ore,* but exhibit no vestige of the upper country, except some solitary blocks of *granite,* which are equally *exotic* in both.

Limestone, in quarry, is found one mile below the ferry; but not in great quantity. The stratum is thin.

The ridges appear to lie east and west, as for sixteen miles we were constantly ascending or descending; and the streams generally flowed to the eastward. The quantity of sandstone is immense. The soil is either a sandy loam, or a loamy sand,—the latter apparently resulting from a decomposition of the rock. Some of this, in texture and in whiteness, greatly resembles salt; it may be rubbed fine between the fingers; and by throwing a lump on a stone, the cohesion was so completely destroyed, that each particle seemed separately scattered. Such might be used for filtering-stones. It may, however, be stated, that it abounds in considerable variety in respect to hardness; and grindstones, building-stones, and even cisterns, may here be procured of any reasonable size. Some of these rocks are faced with ferruginous cement.

At *Little Sandy Creek*, twelve miles from the ferry, iron ore discolours the road, as we descended the hill towards that stream. In many other places, it is said to be abundant.

On entering this sandstone region, we were compelled to remark a difference in the affairs of the inhabitants, for which we were not prepared to account. An almost total want of energy prevails. Many small farms, which had been cleared some years ago,—including fruit trees of handsome growth,—are completely deserted; and the solitary buildings, or the burnt spots where they stood, fill the passenger with melancholy reflections. Even the improvements of former years, now occupied, are retrogressive. The chief part of the remaining inhabitants reminded us of exiles; and if they escape the ravages of famine, they must be nearly estranged to the common comforts of civilized life.

In making remarks so general, though we deem them to be just, it would be disingenuous not to admit every plea that humanity can suggest; and the abuse, which our country has received from roving foreigners,*— whether it be imputed to defects of the head or of the heart,—furnishes a cautionary hint. But though to decide on the manners and intelligence of a people, from what may be gathered in bar-rooms, is a practice sanctioned by custom; though almost every traveller refers to incidents connected with such scenes; and though his estimates of character receive a bias from them unknown

* The writer is unwilling that any person should suppose, that this remark was intended to apply to all foreign travellers. The candour displayed in the Travels of ROBERT SUTCLIFF, [MORRIS BIRKBECK], and JOHN MELISH merit our commendation; and cheerfully would he add any other exceptions equally worthy.

to himself; yet the native patriot would revolt to have his countrymen tried by this rule; for he well knows, that a tavern gang do not represent the population of a neighborhood.

Again, we ought not to forget, that the track of a traveller is but a line drawn through a country. No two inhabitants of the land are alike, and manners and improvements equally vary. The tendency to imitation, inherent in man, however, is continually reducing this difference; though degrees of industry and varieties of soil should not be overlooked.

Further, citizens from different parts of the Union, might vary in judgment. In the Northern States, dwellings are placed near the road, as most convenient for a trading people; but further south, the farmer,— shy of strangers, and unpractised in petty commerce,— retires behind gates and bars, to a situation more remote. Such, also, is the custom of this district; and though we travelled miles without seeing a house, we were assured, that the country is generally settled. It must therefore be admitted, that there is much which we have not seen.

27   We also learn that a road further westward, leading to Pittsburgh through the town of *Mercer*, though more circuitous, is bordered by better settlements. This road, indeed, only deserves the name of *a track*. It is little used and less repaired. Trees, fallen across it, sometimes rendered our progress difficult; and much rain, attended by thunder and lightning from the west, fell on us in situations remote from shelter, except what our waggons afforded. To increase the measure of disaster, provisions of every kind are scarce. Though under the pressure of evils like these, it would be ignoble to despond, yet we suspect that "the soul's calm sunshine," is rarely enjoyed in such scenes.

On some of the hills, notwithstanding the severity of the late frosts, the young peaches remained uninjured.

                                                20 miles.

6 *mo.* 2.—This morning I went with our landlord to view a bed of limestone. The colour is a dull bluish

white, and the stratum appears thin ; but probably there will be no deficiency of this useful material in building.

In the catalogue of calamities that afflict a country, we should place disputed titles to the soil ; and this unfortunate state has witnessed the evil in great variety. Happily, however, on the north and west, the state lines were ascertained previous to actual settlement ; and the circular line, round New Castle, only related to jurisdiction ; but in the contests with Maryland and Virginia, the private right of soil was also involved ; and the Connecticut claim, was a long time, the source of discouragement, and even of bloodshed.

These controversies, though violent, were local. Another existed, less formidable in appearance, but which has tended greatly to diminish the internal prosperity of the state ; and to which, we now find, the present deplorable condition of this district should be imputed.

During Wayne's Indian war, the POPULATION COMPANY failed to procure settlers, according to the original expectation ; and their claim was presumed to be forfeited. In consequence, the state offered one hundred acres for twenty pounds, provided the occupant should remain five years, erect a habitable house, and clear eight or ten acres of land. These terms induced the poorest people to become settlers. Though poverty is not always connected with indolence, yet in our country, where it appears, the union, at least, is frequent ; and the means of doing much was wanting, even where the spirit remained unbroken.

But other causes conspired to retard improvement. The calls of nature for food and clothing, were imperious ; and the slow returns of agriculture were unequal to the urgency of those demands. Necessity compelled them to neglect the labours of the field for the chace. Habits, subversive of industry were thus acquired ; simply *to live,* bounded the view of their ambition, and it has long been remarked, that *hunters never grow rich.* Indeed, he who depends on the forest for his meat, from year to year, ought not to be enrolled as a citizen.

To crown all, the Supreme Court of the U. States declared their titles a nullity, and to ejectment and starvation, we ascribe the desolation noticed yesterday.

Farms, thirty miles below Meadville, with considerable improvements, may be purchased for four dollars an acre, and some say for less. The titles are now indisputable. The timber is valuable, the streams appear to be durable, and the fountains free from calcareous impregnation. Its salubrity cannot be questioned. The soil is loose and easy to cultivate, and the grasses flourish; but wheat and rye, it is said are thrown out in winter. We are satisfied, however, that this evil is to be charged to the farmer, as agriculture is in its most degraded state. A new race of inhabitants is necessary to the prosperity of this place; and we think, that a body of emigrants from the eastward, who could be satisfied with land moderately fertile, might soon acquire wealth.

A company from Virginia are now raising ore for a furnace, about to be erected on *Scrub Grass* Creek*, five miles east of this road.

A morning of bright sunshine has much effect on the spirits; but after travelling a few miles ours were much heightened by the prospect of well improved farms, embellished by decent buildings. No want of industry appears; but that skill, which preserves the fertility of arable lands, seemed unknown.

At *Moore's*, where we took a late breakfast, we were pleased with the view of a prairie, as it is called by the inhabitants. The land is handsomely level, but thinly timbered with white oak and hazle bushes. The young

---

* Scrub Grass is called, in Scipio, " Rushes." Both names are improper, the plant belonging to the natural order of ferns (*Filices*) and to the genus *Equisetum*, or horse tail. To the housewife, it is a valuable burnisher for pewter and tin. It is also employed on wooden ware.

trees have been killed by fires. There is nothing in the soil, however, unfriendly to their growth, as they are shooting up in all directions.

Yesterday, I noticed a fine species of *Lonicera*, with yellow blossoms; and to day, much of it has appeared at the road sides. It is trailing, or climbs on other shrubs. I first saw the *Ascyrum hypericoides* after crossing French Creek, and it continues very plenty through this district.

After passing six or eight miles over hills, which are much encumbered by sand rocks, the country becomes more level and very free from stones. It is not, however, the level of a plain, but the surface is considerably diversified. The soil is a loam, in some places inclining to sand, and moderately fertile.

A smart little boy, of ten or twelve years of age, whom we saw at an inn, was asked if he went to school. No, sir, (was his reply) I have never been to school. We think no child, back along this road for thirty miles, would declare the reverse; and we draw this inference from seeing no building which we could believe to be a school house.

In the evening, I first saw the willow-leaved oak, on a sand hill. The leaves were expanded.

Lodged at *White's*. This, it is said, is the best tavern between Pittsburgh and Meadville.

24 miles.

Slippery rock Creek,* is a heavy mill stream, running 28 westwardly, which we crossed on a bridge. We heard the roaring of falls just below. The country, for twelve miles back, is handsomely diversified with easy elevations; but a little south of this water, we found hills extending to the east and west. Among these, we passed

---

* This stream is a branch of *Beaver*, a large creek, which flows into the Ohio river, at the *North Bend*, twenty nine miles N. W. of Pittsburgh.

through many hundreds of acres destitute of timber. It is called a prairie, and afforded an extensive view of high lands to the westward. The trees have been destroyed by fires, and only in this respect it differs from the land around.

In a bank, we saw limestone in horizontal strata and above it, sand stone in similar form. Coal is found near the surface, and I suspect it has been first laid bare by the torrent or the plough. Many spots of black earth, indicative of this fossil, appeared at the road side.

6 *mo.* 8.—The country continued open a few miles below White's, where it rose into hills of considerable magnitude; but I could not perceive that they extended in any regular direction.* After climbing and winding among them for two or three miles, we came to the *Conequenessing,*† a fine creek which flows westward. Here we saw a coal mine. On examination, we found the incumbent strata to be shale, or clay slate, very similar to what we had seen on the shore of lake Erie. We observed both yesterday and to day, that slaty stones appeared in many places where the road was dug, and, doubtless, coal would soon be discovered by exploring. It is sold at the pit's mouth for sixpence a bushel, and is preferred by the inhabitants to wood for fuel,—the blaze being so brilliant as to supersede the use of candles, even for sewing.

29   * These hills differ from those up the country, not only by the striking characteristic noted in the text, but also by the interspersion of *mica* through the sand stone. While we remained in Pittsburgh, I became fully convinced, by many facts which will be detailed in their proper places, that this country owes the shape of its surface to the first flowing of the streams; and that the alluvial mass, which once filled these vallies, was washed away, while it remained in its loosest state, and before the commencement of petrification. During a journey of more than a thousand miles through that district, in which my attention was daily awake to this idea, I saw nothing to invalidate, but much to confirm it.

† Vulgarly pronounced Kan-a-kan-ace.

We breakfasted late, near *Breakneck Creek*, which flows westward. Here limestone is found in quarry. A furnace, five miles below, near the junction of this stream with Conequenessing,* produces castings of a superior quality, and in great quantity. It is a new work, having only made two blasts. Two kinds of ore are named—one tough and the other hard ; but we were told that four kinds are found further up the country, viz. honey comb, sand or gravel ore, bog ore, and grains of metallic lustre. The sandstone, which is easily wrought into any shape, contains mica, and resists the heat of the furnace.

At *Breakneck*, our attention was arrested by a most singular phenomenon in the progress of vegetation. The hills, which are several hundred feet high, exhibit three well marked gradations. The oak trees, for almost half way up, have not yet opened the buds, and appear as naked as in winter. Such as are higher up, and reaching towards the top are opened in the down, of a whitish grey colour; while those on the summit are completely expanded in the full green of summer. We have not observed any difference of soil, sufficient to account for this extraordinary appearance.

Harmony, the settlement made by Rapp's congregation,—a religious sect, who emigrated a few years ago, from Germany,—lies nearly west of this place on another road, which also leads to Pittsburgh. This people cultivated the vine extensively ; but dissatisfied, perhaps, with the climate, they lately removed to Indiana. So much, however, is related of their extraordinary improvements, that we greatly regret our not taking that place in the line of our journey.

Having travelled twenty-four miles, we stopt at *Brown's* before sunset, seven miles from Pittsburgh. This house is built of stone, and well furnished. The inhabitants are from Connecticut.

* This is also a branch of Beaver creek, before noticed.

The country for twenty miles back is of the most un
even kind. In all that distance, if we except some
small flats on the creeks, we believe that not one acre
of level land can be found. Nor could I perceive that
the hills had any regular course. Its configuration
greatly resembles that part of Chester county, in this
state, which includes Pikeland and Vincent.

Near the summit of every hill, we observed an ochreous earth, reddish, and greasy to the touch. Coal, limestone, iron ore and sandstone are still discovered along
this road; but the last is found but in few places, suitable for building. Strata of this stone, which break up
small on removal from the quarry, are very abundant,
and contain *mica.* The particles of this substance are
thin, and in perpendicular fractures scarcely perceptible.

That the integrant parts of sand rock owe their
origin to quartz is evinced by the actual state of granitic soils. The fragments of these crystals appear to have
been taken up, removed, and subsequently deposited
by water. To this process, we refer the assortment
and horizontal arrangement of sand; and this substance,
departing with the *mica* from the same primitive rock,
accompanied, and settled with it in the specimens before us.*

Since yesterday morning, we have passed many
farms, the proprietors of which have displayed a laudable activity in erecting good houses of durable materials; and this disposition is more apparent as we advance towards Pittsburgh. Yet we cannot exempt them
from much of the censure involved in the following
general statement, though doubtless the degrees of it
will vary.

Agriculture is at its lowest ebb, both in theory and
practice; and we have never seen its operations so miserably conducted throughout the same extent of country. The advantages of clover appear to be unknown;

---

* Sand from the shores of the Ocean, or other large collections of water, is generally rounded by rolling in the waves; but
that which is procured from the soil, or deposited by small
streams in ponds, retains its angles unbroken, and from its sharpness is less suitable for burnishing pewter.

and even that of scattering stable manure ; or that a
soil may be deepened. Consequently, the plough seldom turns it up from a depth of more than three inches ; the roots of the crop take a feeble hold ; and the
moisture of winter, retained at the surface, expanding
into ice, often effects a fatal dislodgment.

The scarcity, and the high price of provisions, with
the low price of land, ought chiefly to be imputed to
the state of agriculture ; for the purchase of all the
contested claims to the soil would only amount to a
small sum. A rage for descending the Ohio, perhaps
should be taken into view, and may assist in explaining why so many deserted dwellings have continued to
begloom our way.

That the women generally perform most of the labours of the field, is an assurance which I am inclined
to distrust, though it may be true in some instances.
We saw many girls, on the road to meeting, who,
though decently dressed in other respects, were bare-
foot. This only denoted simple manners ; but the condition of dogs and swine, with some few exceptions,
are deplorable, and truly indicative of habitual scarcity.

A great proportion of this district is well adapted to
the cultivation of clover, and I look forward with impatience to the introduction of that invaluable plant.
With moderate skill, and the application of Gypsum,
the crops of wheat might be increased four fold, besides the additional supplies of hay and pasture. *That*
manure could be afforded cheap at Erie ; and a portage of
fourteen miles of good turnpike, would place it on boatable waters, to be distributed at convenient landings.

6 *mo.* 4.—The same singular appearance, respecting
the greenness of the trees on the summits of the hills,
continues. It is so very distinctly marked in its height,
that the lower buds of the same tree have not expanded, while the upper branches are perfectly green. We
obtain a correct idea by supposing that a vapour, un-
frendly to vegetation, had filled all the vallies ; and,
doubtless, this is the true explanation.

This country, though infinitely irregular, begins to exhibit more marks of fertility. Wheat and rye are tolerable, and some attempts have been made at introducing clover. Four miles from Pittsburgh, I noticed upland hickory on the hills. Black walnut, which we have rarely seen since we left Erie, appears in considerable quantities; and here we passed the northern boundary of that land where the locust and persimmon are indigenous.

Black earth, denoting coal,—and marl intermixed with lime rock, in small quantities,—we saw by the way side. Coal is sold above Pittsburgh for four cents a bushel, at the mine; but we were surprised to find it carried six or eight miles, when its indications are found on almost every farm.

The three last days have been pleasant summer weather.

Pittsburgh was hidden from our view, until we descended through the hills within half a mile of the *Allegany river*. Dark dense smoke was rising from many parts, and a hovering cloud of this vapour, obscuring the prospect, rendered it singularly gloomy. Indeed, it reminded me of the smoking logs of a new field.

Having been landed on the eastern side of the river, for the *even sum* of fifty cents, we soon found ourselves in the crowded streets of "the Birmingham of America."

We staid in this city until the morning of the 14th. The form of a Diary *will therefore be discontinued until that date.*

On the 8th, our worthy friend J. Ridgway *departed on his journey to Cincinnati. We hoped to overtake him in a few days, and afterwards heard of him on the road, but our next meeting was in Scipio, some months after our return.*

Remarks on this place and its environs, follow.

THIS city stands on a plain, being a point of land formed by the junction of the Allegany and Mononga-hela rivers. Below this point these waters take the name of *Ohio*. It is surrounded by high hills, which close the prospect in every direction; and on viewing this stream in the interior of a great continent, we are surprised that it has worn its way, round so many obstacles to the ocean.

The streets of Pittsburgh are lighted, and conse-quently the useful order of watchmen is established. My ears, however, have not become reconciled to their mu-sic. It is true, I have been more conversant in forests than in cities, and may not comprehend the advanta-ges of these deep-mouthed tones; but breaking the slumbers of the invalid, and giving timely notice to the thief, form two items of much weight in my view as a set off against them.

Pittsburgh is laid out to front both rivers; but as these do not approach at right angles, the streets inter-sect each other obliquely.

It is not a well built city. The south-west part is the most compact, but many years must elapse before it will resemble Philadelphia. Wooden buildings, in-terspersed with those of brick, mar the beauty of its best streets; and as few of these are paved, mud, in showery weather, becomes abundant. A short period, however, will probably terminate this inconvenience.

The slitting and rolling mill, together with the nail factory of *Stackpole & Whiting*, is moved by a steam engine of seventy-horse power. These we visited with much satisfaction. On entering the south-west door, the eye catches the majestic swing of the beam; and at the same instant, nine nailing-machines, all in rapid motion, burst on the view. Bewildered by the varying velocity of so many new objects, we stand astonished at this sublime effort of human ingenuity.

The plate, to be cut into nails, is fixed in an iron cramp with a short wooden handle. The workman is seated; and with a motion of the arm, like a smith who turns his iron under the hammer, he alternately inverts the plate to keep the end square. The breadth of the nail is accurately guaged, as in other nailing-machines; but at the instant of its separation, and before it can move, it is clamped to the spot by a strong iron jaw, which leaves the broader end to project, while an iron mallet at one blow completes the head.

While J. R. held his watch, I made several attempts to count the number of strokes in a minute; but the motion was too quick. The nails would ascertain it, but we never saw the workman keep pace with the machine for one minute. Knowing, however, that between three and four may be counted in a second, I compute the strokes at two hundred and forty.

The smaller nails are cut cold, but the plates for brads are heated. These articles are inferior in neatness to those of Pearson's of New-York; but this defect might be remedied by using thinner plates, though the profit to the proprietors would probably be reduced. The quantity made is about one and a half tons per day; and 20 cents a pound is the common retail price.

The cut nail is an American invention; and the immense demand, for this article, proves its value. Our list of patents shews more than thirty improvements or rather *variations* of this manufacture.

Two cotton factories, one woollen factory, one paper mill, two saw mills, and one flour mill, are all moved by steam, in this city and in its suburbs across the Monongahela. Four glass factories, two for flint, and two for green, are very extensive; and the productions of the former for elegance of workmanship, are scarcely surpassed by European manufacture. It is sent in many directions from this place; one of the proprietors assured us that Philadelphia receives a part, but the great outlet is down the Ohio.

The vast advantages that accrue to this place, from
ts coal, will be appreciated, when we consider, that almost every manufacture owes its existence to this article of fuel. The glass-houses, the furnaces for castings, the steam engines, and every domestic fire-place,
are supplied from the mines. These are situate near the
tops of the hills, in every direction from the city ; and
the vast mass of earth that once buried this plain, appears to have been removed by the waters. A correct
idea will be had, by supposing, (and even believing,)
that the stratum of coal once extended across from hill
to hill, several hundred feet above where the city now
stands.

The shafts of these mines extend far into the hills.
The pick-ax, and the shovel, are the instruments used ;
and on wheel-barrows, the coal is removed to the entrance, where it is placed on scaffolding, from which
waggons are conveniently loaded. The citizens are
supplied in their yards for 7 or 8 cents a bushel.

It is no new idea, that coal owes its origin to vegeta- 31
bles, which have been deposited by water, and compres-
sed by bodies of earth. The facts, that support this
opinion, are numerous. Those before us at present,
however, are less conclusive than some described by
naturalists in Europe ; but sufficiently satisfactory to
unprejudiced minds. Drift sand, cemented into rocks ;
limestone, wholly composed of marine shells ; and
coal, containing the semblance of twigs, all in horizontal strata, impress conviction of this truth.

Though these appearances of twigs are noticed by many observers, I have seen none so distinct as to remove
all doubts of their identity. To take a correct view of
this subject, we must, however, remember that from the
moment these masses ceased to vegetate, decomposition commenced ; and this has been accelerated or retarded, according to circumstances. Generally the
preservation of the vegetable form, depends on the ex-
clusion of air. But whether different mines of this
fossil were formed of plants which grew in different
and distant periods of time, may be a question. Cer-

tain it is,that a change which required a long lapse of ages
to produce, in one situation, may have been speedily effected in another, which was more exposed to the action
of those agents, that nature has multiplied at the surface of the earth.   Thus slate, (here called "horseback,") is the common covering of coal mines; and I
was assured, that wherever the stratum was not deeply
buried, the quality of the coal was injured; indeed, by
its digestion in water, petroleum is produced.   Thus
also by coaking, the bitumen is expelled, and the result
is a coal similar to that found in mines near the heads
of Schuylkill.   As it then chiefly consists of carbon,
like that substance, it affords an intense heat, but emits
no flame during combustion.   Those mines, however,
appear to claim a higher antiquity than those at Ohio;
and by lying in every position, evince convulsions of
nature, which have not reached this country, or which
were anterior to its formation.

The conversion of wood into jet is perhaps the first
part of the process which produces coal.   In some situations at least, this is evident; and in this state it first
assumes the shining fracture which so eminently marks
pit-coal.   This lustre seems to increase till the bitumen is all removed; and may be ascribed, with its greater specific gravity, to a greater degree of compactness.

I learn that a lower stratum of coal has been discovered in the bottom of the Monongahela, and in several wells which were dug in this city.   Some of the natives of England, who have settled here, have been induced to believe from this, " *low main coal*," and from
the strata of that country, that every mine proves the existence of a corresponding bed below it.   However to
those who may be employed in the business of exploring, a few observations on this supposed analogy may
be proper.

The strata of coal countries have been deposited at
different periods.   This is demonstrated by the fact,
that sand of the same size forms layers both above and
below beds of limestone and of coal; for one volume
of water could not deposit all the different substances,
unmixed with each other, as they are found through these

hills. To adopt *that* opinion, the inference would then be clear, that the same or similar floods had strewed equal portions of sand, of shells, and of vegetables, over England and over Ohio. Now, it is very questionable, whether such conformity generally prevails on the opposite shores of an ocean three thousand miles wide; in lands still further separated by lofty ranges of mountains; and where much irregularity attends even some of the strata of small districts.

32

This irregularity, however, prevails less in the coal stratum than in those of sandstone; and round this place for fifty miles in every direction, we learn that this valuable fuel is discovered. At that distance up the Allegany, it forms the bed of the river. But if it is a continuation of this stratum, as some intelligent persons believe, it must have a dip opposite to the strata of Lake Erie; as it is improbable that the falls in that river equal one-fourth of the height of these coal mines.

As the two rivers approach, the hills between them, form a lofty ridge for some distance, but decline towards the city, where they finally terminate. In tracing this elevation south-easterly, no coal is found until we ascend to the level of that stratum; and this is so regular that a workman, with a board and plummet at one mine, could point out the spot on the opposite hill, where another might be opened.

On the day of our arrival in this city, we had several thunder showers from the west. The weather then became clear; and for three days we had brisk gales from the north-west, of unusual severity for summer. The surface of the rivers was rolled into foam, and each night was attended by considerable frost. Indeed, it still continues. (6 mo. 10.)

It is said here, (as at Scipio) that *the seasons* are much colder than formerly; and the conversation always terminates, whenever the subject is introduced, by a reference to the great eclipse of 1806. At this turn, I have always listened with diminished respect.

This popular opinion took its rise, from some cool weather, in the summer seasons of 1806 and 1807. A retardment, in the average progress of vegetation, for a few days was deemed cause sufficient to overlook all terrestrial agents for the absorption of heat, and to charge it directly to the moon.

Of the facility, with which errors not palpable to the senses, may be propagated, we have long been aware; but that men of understanding should adopt this notion,—which originated in the grossest ignorance of the causes of eclipses,—is surprising. Such, however, is the case, and to these I offer a few observations.

The same shadow that attends the moon, has constantly projected its dark cone since the creation. Within every term of a few years, its point has touched the earth; at least twice in every year, our satellite has passed so nearly between us and the sun, as partially to hide it; and once in every month, it has revolved round the earth, and approached as near to us, as it did on the day of the great eclipse. These are facts that admit of no dispute; and the inference is clear and consistent, that, if eclipses affect the weather, the seasons ought to be equalized by such an equality of causes.

Other views of this subject, would justify the assertion, that a solar eclipse has no effect whatever on the atmosphere, except during its continuance. The darkness is nothing but a transient shadow. No reason can be given why the moon, in passing between us and the sun, should produce more extraordinary effects than when the earth rolls between us and that luminary. The latter case happens every twenty-four hours; and the chillness in clear weather is not only much greater, but the duration of the darkness will average more than three hundred times longer than in other eclipses.

But every point of view, in which this belief can be placed, shows its absurdity; and whether it be said, that a pernicious vapour escaped from the shade of the moon, or that the atmosphere received a shock, the supporters of this doctrine are equally discountenanced.

It will be proper to inquire, if the seasons have been uniformly colder since the year 1806 than before that period? A correct answer to this question would shew that much fallacy attends this popular opinion. Pennsylvania has been subject to summer frosts since its first settlement; not, indeed, very destructive, but sufficient to shew that cool weather was frequent. The celebrated DAVID RITTENHOUSE, who resided many years in *Norriton,* twenty miles north west of *Philadelphia,* asserted, " that he had discovered frost at that place in every month of the year, except July." He died in 1797.

This was in times of old. In more modern days, but *before the eclipse,* I remember a severe frost in some parts of Scipio, in the 6th month, 1800 ; and a considerable fall of snow happened at Philadelphia in the 5th month 1803. Many of the citizens were awakened in the morning, by the crashing of Lombardy poplars, the branches of which were in full leaf, and unable to support the load.

We will now notice some seasons, *since the eclipse,* of a different character. The spring of 1808 opened so early, that flax was sown in Scipio, in the 3d month, and on the first of the 4th month, young cattle were turned to pasture, because there was a sufficiency of grass. The whole summer was unusually pleasant, excepting some extremely hot days. Similar observations were made on the year 1811, one of the most remarkable. which the oldest settlers in Cayuga county remember. The spring opened about the 1st of the 3d month, without any subsequent frost; and the autumn was so fine that its mildness was ascribed to *the comet.*

It thus appears, that the popular doctrine of eclipses is inconsistent with reason, and contradicted by facts.

This reference, to which I object, comports well, however, with the operations of the human mind. Whenever two remarkable occurrences, whether real or imaginary, have happened near the same period, the ignorant in all ages, have believed that one depends on the other. Ancient astronomers arranged the disasters of the times with their accounts of comets and eclipses; and in our own day we have had three remarkable illustrations of this principle. In Eastern Pennsylvania,

———— the swift
And perilous lightnings, from the angry clouds,

were observed by some to be much increased, on the introduction of plaster   To the north-east, the frequen-
cy of cold winds, since the great eclipse, has been *observed* beyond all former example; but in the south-
western part of the United States, *where no great
eclipse appeared,* some of the old inhabitants declare,
that this change of seasons arrived with the Yankees,
from the north.

There are causes, however,—not uniform but occasional,—to which we may rationally ascribe a decrease
of temperature in our climate. We have no warm
winds from the north. In winter we experience its severity; and in summer, the more tender vegetables occasionally suffer from frost. On the reverse, continued
south winds uniformly produce warm weather. Even
in the season of winter, the frozen earth becomes
thawed, and we enjoy the warmth of spring or of autumn. All the difference of climate, that we feel, appears to depend on the currents of the atmosphere.

Some reasons, indeed, might be advanced, why the
belief, that the seasons have become colder, might originate without the fact. To one weakness our nature
is incident, which ought not to be overlooked in this inquiry. It has been remarked in different and distant
ages, that old men are prone to censure things of the
present day, and to contrast them with former and hap-
pier times,—not omitting the weather. This is justly ascribed to constitutional decline. The relish for
pleasure has abated; a weaker action of the heart is attended with a corresponding diminution of heat in the
system; and the increasing sensation of chillness is
charged to a change of climate.

We ought also to recollect, that a few years ago, our
fields were sheltered by woods; and every farmer has
observed the difference, in spring, between vegetables
growing in bleak and in secluded situations. The hunter rarely feels the wind in the forest. The recrements
of vegetables, by having imparted blackness to the soil,
also increased its power of absorbing heat. But the
mass has become more compact, and the plough now
turns up the paler coloured subsoil. Stable manure,

partially by restoring this property to our old fields,
produces an important advancement in vegetation.

I have no design to press these arguments beyond
their just weight. I admit that we have many uncomfortable blasts; but I am convinced that in remarks on
the weather, we often witness a morbid sensibility. We
ought not, however, to forget the blessings that surround us, much less to arraign the beneficent order of
nature. We should remember that the balmy breezes
of spring are not those that prepare the most abundant
harvest;—cold rain, and chilling winds, by retarding
the ascent of the stalk, invigorates the root; and that
the richness of our pastures at Cayuga, are unknown
in southern climates.

It has been published, that the *Library* of this city
contains two thousand volumes. Through the politeness of J. Armstrong, the librarian, I gained admittance,
and having examined the catalogue, am enabled to state
that the whole collection is only about five hundred volumes. The books, however, are well chosen, and of
the best editions. How the error originated is of no
consequence except to him who made it.

It is difficult, for a stranger, to obtain correct information respecting the manufactures of a city. But a
traveller is only a gleaner, and ought to bring his mind
to his condition.

Our common fruit trees do well in Pittsburgh. The
peach, the plumb, the apple and the cherry, abound on
the branches, though the frosts have been very severe.
Much of this exemption ought to be ascribed to the
smoke, which constantly, day and night, loads the atmosphere over this place. But this benefit is not without a counterpoise. Often descending in whirls thro' the
streets, it tarnishes every object to which it has access.

The gloomy appearance thus imparted to the houses,
especially to those of wood, whether painted or not, is
such as instantly to fix the attention of a stranger. The
bark of the trees literally "gather blackness;" and a
large honey locust *(Gledistia triacanthos)* growing near
one of the founderies, could receive no darker coat

from the painter's brush. Contrasted with the green leaves, the aspect is strikingly singular.

We cannot conceive that the expense and inconvenience of burning smoke is very formidable; and until such a regulation be adopted, the application of all bright colours, to the external parts of buildings, should be deferred. The additional quantities of light and heat, that might thus be disengaged, would form an item of much value.

I am assured that clothes, sullied before they can dry, are often returned to the wash tub in unfavorable weather.

I had long since remarked, in Scipio, that when south-west wind prevailed, the atmosphere was loaded with smoke; and the cause of this had become an interesting subject of inquiry. We pretend not to have made the discovery in full— we assign not to Pittsburgh the manufacture of all this article; but the quantity produced here is astonishing, and seems sufficient to tinge the air with its sable particles for hundreds of miles.

In calm weather, it rises from the glass-houses and furnaces in columns of great grandeur; and so dense is this vapour, that a poet might fancy it a solid,

" Like the pillars of the skies."

We remark much difference between the manners of the inhabitants of this country and those of Cayuga. In that place, profane language is rarely heard from any person, who pretends to decency, except in a paroxysm of vexation. Here it is an every day amusement. Crossing the Monongahela, in the ferry-boat, with an intelligent gentleman of polished manners, I was shocked and surprised to hear almost every sentence from his lips interlarded with an oath or an imprecation ; yet he was in gay good humour, and, I believe, unconscious of this breach of decorum.

It would be unjust not to express my belief, that honourable exceptions to these censures are numerous; but impiety certainly constitutes a strong characteristic of no inconsiderable part of this people. We had

the first specimen in the teamsters who were taking
flour from Waterford to Erie ; and heard more vile language in one night than in the preceding six months.

A species of *Chrysosplenium?* with ternate leaves,
abounds in moist places round this city.

Most of the *steam engines* used here, are on Evans's
plan ; and a company have established a factory for
their construction. The boilers are hollow cylinders,
nearly two feet in diameter, and twenty or thirty feet
in length. These are formed of thick plates of rolled
iron, connected by strong rivets, and closed at the ends
by pieces of cast metal. When used, they are placed
side by side in a horizontal position ; and being only
part filled with water, a large surface is exposed for
evaporation, while the upper segment restrains the
steam.

It being of the utmost importance that the piston, on
the end of which the steam presses, should accurately
fit the upright cylinder, these parts are *turned and bored*
by machinery connected with a steam engine. These
operations are performed with much regularity. The
borer and chisel move like the log on a saw mill, and
require no manual labour.

Engines, on Watt and Bolton's plan, are also made
here : and great diversity of opinion prevails on the
respective merits of these inventions ; but in fact very
few are qualified to form a correct judgment on the subject.

I have remarked with regret the impiety of some of
these citizens ; but we think, that generally, they are
entitled to much praise for obliging and courteous behaviour. Civility to strangers, in a high degree, even
pervades their factories ; and in all those which I have
visited, the mean practice of permitting children to ask
the spectators for money, appears to be unknown.

The *steam-boat navigation*, we are assured, is a los-
ing concern. The newspapers have announced the
hopes of our western citizens, and the editors now ap-

T
272

pear to be careful to conceal their disappointments.
Two large vessels of this description are lying near the
Point, which have not justified public expectations.
Captain FRENCH, of *Brownsville,* (fifty miles by water
up the Monongahela and thirty-five by land) has built
two vessels of this kind, which it is said have succeeded best. The wheel is placed behind.* The advantages of this construction over the Fultonian plan must
be evident; for the *float-board strikes the advancing current* as it flows into the *wake,* while those of the latter
strike it as it passes the vessel. The wheel is also sheltered from drift wood and ice.

We are told that the captain has been harassed at
New-Orleans, with lawsuits, under the grant made by
that government to Fulton & Livingston. I cannot feel
myself a party in these contests in the most remote degree except where the prosperity of the country suffers,
or the privileges of the citizen are infringed. Doubtless these distinguished men deserved encouragement;
but the propriety,— nay the right,— of a legislature to
fetter genius, may fairly be questioned; and a donation as a tribute to merit, would have comported better
with the dignity of a state, and the rights of a free
people.

The falls of the Ohio will probably be an important
point in the line of that navigation. Intelligent men
affirm, that a vessel, suitable to the river above that
place, is too small to navigate the Mississippi to the
best advantage. The benefits which may accrue from
this mode of conveyance must therefore be greatly diminished above the fall.

Notwithstanding these discouraging appearances, we
look forward with confidence to a period, not remote,
when all foreign commodities, for this country, will move

---

* On the morning of our departure, from this city, we saw a
vessel of ten or fifteen tons burden, on this construction, which
appeared to be intended to accommodate parties of pleasure. and
which was propelled by hand. Both time and place, (the ferry
boat) were unfavourable to our obtaining any further information.

in the train of this powerful agent. The cheapness, the excellence, and the inexhaustible quantity, of fuel, that await the hand of Industry on the banks of these waters, offer facilities to commerce that no other region of our empire exhibits; and a population distinguished by enterprize and awake to this subject will doubtless, soon avail themselves of advantages so beneficently given.

Provisions of all kinds bring a high price in this city though the *market* is fluctuating. Hay, at present is twenty dollars a ton, and oats one dollar per bushel. Butter varies from twenty-five to seventy-five cents per pound. The farmers of this neighbourhood, however, produce neither cheese or pork, that merits a notice. The former of these articles is chiefly obtained from the state of Ohio, and bacon, procured from Kentucky, is now retailed at sixteen or seventeen cents per pound.

Before the late war, this market was distinguished for its cheapness; but with an influx of strangers, induced by the movements of that period, "*war prices*" commenced; and though peace has returned—and though many of those new comers have sought their former places of residence,--the encouragements held out to the farmer, suffers no diminution. Indeed, there are great inducements for the *industrious* to migrate hither. Though the soil is uneven, it is far from being sterile; and exclusive of salubrity of situation, and of durable timber for fences, the coal mines, which pervade almost every hill, constitute treasures of great value.

Farms round this city, at the distance of two or three miles have been lately sold from fifty to one hundred dollars an acre, according to situation.

Desirous of ascertaining the *height of the coal stratum* above the rivers,---but destitute of the instruments for that purpose,--I adopted the following simple method. Though liable to some inaccuracy in practice, it was sufficiently exact for my views, where an error of a few feet was of little consequence. It may interest some of my young readers. **34**

The opposite banks of the river, equal in height, furnish two points in the plane of the sensible horizon, from which may be determined how far back the flats coincide with that plane. A line, from the coal mine on the opposite hill, passing through the top of a long erect piece of scantling, till it touches the plane, forms the hypothenuse of a right angled triangle, the perpendicular of which, is the height of the mine. I therefore drew two (horizontal) lines at right angles to the base of that triangle, one from the end of the hypothenuse, and one from the scantling; because, a perpendicular plane, passing through the mine, to the right or left of the triangle, would cut the horizontal lines of unequal lengths; and by Euclid, B. VI. Prop. 4.

> As their difference (in length)
> Is to their distance (apart)
> So is the length of the first horizontal,
> To the (horizontal) distance of the mine. And,
> As their distance (apart)
> Is to the height of the scantling,
> So is the distance last found
> To the perpendicular height of the mine.

By my mensuration, these proportions determined that height to be 470 feet above the flats.

By the first of these proportions, and the necessary admeasurement, I also found the Allegany River, at a medial height, to occupy about 340 yards of breadth. The Monongahela is supposed to be fifty yards wider.

It is intended to erect Bridges over both these rivers; and persons desirous to contract for these jobs, have been notified to bring in their proposals.*

When we consider, that the land between these streams forms an acute angle,—and constitutes not more than one fifth or sixth of what a circle of ten miles round this city would enclose,—the benefit that will ensue from these to both town and country, will be appreciated; and especially in times of flood and of floating ice, it must be truly important.

* Monongahela bridge was completed about the 20th of 11 mo 1818. The proposed bridge over the Allegany, is not so far advanced.

Having been informed that muscle shells are found in a bed of two or three acres, near the top of a hill three miles south-eastwardly from Pittsburgh, this delightful morning (6 mo. 11,) I traced to that distance one of the roads that diverge over this elevated tract. My excursion and inquiries were fruitless, as to that object; though the search was far from being complete. It was, however, productive of much satisfaction. On ascending to the level of the *coal* stratum, I saw *mines* opened in various places; and the irregular shape of the hills has rendered it unnecessary to sink any perpendicular shaft. Almost every brook runs on a channel which is worn below that level, and consequently the coal appears in the side of the slope.

I mentioned my belief, that the coal stratum once extended from hill to hill, far above where the rivers now flow. Further observations confirm that opinion. A difficulty was at first presented in the questions, Would the rains of ordinary seasons in thousands of years, have removed such immense bodies of earth and sand, as it would now require to fill up all the chasms between all these hills? And, How could such currents carry off rocks, remnants of which strata now project from the sides of the hills? We observe, indeed, that the soil is loose, and wherever the rain is collected by the surface into rills, the fields are extremely gullied; but this is insufficient to account for the extraordinary appearance of the country.

Theories of this kind, often assume the features of extravagance; but the following propositions appear so evident to me, that I feel no hesitation in giving them a place. "The low main coal" is purposely left out of view.

That sand, and some shells, from a base of unknown depth, has been piled up, stratum upon stratum, to the height of the coal mines. That the vegetables, which now form such inexhaustible beds of fuel, were next deposited. That above these, to the height of 150 or 200 feet, sand and earth continued to accumulate. That

then,--before* any part of these materials were cement-
35 ed into rock, a deluge, brought hither by preternatural
means, was led off along the present channels of the
rivers.   That its action, on this loose or half-fluid mass,
was sufficient to dislodge vast portions; thus forming a
surface of infinite irregularity, and yet preserving the
horizontal position of these remnants of the strata.

Crossing one of these hills in a south-east direction,
I was agreeably surprised to find a valley before me,
spreading from the Monongahela to the north-east.   It
appeared to be nearly a mile wide.   The prospect, however, was not limited by this, but embraced the distant
woods to the south-west; and those whose views have
been confined by the hills, as seen from the city, can
have no idea of its beauty and extent.

Several of these farms are pleasantly situated; and
the long rows of cherry trees, near one of the houses,
recalled strongly to mind the scenes of my youth.
This property, the fields of which border on the hill to
the north-west, was particularly pleasing, and would be
sufficient to render any good farmer rich; but though
the soil is naturally fertile, loose, and easily cultivated,
agriculture is so imperfectly understood, that its products might readily be increased fourfold.

On the south-east brow of this hill, I observed the
following plants.   To the intelligent agriculturist,
they will form the best comment on what I have said of
its fertility.

* Not far from *Chartier's Creek*, on our road from Steubenville
to Pittsburgh, we saw a large field on the side of a hill.   Near
the middle of the slope a rocky stratum projects, and for a few
rods, the fragments were collected in piles.   Both above and below this range, we saw no appearance of stone.   Now, it is evident, as currents of water would only remove the sand and gravel, or smaller stones, that this stratum must not have been
a rock at the time of its removal.   But indeed almost every hill
throughout this region, exhibits something- if not so striking,
yet—equally conclusive to the attentive observer.

Juglans nigra	black walnut
cinerea	butternut
squamosa	shell-bark
amara	white or bitter nut
glabra	upland hickory
Laurus benzoin	spice-wood
sassafras	sassafras
Quercus alba	white oak
prinos v. *palustris*	swamp-chestnut oak
rubra	red oak
tinctoria	black oak
———	pin? oak, black-jack.

(Leaves long and smooth, with neither serratures nor indentures.*)

Robinia pseud acacia	black locust
Gleditsia triacanthos	honey locust
Cercis canadensis	fish blossom
Vitis vinifera	grape vine
labrusca	———
Sanguinaria canadensis	red root
Actea racemosa	black snake root
Arum triphyllum	Indian turnip
Pyrus coronaria	crab apple
Podophyllum peltatum	mandrake, or May-apple
Platanus occidentalis	buttonwood, or syca-more
Rubus villosus	black berry
Rhus typhinum	stag's-horn sumach
Morus rubra	common mulberry
Acer saccharinum	sugar maple; and

doubtless there are many not noticed.

I sought much for the magnificent *Aristolochia sipho,* but in vain.

As I sat writing, near the summit of the hill, I was disturbed by the racing of two *grey squirrels,* which

---

* To the westward this is known by the name of black-jack. It is, however, a different species from the true black-jack, which is, or ought to be, Quercus *triloba.*

"scarce shunned me," though not because they had

"Grown so familiar with their frequent guest."

Such incidents, truly, are trifles; but to him who
enjoys solitude, they constitute some of the most pleas-
urable moments of life.

That these squirrels are a different species from the
black, (which I also saw not far back on our route) is
very questionable. Certain it is, that the latter appear
in every possible shade between black and grèy; and
that they associate together in Scipio. They are also
alike in their migratory disposition, traversing extensive districts, and swimming through rivers, and even
lakes.*

A total change from black to grey, it is said, took
place amongst them in New Jersey, after the settlement
of the upper part of that country; and when we consider the uniform colours of wild animals, the varieties
which attend domestication, together with the fact that
these quadrupeds now procure a new kind of food from
our fields, we shall cease to wonder at the change.

This is the native country of the opossum *(Didel-
phis opossum ;)* and also of the brown rabbit, the *Lepus
whabus* (of JEFFERSON.) The latter I have never known
further north than the foot of the Allegany, near Mun-
cey; but am unable to determine how far it is found on
the road towards Erie.

This animal, like the quail, delights in open winters,
and a cultivated country. In this respect, it forms a
contrast to the white hare *(Lepus timidus?)* which is
most numerous in the wildest parts of the Allegany
mountains. Different regions seem thus to have been
assigned to them; and though it has been said, that the
latter is extending its territory to the south, that opinion
may fairly be questioned, from the circumstance, that
since the great reduction of the woods, in Scipio, and

---

* This is frequent at Cayuga, where the lake is two or three
miles wide On landing, drenched and exhausted, they lie awhile
on the shore before they can escape to the woods.

The use of "bark" or "shingles," in such voyages, appears to
be unknown to these foresters.

the consequent diminution of snow, this quadruped is rarely seen.

On my return, I passed over sinks, occasioned by the incumbent earth falling into a coal mine. These, I conjecture, were forty or fifty rods from the mouth of the shaft. The great theatre of combination and dissolution is at the surface of the earth, and this fossil, in many places, is not sufficiently sheltered from the atmosphere. The miners, therefore, by passing directly into the hills, procure coal of a better quality.

I observed the peaches green on the trees, though the frosts have been very severe.

A few feet below a coal mine, where the hill slopes towards the city, I observed a thin lime rock, which seemed wholly composed of shells; but unskilled in Conchology, I can only state that they were smaller than those in the rocks of Cayuga, and of a different kind. The earth below it, as usual, was a marl.

The adjoining hills contain inexhaustible quarries of sand rock, suitable for grindstones; and several establishments, for the manufacture of these useful articles, are extensively conducted. As no marble is brought hither, except from the neighbourhood of *Philadelphia*,* those quarries also supply the citizens with gravestones. Near *Breakneck*, I noted that *mica* was contained in the sand rock and this singular addition is also found here, in all the strata of that stone which I have seen.

Zadok Cramer, who died some time since, near Natches, and late of the firm of Cramer, Spear and Eichbaum, of this city, was an estimable character; and his friends speak of him with a warmth of feeling and regret, honourable to him and to themselves. He had done much to disseminate knowledge, and introduce

* I was told at one of these factories, that no marble could be procured west of the mountains. It is a mistake: Marble is found in Kentucky, and might be brought hither by water, much cheaper than from Philadelphia.

just principles of economy through this section of the
country.   No opportunity of doing good was omitted;
and the circulating Library, the Magazine Almanack,
and various miscellaneous Tracts, were employed for
36   that purpose.   But the *Navigator* is his chief work,
and will remain a lasting monument of his industry and
usefulness.   Though we observe, in some few passages,
a deficiency of taste, both the plan and the execution
bear strong impressions of genius.   Finding himself
sinking under a consumption, he removed from the
dense, suffocating air of this city, to the Mississippi
Territory; and found so much relief from a southern
climate, that he returned to his former and favourite residence.   In a few months, however, he experienced a
relapse, and the balmy climate, which had once restored
him, was now tried in vain.

In his Navigator, he has detailed some of the villan-
37   ies of ASHE, well known for a volume of Travels.
This man is still remembered in Pittsburgh by the name
of ARVILLE, where he assumed the manners of a gentleman.   I had long since observed the indignant con-
tempt with which every enlightened mind viewed that
miserable production; and now have to remark, that a
prostration of truth is nearly allied to a departure from
every moral virtue.

Birmingham is a small village across the Monongahela, about one mile south of Pittsburgh.   It has works
for green glass, furnaces for casting hollow ware, &c.
from pigs,* and a saw mill, which is moved by a steam
engine.   The coal for all these, is used fresh from the
mine, without mixture, coaking or desulphuration.

Many of the balls for Perry's fleet, were cast in this
foundery.   But instead of forming such ministers of
havoc, the metal is now moulded for softer hands, and
flat or *smoothing* irons are produced in abundance.
These are ground on a stone which revolves by a band
from the steam engine.   On remarking, that its velocity was so great as to endanger those near it, I learned

* Pit coal is not used in reducing ore.

that one of six feet diameter (part of which I saw lying there) had parted, and broken its way through
the sides of the building. The grinder at that instant,
providentially had stopped, and was standing beside
it.

As many instances of such disruptions are known,
some explanation may proper.

" I speak it to the thoughtless and the young."

Bodies, which acquire velocity by a single impulse,
have a tendency to move in right lines. Water, poured
in small quantities on a grindstone, when it revolves
slowly, is attracted by the stone ; and here we see that
tendency, feeble, and overbalanced by such attraction.
But as the velocity increases, that law becomes more
apparent ; and the water is thrown off with violence, in
the same instant in every direction. Now it is evident
that every part of the stone is also urged to a separation ; and that, whenever the motion applied, overbal-
ances the cohesion, a disruption must ensue.

The *purple mole* is not known to be a native of the
western parts of New-York, and at Birmingham I first
noticed the traces of this troublesome creature.

A *Society for the promotion of Useful Knowledge,* including Chemistry, Mineralogy, &c. was instituted here
about three years ago ; but the dispersion of some of
the members, and a want of zeal in others, have occasioned its decline. This is to be much regretted ;
it falls to the lot of few, however, to be eminent in literature and in business ; and for the latter, the citizens
of Pittsburgh are particularly distinguished. For a view
of their Cabinet of Mineralogy, I was indebted to the
politeness of A. BOLTON, one of its most active members.

The *horses,* in this place, are a much larger breed
than those commonly raised in New-York ; and as the
utmost regularity in feeding and currying prevails, their
appearance is well calculated to excite the admiration
of strangers, from the eastward.

Horses are cheaper in this city, probably, than in any part of the state. This is chiefly occasioned by the western merchants, who, on their return from Philadelphia, sell their hacknies for whatever they can get, and descend the Ohio in boats.

J. Swan had provided a quantity of *small bank bills*, which proved very convenient; as it enabled him to pay our bills without *change;* and exempted us from the daily imposition of receiving *trash*, in all its varieties, of notes counterfeit, insolvent, &c. Desirous to retain an advantage so important, we applied to both banks of this city for a new supply, but this species of currency, so necessary in a *paper age*, could not be procured.

6 *mo.* 14.—Having been detained, day after day longer than we expected, this morning about sunrise, we left Pittsburgh with all the joy of a bird which escapes from its cage.

" From the tumult, and smoke of the city set free,"

we were ferried over the Monongahela, with elated spirits; and I repeated that line in Montgomery, with an emphasis, which it never before seemed to require.

I was told as we crossed the river, that coal was dug near the top of the hill ; and as what we could see of it, had been estimated by Cramer at 300 feet high, I began to doubt the correctness of my observations. I found, however, that we had to ascend a considerable distance beyond the first ledge, before we came to the coal stratum. Having passed it, we saw no more till we descended the opposite side of the hill, when its dark zone extended across the road. Again, in ascending the next hill it became visible, and these appearances continued to the south-west of *Canonsburg*. At *Chartiers' Creek** we saw the last. The bank just above the water, was a dark slate, and in digging for it, the flats had been greatly excavated.

* Vulgarly pronounced Shurtee.

Two or three miles west of Pittsburgh, we passed a farm which is very neatly cultivated—a singular object in this country. The resident is of the name of PLUM-MER, and from New England. It is greatly to be wished that there were more, equally intelligent and active.

The fruit, over these hills, has been nearly destroyed by the late frosts.

North of Pittsburgh, I observed that the locust (*Cicada septemdecem*) had killed many branches of the oaks last summer, as the dead leaves were remaining. During this day, we also saw much of their work. It is well known, that this insect deposits its eggs in the branches; and that the destruction is caused by the numerous perforations.

Towards *Canonsburg* the country becomes less hilly. If the coal stratum, from Pittsburgh, has preserved its level to this place, which is probable, there is then only the remnants of the superstratum of 150 or 200 feet to constitute the hills; as the channel of the creek is level with the mines. The relative elevation must be consequently diminished.

Limestone, which through all these regions is in very limited quantities, becomes more plenty in this vicinity, though the stratum is thin.

Canonsburg is pleasantly situated on a hill, or rather on its south side, and contains twenty or thirty well built houses. These are chiefly of stone.

White oak, neither large nor lofty, is the principal timber of the country, though hickory, pin oak, black oak, black walnut, &c. form a part.

After a ride of seven miles, southwestwardly from this village, we reached the town of *Washington*. It is situate on the summit of a hill,—from which we have a fine prospect of the surrounding country,—and consists of about 100 houses, many of them handsomely built of stone and brick. The streets are paved. The tops of the chimnies are generally formed of white sandstone resting on bricks, which gives them a neat appearance. These casings are entire, and made by cutting away the middle part of the stone.

Courts for Washington county, are held in this town; and the great number of roads, that centre to it, give some idea of its importance. A steam mill, with three pair of stones, is in operation; the engine is of Evans's construction; and the supply of coal is brought from Canonsburg.

It is a reasonable belief, however, that coal is abundant even under this town; and the depth, by comparing the appearances of the stratum at Canonsburg and at Wheeling, might be nearly ascertained. It would then become a matter of calculation, whether a steam engine, at the mouth of a perpendicular shaft, could hoist coal at a cheaper rate than horses could draw it in waggons from a distance of seven miles. Coal of a superior quality might be expected from the depth of 100 feet.

This neighbourhood appears to be the height of land; and the alluvial flats are more extensive than those towards Pittsburgh. The Ohio river, which flows northwestwardly from that city, describes nearly the arch of a circle round this town, at the distance of twenty or thirty miles.

The streams, after the heavy showers which fell today, were remarkably muddy; though thirsty, our horses refused to drink, and the water had a marbled appearance, like soft soap. The colouring matter is an ochreous clay, and its suspension in the water may result from the fineness of the particles; but in some of the western parts of New-York, the brooks, at such times, are comparatively clear; and we incline to believe that this difference should be ascribed to the clarifying properties of lime. *There* much of the soil is a marl. *Here* only a thin stratum of limestone appears in the hill side.

We have seen no finer meadows than in this vicinity, nor do we think there are any better in New-York. The soil is not replete with vegetable matter; but with proper culture it produces abundantly.

We now took the road to Charleston in Virginia, which is situate on the banks of the Ohio; and travelled almost at right angles to the course from Canonsburg.

It has been justly said, that "manners change with climes." In New-England, for light work, a single yoke of oxen, assisted by one horse, is a common team; and when greater draught is required, additional yokes are applied, even to waggons, for performing long journies. In New-York, the two-horse Dutch waggon is fashionable. Near Philadelphia, the single team of eight or nine horses is seen; in the lower parts of Maryland and Virginia, the light three-horse team is common; while in this country, the heavy Lancaster waggon, drawn by five or six horses, which vie in stature with the elephant, is continually before us. The extreme slowness of these overland sloops, often attracted our notice; but heavy teams in all countries, perhaps, move slowly; and Wordsworth, in describing the crippled beggar of England, says,

> Him, even the *slow-paced waggon* leaves behind.

We are told, that this business has been very profitable. In the present state of things, indeed, it appears indispensably necessary to the commerce of many parts of this state; yet we think the raising or keeping of fine horses is carried to excess. Man is prone to follow the beaten track; and in many instances, the inducement, to pursue a business, proceeds more from habit than from calculation. It will be found after enumerating the prices of the waggon, the horses and the gears, that no inconsiderable capital is required to start a team; and when the regular expences of provender and the incidental expences of *wear and tear*, are included, a very large deduction must be made from the

gross profits.   In times of scarcity like the present, it is
ever conducted with loss.

On the reverse, when we estimate the quantity of
grain which the driver with one half of his team could
produce ; and consider that bacon is sold in this country from 12 1-2 to 25 cents a pound, it will appear probable that a different system of rural economy might
be advantageously adopted, at least to a certain extent.

The pride of owning, or driving, a fine team, however, is a powerful inducement to pursue the present
practice ; for no general, at the head of an army, feels
better than the Pennsylvanian whip-cracker.*

The features of this country are singularly interesting.   For mile after mile, we saw strata of earth and
of stone, in both sides of these rounded hills, at equal
heights ; we saw the same on the sides of the next hill,
if equally elevated ; but sometimes we passed a considerable distance over those which did not rise up to
that level ; and on ascending some which are higher,
again the same strata appeared.   Never have I seen a
land whose internal structure is so easily ascertained ;
and the idea is clearly presented that the vallies were
cleared out after the strata had been formed by depositions.

A stratum of limestone, near the summits of the
higher hills, particularly engaged our attention.   It rests
on one of a dark slaty earth, which is doubtless a residuum of coal.   From its resembling marl, I tested it

---

* Whatever employment calls men far from home, into com-
panies where no subordination prevails, has a tendency to injure
their manners, if not their morals; and this is much increased
where spirituous liquors are liberally administered.   Of this remark, teamsters and watermen furnish illustrations.   From the
former, common civility is scarcely expected; and persons of
genteel appearance sedulously avoid situations in the road, where
it might be necessary to ask of them the smallest favour.   Yet,
in almost every walk of life, we may find exceptions to
general remarks.   Some of those persons are the sons of independent farmers, who have been well educated ; and on our return home, we met with instances of generous civility, which
were equally pleasant and unexpected.

with diluted muriatic acid, but it exhibited none of the characters of calcareous earth. These strata extended many miles, but at last disappeared,—proving the notion of regular strata round the globe to be an erroneous extreme. 30 miles.

6 *mo.* 15.—We breakfasted at *Middletown,* a village of thirty or forty houses, situate on high ground. Coal has been procured near the summits of the hills, but the quality is inferior. A better kind is discovered in low situations.

During the preparations for our breakfast, my attention was excited by a red-bird, *(Merula marilandica?)* confined in a cage. No prisoner was ever less reconciled to his cell; and time, that eases the burden of life by adjusting it, seemed to have treated the poor fellow with neglect. He had never learned to articulate, " I can't get out!" but wearied with jumping down, and then up, he broke forth at last in his own language with notes expressive of grief and anger.

Our landlord said that he had procured a companion for him, of his own species, which he received with the utmost animosity; and in a few minutes, after its introduction, he found it dead in the cage.

These birds are of a beautiful red colour, with a dark crest. As they are natives of this quarter, and also of Cayuga, it is probable that they inhabit all the intermediate country. They are not partial to the haunts of man, and I suspect are incapable of domestication.— There is a singular wildness in their notes.

We have never seen better sandstone than this region furnishes. It is easily cut, and the harder sort stands the fire; but the cement in some is too weak, and it crumbles. Particles of mica are dispersed thro' all that we have seen. At Washington I observed mica-slate used for paving stone, which retains the curvilineal surface, and breaks in the fire.

This morning we passed men who were repairing the road. As their only implements were the grub-hoe and the shovel, or occasionally the plough, it will not be difficult to determine that the amount of their labour was trifling. Seldom, indeed, have we discovered any traces of improvement. The performance of this important public duty is more nominal than real ; and the western Pennsylvanian, depending on the strength of his team, appears to be an indifferent spectator to the state of the roads. Little, however, can be achieved without instruments. The *scraper,*—which, in road-making, is almost as much superior to the shovel, as the plough, in farming, is superior to the hoe,—is unknown ; and we have neither observed it, nor its marks south of Meadville. Frequently, we have seen the way confined by high banks, scarcely exceeding the breadth of a waggon, and sometimes covered by large stones, which remained after the loose earth had passed off with the torrents in heavy rains. As the difficulty of travelling through these channels, increases, the load is diminished, or fresh horses are added to the team ; and when a passage becomes quite impracticable, a new opening is made through the woods, which gradually deepens to a chasm. Many of these will doubtless remain for the inspection of future ages.

It is worthy of remark, that the New-York farmer with two small horses, traverses an equal length of way, and carries a load as heavy as the Pennsylvanian does with five or six horses, each nearly twice the cubic volume of the former. If the state of the roads constitute all this difference, we are furnished with a strong argument against neglecting one of the first duties of a civilized people.

There are other considerations, respecting the comparative state of the roads, that will excite some interest with *the humane.* Steep hills, and miry places, often require the whole united strength of the team ; and a small inequality of movement, which among so many horses sometimes takes place, will cause all to stop. In these circumstances, dismay is highly contagious ; and the voice of the driver, if it betray his fears, will spread confusion throughout the whole team. When the difficulty advances so far, it is not easily overcome. A free use of the whip succeeds, and to let the lash fall on the animal, almost without cause, becomes like other vicious indulgences, at last easy to the conscience. In the state of New-York, this severity is much less observable.

We shall err, however, if we believe, that these people are as far behind in every branch of rural economy. For a sum, seldom exceeding five dollars an acre, the farmer causes all the young oaks and hickories to be taken up by the hoe, from his new fields; and is commonly reimbursed for this expenditure in the first crop. But in the states to the north-east, the cultivator contends with these grubs for many years; and only subdues them at a tenfold expence.

In several of the mechanic arts, these people also excel. The blacksmiths, especially, are a very superior order of workmen.

About five miles west of Middletown, we passed the west bounds of Pennsylvania. This part of Virginia, is a strip, here seven miles wide, but becoming narrower to the north, and terminating about thirty miles above Charleston. After a long descent between the **38** hills, we reached that town; and here we had the first fair view of the Ohio.

This river is not strikingly beautiful, though it is a fine flowing stream ; and at this place more than 600* yards wide. The singular luxuriance of vegetation

---

* So we were assured by the ferryman, whose apparent candour gained our credence. It may be proper to remark, however, that ferrymen should be considered as very slender authority. When we crossed the Allegany, north of Pittsburgh, I was told that the breadth of the river was five-eighths of a mile ; and at Cincinnati, it was said, with a promptness which should only accompany truth and knowledge, that the Ohio was one mile wide. At other places I have been suspicious of deception. I can discover no plausible apology for such behaviour, although answering such questions frequently, may render them impatient; and though a broad river may seem to justify high rates of ferriage.

My estimate, at page 64, makes the Allegany river less than one fifth of a mile wide; and Dr. Drake states that the breadth of **39** the Ohio, at Cincinnati, is considerably less than one-third of a mile.

that decorates its hills, whether precipitous or sloping,
constitutes its principal beauty, and in this respect it
is probably unrivalled.*   We refer the cause of this to
the admixture of earths from the different strata, and
which produces a soil perpetually fertile.

Agreeably to what I have remarked, it has formed,
for itself, a valley 500 or 600 feet deep.   The flats appear to possess an equal width with the channel; and
though fertile, are scarcely first-rate, as sand forms too
large a proportion of the soil.

The opposite bank of the river is in the state of O-
hio; and after a short delay, we entered the ferry-boat.
On the line between two states so different in internal
regulations, it was impossible to reflect without a strong
moral feeling.   Indeed, I stept on shore with emotion.
It was the first I had ever trodden uncontaminated by
slavery; and I exulted to find one spot of earth where
freedom is the *legal inheritance* of all.   Yet I was
chilled at the recollection, that the poor fugitive from
the opposite shore, who had never committed a crime,
could be pursued, taken, and chained, *even in this land*,
and dragged back to slavery.   This is an evil resulting
from our federal compact; but the idea is humiliating.

However, it is not less so to reflect that our civil and
political history furnishes the extraordinary fact, that
those who have contended most strenuously for the ex-
patriation of Europeans, have rigidly denied it to the
descendants of Africans.

But, although the progress of moral sentiments is
slow, when at war with interest, yet there is much to
encourage the philanthropist.   Half a century ago, this
vast portion of suffering humanity, had only a few solitary advocates.   Since that period, we have seen the
slave-trade prohibited by Britain, which was justly
characterized,

“ As human nature's broadest, foulest blot.”

We have seen, not long ago, whole religious societies,
for the first time, relinquish the practice of slavery.

* With the exception of its own tributary streams,

We have seen several states provide for its gradual
abolition; and some for its immediate extinction. We
have seen large majorities of Congress erect new states,
on the positive condition that it should be wholly abol-
ished within their limits; and though there is much to
deplore, there is cause for encouragement.

Some fine fields have been cleared on the banks of
this river; but no building of decent appearance is seen
in seven miles. We suspect this part is cultivated by
tenantry.

On these flats, we first saw mounds—the remains of
a race unknown to history; but as these were distant
from the road, we passed without stopping.

Warrenton, is a small village, on the flats, near the
mouth of Indian Short Creek.

Soon after landing in the state of Ohio, I first observed, in its native soil, the buck-eye *(Æsculus flava)*
which grows abundantly on these banks. Sometimes
it attains a diameter of more than two feet. Its foliage
is beautiful; but the wood is soft, and of little value.

Leaving the *Mount Pleasant* road on our left, we
went up the deep valley of *Short Creek*, frequently
crossing that stream. At the distance of five miles
from the River, we arrived at D. STEER's, where we 40
were kindly and hospitably entertained.

28 miles.

We staid in this neighbourhood, until the 21st, when
accompanied by D. S. we resumed our journey on
horseback. The reader will not require an account
of hospitable rites performed in the most engaging
manner,—by old friends whom I met in a strange land,
and by acquaintances of recent date,—though we hold
them in grateful remembrance.

Some remarks on the country adjacent to Short Creek, are subjoined.

——•—•——

41   *Mount Pleasant,* a village of about 100 houses, built chiefly of brick, claims no older date than ten years, when its site was a forest. It has a post office; and a bank is about commencing operations. It is ten miles from the river. Many of the inhabitants are *Friends;* and the house in which their yearly and quarterly meetings are held, is in this village. It is a spacious brick building; and is only occupied on such occasions,— the meeting house which they usually attend, being half a mile further west.

The library at this village contains about 200 volumes. It is a recent institution, but indicates a laudable thirst for knowledge in the inhabitants.

We have frequently remarked since our arrival in the neighbourhood of Pittsburgh, that fruit trees are more flourishing and *clean* than at Cayuga. We recollect not of ever having seen peach trees so large as in Washington county, (Pa.) I find, however, that *lice,* as they are called, live even here; but they are not numerous, and the apple trees grow so thriftily as to be but little injured by their encroachment.

From Pittsburgh to Short Creek the country is thickly settled. Large orchards of peach and apple trees are numerous; but the fruit has been chiefly destroyed by the late frosts. This is the only season, however, in which it has failed here in ten years. On the banks of *Long Run,** a small branch of Short Creek, the wild plumb trees retained their fruit. The preservation of these may be ascribed with propriety to exhalations from the stream.

Iron ore has been found here, (on Long Run) but we were disappointed in obtaining specimens. On the hill side there is red ochre in great quantities, and

---

* Three or four miles north westwardly from Mount Pleasant.

we think superior in brightness to any imported. It appears to have been furnished by one stratum, and conveyed to the surface by water; at least we traced it twenty or thirty rods along the hill, in a horizontal direction. In some places, it is mixed with concreted limestone, which also owes its formation to the agency of water. Whenever it is unmixed with this stone, the ochre is soft like clay. We have recommended a trial of its qualities as a pigment.

Coal is found half a mile up this stream, and large **42** lumps have been carried down and mixed with the sand and gravel. The stratum is found in the hill side, at this place 100 feet above the water.

On the flats, near this *Run*, the *Jeffersonia diphylla* grows in abundance. I have never seen it in any other place, excepting the western parts of Scipio.

In this quarter, wheat is generally free from smut and blast. Even in the last season, when the latter disease was so injurous in the western district of New York, and the adjacent parts of Pennsylvania, no damage was sustained. This grain commonly weighs from 63 to 67 lbs. a bushel.

The attachment that binds man to his native soil, frequently is founded in prejudice. The whole of our population consists of adventurers, or their almost immediate descendants; and from this cause, perhaps, that attachment is more feeble, in the United States, than in any other country. Yet many unerring symptoms of it are apparent. In the true style of this species of patriotism, we had been latterly told, with reference to the state of Ohio, that southern climates are unhealthy; that the grasses do not flourish; that potatoes degenerate, and produce a crop so scanty as to be generally neglected; and that the milk of cows is extremely diminished. Now we cannot perceive that any of the vegetables, cultivated in the western part of New York suffer any injury from too much warmth in this climate, and milk and butter are plenty. The meadows, J. S. thinks are finer than ours, and even the potatoes are excellent.

Certainly these facts are hostile to such prejudices ; but when we have seen more of warmer climates, we shall be better qualified to resume the subject.

In this district, the brown rabbit, the raccoon *(ursus lator)* and the woodchuck, or ground hog *(Arctomys monax)* are numerous. The hare of the lake country is unknown.

Much of the soil, in this neighbourhood, is a clayey loam, from which bricks and earthen ware of a good quality are extensively made. But it is evident that where limestone, sandstone, clay-slate or coal, appears on the hill side, the soil must vary accordingly.

We were shown a small tract of land without improvements, and told that it would sell for forty dollars per acre, although it was upland and possessed no particular advantages. Better in Scipio might be purchased for twenty five dollars an acre. We were surprised at this, because grain is commonly from 33 to 100 per cent higher in that country than at Short Creek. It appears, however, that the price of land is much less dependant on the quality of the soil, and the commercial advantages, than on the number of purchasers. Numerous as are the sales of farms in Cayuga county, the spirit of emigration is nearly sufficient to balance all the effects ; and a surplus of land remains in market. In this district the society of *Friends* are numerous ; and the desire to be convenient to the yearly meeting is so strong as greatly to affect the prices of real estate.

43　I have frequently noticed in this vicinity, that large bodies of earth, with a surface of several square perches, slide from the hill sides, carrying the trees along. Water, by lubricating some parts of the subsoil, is considered as the agent. The rough and mangled appearance T of the fields is singular, but such views are not con-
273　fined to this country. The west bank of the Cayuga lake above Aurora, from the same cause, presents an aspect equally rugged ; and it is recorded that in England, many acres have moved off together in a body.

The danger to buildings, erected on such hills, or even near the bases, must be evident.

From J. S's, on Short creek flats, with the assistance of a quadrant, I found the east hill to be nearly 400   **44**
feet high. It contains a valuable coal mine. But the west hill, which appears higher, seems destitute of this fossil, and furnishes another proof of the irregularity of coal beds.*

This distinguished Friend, besides his other mills, has erected a woollen Factory. Fine wool is an object of much attention, and the merino breed of sheep appears to be widely spread over the western country.

The *wood house*, so common in the eastern states, and which, when properly furnished, supplies the house-wife at all seasons with fuel ready cut and dried, is unknown in this district. On the reverse, the *spring house*   **45**
is considered, not only here, but in every part of the middle states, south of New-York, as a necessary appendage to a farm. Having no fountain near his dwelling, over which such a building could be erected, J. S. has provided large stone cisterns hewn out entire, five or six inches deep, and raised to the height of a table, into which a stream,—brought under ground, from a distant spring,—is constantly pouring. In these, milk is placed in vessels; and during the sultry heats of summer, acquires the most refreshing coolness.

In this vicinity, waggons are but little used for the conveyance of persons. Both men and women generally ride on horseback, and indeed this mode of travelling is most convenient in such a hilly country. The great number of saddles, which were suspended in front of many of the farm-houses, frequently excited our attention.

––––––––––––• ❉ •––––––––––––

6 *mo.* 21.—This morning, about sunrise, we resumed our journey, passing through Mount Pleasant. *Harris-*

* The stratum, however, may only be hidden by fallen masses of earth from above.

ville, a small village of a dozen houses, the building of which commenced about one year ago, is five miles further west. Two others of less note are laid out between these places.

46   *Morristown*, fourteen miles west of the latter, and consisting of twenty or thirty houses, is situate on a hill.

A large limb of a dead oak, that broke over our heads, and from which danger we were mercifully preserved, recals to memory a circumstance that happened two weeks ago, in Washington county, on the road which we travelled. The tale is sad but simple. A young woman was returning from a visit to her relations in Kentucky, as preparatory to her marriage. Her intended consort accompanied her on the journey. Alarmed at the prospect of a storm, and anxious to gain a shelter, they pressed forward, but were overtaken. A decayed oak, impelled by the blast, began to fall as they approached; the trunk struck the neck of his horse; but hers passed from under her, the moment she was crushed to death.

Lodged at *Bradshaw's*, a good inn.

From this elevated spot, after sunset, we observed fog, filling the whole valley of a small creek to the north-west. Such a sight would be peculiarly novel to an untravelled native of Scipio. This morning the prospect of Short creek valley, when filled by that vapour, was also remarkably fine; and being seen indistinctly through the trees, strikingly resembled one of our northern lakes, encircled by forests.

34 miles.

6 *mo.* 22.--We breakfasted at *Smithtown*, after a ride of ten miles. The company at table was large, consisting of a curious medley, from different states; and the conversation was often rapid and vociferous. The names, " Yankee," and " Wabash," were frequently repeated; and indeed we have heard them at almost ev-

ery place where we have stopt. I mention this as connected with the facts, that our eastern citizens are pouring through this country in all directions ; and that the lands on that river are objects of general attention.

Bemustown, five miles further west, consists of about forty houses ; but there is nothing very pleasant in the appearance of any village that we have seen since yesterday morning.

Up hill and *down hill* constitutes more of the roads throughout this country than of any others that we have ever travelled. The fatigue, which is induced by calling into action only one set of muscles, is here unknown. Endeavours have been made, however, to lead the roads round the winding summits of the hills, but this adds greatly to the distances between places.

In this district, the bottoms, or flats, even on small creeks, though clayey, have become quite extensive ; and the hills commonly have less relative elevation than those of *Short creek,* though we have crossed some which commanded distant prospects. We first noticed this change six or eight miles west of Mount Pleasant ; but perceive no other material difference in the formation of the country. Perhaps coal is less plenty, though **47** some is still found.

The principal timber on the hills is white oak ; along the streams, sugar maple. In some places, black oak and black walnut are interspersed with hickory, but chestnut and locust are rare. The wild plumb tree alone retains its fruit.

Twenty five miles east of Zanesville we crossed *Will's creek,* a branch of the Muskingum, on a toll bridge. The stream is narrow, but the bridge extends some distance over the flats. Immediately east of this, is situate the town of *Cambridge,* where the courts for *Guernsey county* are held. It contains about 100 houses, some of which are brick, and many of the inhabitants are from the island of that name.

38 miles, to *Few's* an excellent inn. **48**

6 *mo.* 23.—Much of the upland, through which we
49 have travelled to-day is far less inviting than the country round Short Creek. The hills are more abrupt,
the soil less productive, the timber stunted, and the
crops were promising in proportion.

After a ride of thirteen miles, through a rough country, we breakfasted at *Zanesville.* From the hills,
above this place, we saw the dense smoke of a furnace,

" —— high curling to the shaded skies,"

but this was the only column which we observed. The
heat of the day had probably suspended the ascent of this
vapour from domestic chimnies. The neighbouring hills
supply the coal ; but much, of a better quality, is pro-
50 cured from the bed of the river. We are told that it
is not found further westward.

This town is situate on the east bank of the *Musk-*
ingum river. It is the capital of the county of that
name, and is the largest that we have seen in this state.
It consists of several streets. Probably it contains
200 houses, many of them well built of brick ; and the
whole view gives us the idea of a place of considerable
business and capital.

A small meeting, of the religious society of Friends,
is established in this town.

The course of the river is southwardly, and its sources
are said to interlock with the Cayahoga, which flows
into lake Erie. The portage is seven miles. Some of
the inhabitants of this place, feel much interested in
the plan of opening a communication with the lake, by
connecting these waters, which a small expence would
effect; and they fully believe, that the completion of
the proposed canal, through the western parts of our
state, would confer even on them, the most important
advantages.

There are rapids in the river opposite to this town.
A canal, with locks to improve the boat navigation
round them, is now in a state of progression

Half a mile below, on the western bank of the river, stands the village of *Putnam*, (formerly *Springfield*) consisting of twenty houses, of decent appearance. The inhabitants are chiefly from New-England. By their emulous exertions, a wooden bridge, supported by stone piers, has been erected; and on which we passed the river. A toll is collected to reimburse this expense, which must have been great, as the river is 200 yards wide.

Above the toll-gate, we observed a notice, that any person who shall drive a horse over the bridge, faster than on a walk, will be liable to a fine of two dollars.* This is a novelty to us; but, doubtless, it merits the attention of all who construct wooden bridges.

From the hill side, west of Putnam, great quantities of white sandstone have been quarried. Between these we observed a stratum of coal,† two or three feet in thickness. It is difficult to dig when the stratum is less than five feet, as workmen must be either constantly bent, or remove a part of the incumbent mass.

During the two last days, we have travelled in company with C. L. Harrison, a native of Louisville,‡ in Kentucky. His easy manners, and good sense, render him an agreeable companion.

The channel of *Jonathan's creek*, seven miles south-west of Zanesville, presents a singular appearance. It is about two rods wide, and the sides and bottom are of limestone, which lies in horizontal strata. Through this, fissures six inches wide, at one rod distances, extend diagonally across the stream. The quantity of

---

* This precaution appears to be common throughout the state, (as well as in the eastern parts of our state.)

† An intelligent friend of mine, who staid a few days in this place assured me that he saw a cellar, from which was taken, sandstone for the wall, sand for the mortar, limestone for the same purpose, and a sufficiency of coal to burn it.

‡ At the falls of the Ohio.

limestone, at this creek, is greater than we have seen at any place since we left Buffalo.

Springs, though frequent, are low down between the hills; and often inconveniently situated from the dwellings. This remark will apply to all the country west of Pittsburgh. Sometimes the water is *hard,* or unfit for washing, and not agreeable to the taste. At this creek, though the weather was warm and dry, and though our horses doubtless were thirsty, yet the water was so foul that they refused to drink.

About one mile west of Jonathan's creek, we observed peaches, for the first time in this state. The trees are not regularly loaded, and we find the most fruit on the hills. Even there, in some places, it has been destroyed by the frost.

T
273   *Middleton* consists of twenty or thirty houses, situate twenty miles west of Zanesville, and eight miles east of *Clinton.* At this last named village we arrived about dark, excessively fatigued; but found excellent accommodations at Marquatt's.

While our hostess was preparing supper, a neighbouring physician made many remarks on the nature of the mounds, which appear through this country. He stated that snakes of different kinds, but especially the rattlesnakes, had taken up their winter quarters in one of these *tumuli*; that the inhabitants of the neighbourhood collected to destroy them; and that in digging, they removed several layers of human bones which were separated by pavements. They found, however, that the undertaking was too great; accordingly the siege was changed to a blockade by enclosing the mound, and in daily visits to the spot, they completely extirpated these reptiles.

A coal stratum, two feet in thickness, is found near this place.   41 miles.

6 *mo.* 24.—This morning we met upwards of 300 head of cattle destined for the Philadelphia or Baltimore market. The road was filled to a great distance;

and their long line seemed to recal the pastoral days of Theocritus.*

After a ride of ten miles, through a country diversified with hills of moderate elevation, we breakfasted in *New-Lancaster*, at Green's, an excellent house. This **52** town consists of about seventy five dwellings, situate on the west side of a hill, so that it is scarcely seen until we are almost amongst the houses. It is the capital of Fairfield county. Materials are prepared for erecting a new banking house. Many of the inhabitants of this place and its vicinity are High Dutch Pennsylvanians.

Coal is brought about twelve miles from the eastward, for the use of the blacksmiths; and I am told that none has been found further to the west. The chance of finding coal strata in the sides of the hills, diminishes as the country becomes more level; and we know of no attempt to explore the regions under foot.

The standing rock is seen to the north east, from **53** this town. It is only a hill several hundred feet high, whose west side is a naked sandstone rock, so loosely cemented as to be crumbling and wasting away. Several other rounded hills stand in a line to the north-west of it; and from their summits, the eye must doubtless take in a most extensive range of country.

The newspaper of this place contained much of abuse from a mechanic, who was offended at some of his neighbours of the same trade. That a printer should

* To a quotation from this ancient bard, Capel Lofft has subjoined a translation, at once simple and elegant:
————The Kine in multitudes succeed,
One on the other, rising to the eye;
As watery clouds, which in the heavens are seen,
Driven by the south, or Thracian Boreas,
And numberless along the sky they glide;
Nor cease; so many does the powerful blast
Speed foremost and so many, fleece on fleece
Successive rise, reflecting varied light.
So still the herds of Kine successive drew
A far extended line: and filled the plain,
And all the pathway, with the coming troop.

pollute his columns by such miserable and ill-natured effusions,—become the herald of private quarrels,--corrupt the public taste —annoy his distant readers—and injure the reputation of the town,—excites serious regret; and our estimate of character must be low, where a disposition to engage in dirty work for paltry wages is so apparent.

Many printers, however, in this western country, set an example to their eastern brethren of the type, which might be profitably followed.   Notices of the curiosities, antiquities, situation, and particular advantages of certain districts, frequently enrich their pages; and the emigrant, the traveller, and the settled inhabitants of the land, become possessed of much useful knowledge which cannot, at present be obtained from books.

Having determined to visit E. Johnson, who lives on the *North Fork of Paint creek*, we left the main road to *Chillicothe*, and took the right to Circleville.

We crossed the Hockhocking on a toll bridge.   This *river* is about *two yards and a half wide*, and skirts the town on the west, but the causeway is of considerable length.   The bottoms or prairies are perhaps two miles wide, and the hills at the borders, (excepting those already noticed) are low.   These flats produce fine corn.   The soil is black and fertile, though the subsoil is a yellowish ferruginous clay.   The honey locusts are very large and numerous.

We perceive, by the size of the corn, and the colour of the wheat and rye, that we are rapidly changing our climate.   Two days have almost brought us within sight of harvest; but two weeks hence, the fields which we left will be green.   The weather continues warm, but not more so, than our summers in Scipio.   A thunder shower from the west, passed to the north of us last evening.

Four miles west of New-Lancaster, a fine chalybeate fountain poured through bored logs, and coated every substance, over which it passed, with ochre.   On observing us alight at the spring, a young woman, with singular politeness, brought down a mug for our accommodation. The medicinal qualities of this water, in days not distant, will probably confer celebrity on the place.

Ten miles west of New-Lancaster, we first observed the *blue ash*. It is a fine stately tree of two or three feet diameter, generally of a straight grain, and may be easily split into rails.

The *cotton wood*, of which so much has been said by travellers from the western country, and which had become an object of curiosity, was first pointed out to me near the same spot. I found it, however, to be an old acquaintance—the *Populus angulata* of the botanists. It grows plentifully at Cayuga, where it is called, though improperly, the *balm-of-Gilead poplar*. The true balsam poplar,* differs greatly in the leaf; but the buds of both being resinous, have occasioned the names to be confounded. Its resemblance to the Lombardy poplar,† is striking ; CRAMER believed it to be the same, but a *specific* distinction is visible.

Thirteen miles west of New-Lancaster, we passed through a tract about four miles wide, nearly level, and very fertile. Buck-eye, blue ash, honey locust, black walnut, hickory, and oak, constitute the principal timber trees,—the growth of which is luxuriantly fine.— The soil is black and loose, and the cultivator will rarely see any more inviting; but marshy ponds are interspersed, from which disease will stalk forth, whenever his labours commence.

Within the last two days, we have passed several circular mounds, which appear to be sepulchral; and with the exception of one or two on the Ohio bottoms, are all situate on dry, elevated ground. This afternoon, we saw one of thirty feet diameter, and twelve or fifteen feet high, which was diminishing under the hands of the brick-maker ; and, on stopping, we were shewn pieces of red indurated clay, which appeared to have been slightly burnt. Stones are also a constituent part, though this mound contained but few. These

---

* Populus balsamifera. † Populus italica.

were water-worn; and must have been carried at least
half a mile, as the nearest stream is at that distance.
A pavement was thus formed, under which human bones
were discovered. No excavation appears in the adjacent soil; and from this circumstance, the idea, that
the clay was brought hither on funeral occasions, and
at different times, derives some support.

Two hours before sunset, we arrived at *Circleville.*

This town, of about fifty houses, is situate on the
east side of the Sciota river. The features of the place
are singular in the highest degree; and it may be considered as an *unique* in village building. The court-
house for Pickaway county, an octagonal brick edifice,
stands on a mound, in the centre of an old circular fortification; and round this, on a circular street, at a re-
spectful distance, the principal houses are built.

But the labours of modern times, on this spot, excite
small interest in the mind of the traveller, when compared with the monuments of a race, whose very name
is lost; and whose works only inform us that they were
numerous, civilized, and apprehensive of invasion.

54   I have noticed the circular fortification, which has
shaped the town. There is also a square enclosure that
touches it on the east. But though these are stated to
be equal in area, the difference of figure is not greater
than the mode of construction. The circle is formed
of two banks, which are separated by a ditch, or fosse,
about thirty feet wide at the natural surface of the
ground, but sixty feet from the top of one bank to the
other. Much of the fosse, doubtless, has been filled
from the banks, in the lapse of ages; but, even at this
day, a great excavation is visible.

The square, on the reverse, has no ditch. The bank
is about thirty feet wide at the base, twelve feet high,
and sufficiently broad on the summit for a waggon road.
It is a stupendous work; and yet the whole mass appears to have been *carried* hither from a distance. This
is evident, in respect to the north and south sides, which
are formed of clay resting on a gravelly soil; and near
the west bank, which is composed of the latter material,
I saw no excavation from which it could have been ta-

ken. Near the north-west corner, a swale or draught for water in heavy rains, appears both on the inside and outside of the wall, and proves that it could not have been gathered from the adjacent surface of the ground.

It is a great singularity, that these materials should have been kept separate and distinct. At the corners, each kind terminates; and the inner bank, of the circular fort, is clay, but the outer is gravel. Doubtless, the latter was thrown from the ditch; and a stratum of clay *may* have supplied the other; but it is questionable, whether the excavation yielded earth sufficient for both banks.

The following diagram, will shew the position of these fortifications. The middle of the west side touches the circle, and the two gravel banks become one mound for a short distance. At every corner, and in the middle of every side, there are gateways; and in the inside, a small circular bank, opposite to each. But, if these were ever high enough to guard the entrance from missile weapons, which is probable, a great depression must have taken place. The main road now enters the eastern gateway, and leads westward, through the opposite passage, into *Circleville.**

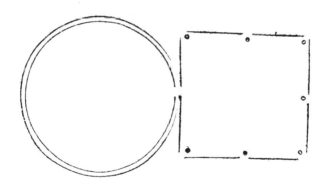

* Kilbourn, in his Gazetteer of the state of Ohio, remarks that "originally there was but one entrance into the circular fort, and that was in the east side which communicates with the square

T
281
    We are told, that the east and west sides of the square vary 17° to the right of the meridian. From this isolated fact, it has been confidently asserted, that this people were acquainted with the polarity of the magnet; that by it the square was drawn; and that the time can be calculated from its variation. To me, however, this appears a frail foundation for such important deductions. The knowledge of geometry, which is here exhibited, is trifling indeed, when compared with what the Greeks knew of that science; and yet, the whole learned world was ignorant of the compass prior to A. D. 1302. But no degree of improvement in the Arts, would authorise us to adopt that belief, unless the fact was particularly specified; because it is one of those discoveries, to which man never could arrive by reasoning *a priori.* It was the result of accident; and ages of experience in the manufacture of iron might pass,—as we know such did pass,—without that discovery. Yet it has not been even ascertained, that these people had any knowledge of iron.* Neither has it been shewn they possessed any glass, without which it would be difficult to construct a compass.

    Were it even known that this instrument had been employed, and that the magnetic meridian was coincident with these walls at that time, all reasonings from variation, must be futile. Admit the magnetic period to be 1000 years,† and then we know not how many periods have elapsed, since the date of these works; for there is nothing to determine such date within 1000 years.

    The first adventurers of our nation, found this spot overshadowed by a forest. On the mounds, oak stumps

enclosure. The avenues in the latter fort, are from twelve to fifteen feet wide. The diameter of the circle, is forty-seven rods." It will, therefore, contain nearly eleven acres.

Cramer says, that "each embankment [fort] contains about five or six acres of ground;" but this statement was conjectural. Our host said that nineteen acres were enclosed.

    * Though iron has been discovered in some of these mounds, the *smallness of the quantity* evinces that these people could not have been acquainted with its manufacture.

    † Which is twice as great as we believe.

How remain, which indicate trees of great magnitude ; and there is nothing to authorise us to say, that this was not the tenth crop since these abodes became desolate.

No inconsiderable part of the north and south walls, have been made into brick ; the workmen are constantly employed, and probably in a few years will convert all the clay into walls of another kind,—furnishing a *practical comment* on the words of the poet,

" All forms that perish, other forms supply ;"

but when we recal in fancy the unknown people who once walked where we now walk, the solemn truth of the counterpart is impressive,

" By turns we catch the vital breath and die."

32 miles.

6 *mo.* 25.—Our route now lying through *Old Chilli-cothe*, we left our fellow traveller C. L. H. with regret. Our best wishes attend him.

We estimated the Sciota, which we forded below the town, to be twenty rods wide. The bottoms, like those on all the streams of this part of the country, are very extensive ; and fertile in a high degree.* Much however remains uncultivated. This is partially owing to the unsettled state of the titles ; for the west side of this river is military land, and it is singular that almost all

* The formation of the western country was noticed at page 65 It is remarkable, that every where near the Ohio river, along which that preturnatural flood was led off, the country is gullied in a peculiar manner and vast portions of the uncompacted strata having been removed, the brooks are placed in deep and narrow chasms. On approaching through the high lands on the east side, and within twelve or fifteen miles of the Muskingum, we observe similar effects. Distant from these rivers we noticed a great difference of aspect. The streams, flowing near the natural surface, have spread far and wide after heavy rains and formed flats singularly extensive Indeed, so regularly does this obtain that some computation of the distance from the rivers may be made from these features of country The prairie lands are generally forty or fifty miles from the Ohio.

the old donations within the United States, are a constant source of litigation. The irregular method of locating land, authorised by the state governments in years past, has been of the most baneful consequences.

On reaching the upper Flats we passed through some farms which greatly attracted our attention. This land we expect was originally prairie. It is not a dead level, but beautifully smooth; the soil dark and fertile, with a proper proportion of sand, and the crops of a luxuriant green. Yet its proximity to stagnant water renders the situation sickly, and on him who lacks health, the bounties of nature are lavished in vain.

About six miles from Circleville, we came to a prairie, or tract of several thousand acres, on which there is but little timber; and that little is in groves through it like islands. It is composed of swales,* in places very wide, and which communicate with each other. At present these are dry. The soil is black, and produces a luxuriant growth of herbaceous plants,—nearly one half of which to me are new objects. Among these I noticed the wild Indigo *(Podalyxia alba?)* with white blossoms and a larger growth than that of the granite hills; a rose, *(rosa carolinensis?)* of a pleasing red colour with stalks resembling the raspberry; yellow *bartsia,* and many not in flower.

I conjecture that this tract is bottomed on rock or hard pan, which completely retains the water. That the subsoil is impermeable, is indicated by the oaks which are shrubby. Notwithstanding the general levelness of the soil, there is some irregularity; and the

---

* Our countryman, NOAH WEBSTER, who judiciously introduced into his dictionary many words peculiar to the United States, has omitted this term; yet I know of none which will strictly and literally supply its place. In the country east of the mountains, its use would be very limited, for *swales* are nearly unknown; but in the western parts of New-York, these are so numerous that without it our language would be defective. I define it, a draught in the land, which receives and conveys off the superfluous water, without being gullied; moist, but furnishing no stream fed by fountains.

rains of all seasons inundate the lower parts. Hence
the black vegetable mould, which is formed or carried
there ; and hence trees or shrubs, which require a dry
soil are drowned, and those which require a wet soil
perish in a drought. No settlements have been formed ;
yet we consider this tract very valuable, and hollow
drains of small expence would render the whole suitable for the growth of corn or wheat.

South of this tract, the surface is more uneven, though
sufficiently smooth for the plough. The trees are of a
larger growth, and the land is cultivated in places ; but
water is scarce. We found the well of one farm walled
up with wood, and the water too nauseous to drink.
How health can be preserved under the daily adminis-
tration of such poison, can only be explained by referring to the power of the constitution to accommodate
itself, within certain limits, even to poison ; but the
experiment is always dangerous. Indeed we learned
that some of the family were sick.

Stones in this district are very scarce ; but bricks,[*]
completely burnt, might form a substitute for walling
wells, which in many instances should be preferred.
All limestone injures the quality of water for washing ;
and the extraneous matter which it encloses, often injures that fluid in flavour and salubrity.

The flats on *Deer creek*, like others through this district, are fine ; and contain but little sand. The soil is
underlaid by calcareous gravel.

Granite, we observed for the first time in this state, a   **55**

___

[*] Brick moulds for this purpose, should be formed by two concentric circles intersected by *radii*, the inner circle determining
the cavity of the well. Reduced to the fusing point, clay constitutes one of the most imperishable substances in nature, and
Clarke remarks that *terra cotta* has lain in the ground for thou-   **56**
sands of years without injury.

By possessing the peculiar property of contracting in fire, this
earth may acquire great closeness of texture, and a proportionate
degree of cohesion. On this degree, the strength of all articles
of this manufacture, depends.

few miles east of Circleville; but the quantity is small. It continues to be thinly scattered round; and must have arrived, like that in the western parts of the state of New-York, after the formation of the country.

On the west bank of Deer creek, we were attracted by a fine stream which poured from a milk house. Suffering so long from thirst, we alighted with alacrity; and the pleasure was heightened by the kindness of the mistress, who treated us to milk, in the true spirit of southern hospitality.

Many of the inhabitants, in this quarter, are from the state of Delaware.

57 *Old Chillicothe* is situate on the north fork of Paint creek, seventeen miles from Circleville. In years past, it was a place of some note, from being the site of an Indian town; but now it is a small village of two or three houses.

Having been detained on the road, by frequent showers from the south-west, it was two o'clock before we arrived at E. Johnson's. His house is one mile from the old village.

His farm contains nearly eleven hundred acres, and one thousand of bottom land of the first quality. Much of the soil consists of "finely divided matter." This branch of *Paint creek* is a common mill stream in size; yet we saw much drift-wood far from the channel, and in places, both the soil and the fences exhibit proofs of its ravages.

Here we acquired new ideas of the great production and consumption of corn in southern climates. Our friend receives 3000 bushels annually into his cribs, and he assures us he has had one hundred and fifteen bushels to the acre; but more frequently after depositing fifteen or sixteen bushels for rent, his tenants have eighty or ninety bushels an acre left for themselves.

However, the consumption keeps pace with the production. Part is consumed in bread; a larger proportion as horse feed; and I noticed that a herd of thirty or forty hogs never petitioned without receiving a plentiful supply.

The gourd seed corn is generally cultivated ; and in many fields we noticed the old stalks standing, twelve or fifteen feet high. The ears of this kind of corn are thick ; and the grains so crowded as to be elongated like the seed of the gourd or calabash. The grains, when thrown in, fill the paper case which enclosed the ear. But a bushel of this has less weight and less value than a bushel of flinty corn.*

It is commonly believed that the gourd seed is more productive than the common kinds ; and this would be admitted if the grain was proportionate to the quantity of stalks. But where each kind produces the same number of bushels to the acre, there is a great difference in this quantity ; and the following hints may be suggested to the experimental agriculturist.

The first draught made on the stock of nourishment, in the soil, is for the stalk. In the larger kinds of corn, sometimes we observe the whole nutriment exhausted on this part of the plant; and no grain is produced. The smaller kinds, therefore, by requiring less for the stalk, will have a larger supply for the ear; and be consequently more productive.

Yet this reasoning has not been in all cases supported by experiment. Those that I have seen made on the corn of the lake country, in warmer climates, have not been successful. Neither did I consider such to be conclusive. In these climates, the mode of culture is much more imperfect than in the western parts of New-York ; and a small plant cannot succeed so well among weeds, as one of more vigorous growth. How much of the failure should be imputed to this cause, or how much to the climate, I cannot decide ; but it is certain that at Cayuga, the small kind has produced nearly 100 bushels to the acre ; and probably in aggregate weight, and in

* *Corn* is a general and proper term for all kinds of grain, and consequently includes wheat, rye, barley, oats, &c. but a fondness for brevity has discarded the adjective " Indian," and we now confine the name to the Zea mays.

nutriment, has equalled the greatest crops to the
south.

Here we first noticed [in this state] the sweet potatoe *(Convolvulus batatas.)* This plant thrives best in a
rich sandy loam. A considerable degree of warmth is
requisite for "a healthy vegetation," and a loose soil
best admits its large tuberous roots to expand. The
culture chiefly consists in heaping the earth into obtuse
cones, one foot in height, ; and in preventing the trailing stems,—which would spread down in every direction,—from taking root. This is effected by gathering
and rolling them on the summit. Without this precaution the energy of the plant is continually applied to
the production of new branches, and the root is bereft
of its proper nourishment.

We observe the change of climate with surprize.
The wheat is considerably embrowned, and some
patches through the fields are nearly fit for the sickle.
We have never travelled where wheat and rye were
more abundantly fine.

Our friend has a cluster of small peach trees to spread
clothes on, as a substitute for box.* These are sheared
at the height of two feet. The novelty of this culture
claimed our attention ; and as an object of convenience it merits this notice.

The *Buffalo Clover,* though found at Short Creek,
here first came under our examination. It most nearly
resembles the white clover ; and to the careless observer appears only to differ in a more luxuriant growth.
However it is not much esteemed for pasture,— being
considered watery, and nearly destitute of that nutritious property which so eminently marks many other
species of this Genus.   18 miles.

6 *mo.* 26.—E. J. is distinguished for his hospitality,
and delights in treating his friends with kindness.

* Buxus sempervirens.

Anxious, however, to pursue our journey, about nine o'clock we departed.

On a small branch of Paint Creek, one mile west of this place, we observed three mounds; two of these were ten rods apart, and the third forty rods further up the stream. The last appeared to be one hundred feet diameter at the base, and twenty feet high. All mounds of this class are obtusely conical.

At *Greenfield,* there is fine limestone for building; **58** and there we saw the first stone house that we recollect below Washington. This village (ten miles from E. J.'s) consists of a dozen houses, on the south bank of Paint Creek. Improvements, on a small scale, are advancing. Coal is found in the hills, five miles to the south-east; **59** but we heard of no search for this fossil except on the sides of such elevations; and all that merit that name in this quarter are few in number, and of moderate height.

Leesburgh, a collection of twelve or fifteen small houses, ten miles from Greenfield, is situate near a small creek flowing to the eastward. It is a new establishment.

At this place a tract of country commences, ⌈and which extends to the Little Miami⌉ distinguished for timber of thrifty growth, and in great variety. Perhaps white oak is the most numerous kind; but black walnut, sour gum,* or pepperidge, shell bark and upland hickory, red and black oak, beech, and sugar maple, are abundant. The soil is a calcareous loam; and a substratum of limestone is found at the depth of a few feet. There are no hills, except along the creeks. In its smooth but varying surface, it resembles the lands near the Seneca and Cayuga lakes, and when properly seeded, *timothy* grows finely. We observe nothing in this climate, unfavourable to the larger grasses.

* Nyssa integrifolia.

The *peach tree* attains a greater size in this quarter than we have ever witnessed to the north.

28 miles to Harris's, a good house.

6 *mo.* 27.—In this district, the *papaw* grows in profusion, and forms the principal part of the underbrush. Indeed it is a common shrub through much of the state.

Our road still led through the Military Lands; and we were often reminded of the evils of monopolizing wealth. To-day, sometimes we travelled several miles without seeing a house; no inconsiderable portion of the central and finest part of the state remains a wilderness, and young cattle, sheep and swine are often destroyed by the wolves.

The manner of clearing land in this state is very slovenly; and from the great quantities of dead timber left standing through the fields, the farmer with his family and cattle, is not only in jeopardy, but the traveller, who approaches their borders, is necessarily compelled to partake. However, in a few years, the cause of these complaints will be removed.

Since we left Erie, we have noticed an extraordinary number of poor hogs, roving about the woods. Their aspect induced us to think that they receive no food from their owners; and this want of economy is remarkable, for good meat ought not to be expected from such carcases, however they may be pampered hereafter.

To-day, we observed one of these animals with something resembling a porter bottle fastened to his tail. When walking or trotting, his legs alternately were beaten, and sometimes entangled by its swinging; and his emaciated figure indicated the labour that attended all his motions. This singular incumbrance appeared to be formed of clay, which adhering to his bushy tail, coat over coat, had acquired a bulk so distressing. Soon after we saw another similarly accoutred. In these instances, the truth of the quaint adage in our country, that "it takes a bushel of corn to fatten a pig's tail," will be plausible.

6 *mo.* 28.—EARLY this morning we crossed *Todd's Fork,* when our road led for eight miles near the east side of the *Little Miami.** The flats for that distance are fine; but at the ford (twenty rods wide) these totally disappear, and the river is confined between low limestone hills.

The late frosts have been very severe. We saw neither peaches nor apples till we approached this river; and, indeed even here, these fruits are scarce. Dead leaves, in tufts, are hanging on the papaw, and on most other trees,—the first growth of this spring having been entirely destroyed. This remark will apply to much of the state where we travelled.

On the west side of the Miami, the land is inferior in quality. The trees are white oak; and the soil inclines to a cold clay. There are no flats on the streams. Near Montgomery, the surface is more irregular; but the elevations are moderate. Horizontal limestone appears; and the soil amongst these rocks is evidently more fertile than on other parts of the hills. This results from a decomposition of the stone, which is chiefly formed of marine shells in fine preservation. The stratum is only a few feet in thickness. Clay-slate, of a greenish blue colour, underlays it; and amongst this we obtained no good water. Some of the wells in this neighbourhood are deep.

At *Montgomery,* a village of a dozen houses, twelve miles from Cincinnati, we stopped to see a carding machine which was turned by the treading of a horse on a wheel. A circular floor is attached to the upright shaft, which is so much inclined as constantly to present to him a small ascent. He is blindfold, and his traces are

* Pronounced Mi-am-e.

fastened to a beam.   On stepping, the wheel moves towards him.

Near this place, peaches and apples load the trees, especially those on the hills ; and this pleasing appearance continued.

Having so often seen the miry soil of Cayuga most expeditiously converted into excellent roads, by means of the scraper ; and knowing how much the prosperity of a country depends on such avenues of communication, it has been with real regret, that we have observed the grub-hoe and shovel generally employed on highways.   At Short creek, indeed, we saw an instrument of that description, encumbered by shafts, and designed only for one horse, which, however, was very useful ; but except in this neighbourhood, we had not seen one properly constructed, within the state.   Here two were in operation, but from these attempts we were not encouraged to hope for much ; for the loosened earth was left wide and flat.*   To such injudicious management we ascribe a prejudice, which is here very prevalent, that artificial roads are not so hard as the natural soil.   But raise the middle by heaping on it the more solid parts of the subsoil; let this be done in the early part of summer, so that it can be compacted before the commencement of autumnal rains, and Ohio will lose much of its celebrity for mud.   Until these operations are performed, it will be most eligible to visit it on horseback.†

* It is also a great mistake to form roads too narrow.   Several have been made in the present season (1813) where the driver must be vigilant to keep his waggon on the top; and if two, heavily loaded should meet on such ditch banks, the consequence must be unpleasant

† My ingenious friend Jethro Wood, suggests that roads on the natural soil. secured from the water of higher grounds by deep ditches, will be preferable to such as are raised by the scraper. He remarks that the ruts close much sooner in level lands than in artificial ridges.   We have also observed that roads on level banks near deep gullies, which receive no water except from the clouds, need no repairs ; but we believe that ditches made with the instruments now in use, would be too expensive for general practice.

About three o'clock we descended through the hills, along a hollow way, into the valley of the Ohio, and *Cincinnati* appeared before us. It is a great town. Brick buildings are very numerous, and many of these are elegant; but compactness constitutes much of the beauty of our cities; and in this it is deficient. Some of the streets may form exceptions to this remark; and we ought to remember that few towns (if any) ever rose from the forest more rapidly; that its date even now is within the memory of the young; and that its mammoth form, at no distant period will be filled up and completed. By some, it is suspected, however, that its present greatness is premature; but this can only apply to its mercantile concerns; for its manufactures cannot be materially affected by any change in the current of commerce. Neither need the merchants fear a rival city, unless it rise to the north.

Among the most respectable of the manufacturing establishments we notice the brewery of D. & J. Embree. The works, though in a progressive state, are now sufficiently extensive to produce annually five thousand barrels of beer and porter, and the quality is excellent. A treadle mill is attached to these buildings, similar in construction to that at Montgomery. It is turned by two horses, and grinds one hundred and twenty bushels of malt a day. In the present recess of business, it is employed in the manufacture of mustard.

Works for green glass have lately gone into operation; but some of the articles produced are very imperfect. We can smypathize with the proprietors of new establishments; for we are aware of the many inconveniences and discouragements that beset them at the commencement; but we cannot too strongly inculcate that TO ATTAIN EXCELLENCE WILL BE THE FIRST OBJECT OF THE PATRIOTIC MANUFACTURER; and such virtue could scarcely fail of its reward.

A monthly meeting of the society of *Friends*, comprising about forty families, is established in this place.

Walking out in the evening with D. S. we were accost-
ed by one of this community, who, on learning that I
was from New-York, led us directly to his house. This
was J. N. and were we not impelled on our journey,
early in the morning, we feel confident that we should
owe much to his friendly attentions and hospitality.

We are informed, that *Vincennes* is almost 200 miles
to the west; and we are advised to cross the Ohio, and
avoid the circuitous route of tracing "*the north bend*"
of this river. Opposite to *Cleves*, Kentucky attains its
highest latitude.

6 *mo.* 29.— About sunrise we crossed the Ohio.
From the ferry boat, the prospect was interesting; and
though we were far beyond the mountains in the interior of the continent, memory, at once, associated the
crowded scenes of the Delaware. Cincinnati spread
out behind us, with the steam mill towering from the
edge of the river; while in front *Newport* and *Covington** enlivened the landscape.

The idea is so prevalent, that we say it is natural to
look for a new people in a new state. Yet here, we
could not really expect any difference, except what is
produced by a slave population. Negro quarters, which
are shabby log buildings in the rear of the *great house,*
were objects, however, not to be overlooked.

This part of Boone county appears to have been recently a wilderness; and in the course of our journey
through it, we rode several miles without seeing a
house.

Our road led south-westerly, by *Boone court-house,*
to *Meeks's ferry,* a distance of twenty-five miles. This
tract, like that immediately south of Cincinnati, is remarkable for having no flats on the streams, the hills
coming down on both sides to the water, and constitu-
ting a surprizing contrast to the Sciota country.

* The former town is above Licking. and the latter. a new
village where we landed, is immediately below that river.

The stones are calcareous. From the last crossing of French Creek to this Ferry, the land, in which the plough would be obstructed by stones, is in very small proportion. Granite has been rarely observed; and in these cases, not one hundredth part of the quantity appears, that is scattered at Cayuga.

Basswood is very scarce, on our route through the state of Ohio. After having travelled the whole distance from Short Creek without observing it; and having believed, that we had left the region of its growth entirely behind us, we were surprised to observe it near Cincinnati.

To see black walnut, papaw, and honey locust, with horse-chestnut three feet in diameter and sixty feet without a limb,—growing amongst sugar maple and beech of gigantic size,—was to us a novelty; and we were not less surprised to find the weather not warmer than that of Cayuga;* but corn four or five feet high, and wheat nearly fit for the sickle, which makes the difference of a month, clearly indicates the temperateness of the climate.

Certainly, the fields are better cultivated in Kentucky than in Ohio round Cincinnati, where freemen only can be employed. This is so different from what I have observed in Maryland, that I ascribe it to the small number of slaves which are kept here, and to each farmer's being his own overseer. On the contrary these degraded beings, probably, have a prejudicial influence on their neighbours across the Ohio; for labour is disgraceful in the vicinity of slaves. But whether this,

* We were not aware, at this time, of the unexampled coldness of the summer in this place. This is copied from my minutes, unaltered, to shew our opinion of the climate, at that time; but we were deceived in comparing this season in Kentucky with other seasons at Cayuga. On our return home, after a lapse of sixty-three days, we found that the wheat had only been harvested ten days. Though this difference of climate is remarkable, yet on the same day, in the high lands near the road between Owego and Ithaca, fields of this grain were standing, just ripe, but untouched by the sickle.

the price of labour, the scarcity of hands, or all combined, is the cause, certain it is we were surprised at many marks of slovenliness in the agriculture of that district; and we noticed stacks of wheat* and oats unthreshed, which were apparently three years old.

Some small fields of tobacco made a handsome appearance. Sweet potatoes are cultivated in places, but the soil is not sufficiently sandy to suit them. Hemp also engages the attention of some farmers; but the prospect is not flattering at present, and the flats on the Ohio are much better adapted to its growth.

In this district, *cut money* is very common. If change cannot be made, the chisel and mallet† are introduced; but there is a speculation, even in this business: for,

> " As coin that bears some awful monarch's face,
> For more than its intrinsic worth will pass,"

so one-fifth is often palmed on the traveller for a quarter.

This invention is supposed to be of Kentucky origin, and was probably caused by necessity. In this country, as far as we can discover, the *banks* have done nothing to accommodate the people with change. Private bills, at present, are sufficiently numerous.

We had apprehended much difficulty in travelling through this western country, as it had been published at Albany, that heavy discounts were exacted for all kinds of *paper* out of its own immediate neighbourhood. Now, so far was this from being true, that we have seen no people more accommodating; and no discount whatever has been demanded.

At *Meeks's Ferry,* below Lohary Island, we crossed the Ohio River, and landed in Indiana. We went down the flats half a mile, and stopped at the house of a man, from the state of New-York, who treated us to

* Wheat is was 62 1-2 cents a bushel.

† Ashe's statement on this subject, is one of the very few truths which his voluminous work contains.

ripe morella cherries.   The trees were large, and grew in two fine rows, which he assured us had only been planted five years.   On my remarking the great height of the sandy flats, on which his house stood, he pointed to a mark on the wail, about four feet above the first floor, and observed, that the river had been there ; and that they had taken refuge on the neighbouring hills.   It is said that the difference between high and low water mark, sometimes equals sixty feet perpendicular, and our observations tend to give credence to this statement.   The volume of water which pours down the channel at such times, must therefore be immense.

Our path now led through bars into a vineyard of one or two acres, and the vines appeared thrifty.   This road is only travelled by horsemen.   The rank vegetation of the river flats crowded so close as sometimes to brush both sides of us as we rode along; and indeed every thing conspired to remind us of being in a new country.   After a traverse of three or four miles we came to the *Rising Sun*.

This village, of forty or fifty houses, is built on an easy slope that fronts the Ohio.   We recollect no situation more pleasant.   The buildings are not first-rate, but the town only claims, as it were, the date of yesterday.   A floating grist-mill was anchored in the river, near the shore ; and the float-boards of the water-wheel were turned by the current.

On leaving the river, we ascended the hills, the soil of which is very fertile, and the vegetation uncommonly fine.   We had gazed at the majestic beech of this country, three feet in diameter, with branches of a great size ;—we had seen the honey locust, the black walnut and the horse chestnut* of equal magnitude ; —and here we saw, with surprise, the black locust almost a rival

* This is called " the sweet buck-eye," to distinguish it from the kind which we first noticed on the Ohio.   Dr Drake has shewn these to be specifically distinct, and has named the former *Æ. marima.*   " It frequently arrives to the height of one hundred feet, and the diameter of four."

in stature, with grape-vines, like cables, hanging from
the tops of the trees in every direction.

6 *mo.* 30.—I have avoided remarks on our treatment,
except where gratitude required us to treasure the remembrance. When our fare has been *slim*, and our
bills high, we have passed on quietly, in the hope of
something better. Occurrences of this kind are but
trifles of a moment; and my only motive, for departing in one instance from this practice, is to give some
information which the untravelled reader may wish to
acquire.

It does not appear that any regular tavern is kept on
these hills; and as the chief part of the inhabitants
have arrived since the war, at evening, we were induced to abide at the first place where food for our horses
could be procured. Our host and his family were very
civil and attentive; but on awakening from the first
sound sleep, we despaired of all further repose. The
bugs ran riot. Our friend D. S. who through conde-
scension had taken the floor in the evening, with a sad-
dle under his head, escaped the disturbance; but we
were kept in a state of continual activity. Though
greatly fatigued by travelling, we saw, through the
chinks between the logs, the slow approaches of the
dawn with impatience, and long before sunrise resumed
our journey.

Our road led for several miles over high, level land,
apparently cold and wet;—timbered with beech, white
oak, &c. and soon becoming covered with briars* where
the fields are neglected. The aspect of things is discouraging to new settlers. What their progress will be,
is uncertain; for though the soil is moderately fertile,
and well adapted to grass, all the improvements are
very recent and scattering.

It is remarkable, that on descending from the tops of
the hills, the soil becomes excellent. The fact is, that
near the summit level, the superstratum is clay; but

* *Rubus villosus,* or blackberry.

not more than twenty or thirty feet below it, there is limestone in horizontal strata. In the side of every declivity, at that depth, this rock appears; and by decomposing, imparts to the soil beneath it, a dressing of marl. These constitute a mixture of elementary earths which cause perpetual fertility.

This country, including much of that above Cincinnati, and all that we saw of Kentucky, is more destitute* of durable water than any other region that we have traversed.

Plants, whose features are new to me, appear almost every day. Some occupy but a small region, while others are extensively scattered. The idea, that *every district marked by small differences of soil and climate, has plants and animals peculiar,* presents itself at an early date to the naturalist. To-day, I first observed the southern Aralia *(A. spinosa,)* and some are twelve feet high. No shrubbery should be without these singular and beautiful plants.

The *buffalo,* or *wild clover,* grows abundantly among the bushes, on the fertile though narrow flats of a small brook, down which the road winds. It appears to vegetate earlier than the white clover; or at least, the seed is sooner ripe.

The Columbo root *(Frasera Walteri)* which abounds between the Sciota and the Miami, is a large *tetrandrous†*

* Dr. Drake, in noticing that part of Kentucky which is adjacent to Cincinnati, remarks, that " wells cannot be dug on account of the limestone rocks, which, except in the valley of the Ohio, are every where found at the depth of a few feet " Water was very scarce, when we were at Boone Court-house; and of this place he adds that " it is not likely to be of any consequence as in summer and autumn, water even for domestic use, cannot be had within the distance of two miles."

It is evident that the Ohio River never wore these rocks away after the petrification was complete.

† Dr. Drake says that Professor Barton proposed to call it *Frasera verticillata,* and he has adopted the alteration. The name is very appropriate. It is founded on one of the m ost striking fea

plant four or five feet in height. As a bitter tonic, I am told that it is much used by physicians in this country; and some consider it equal in efficacy to the imported. I first noticed it on the oak plains, west of the Genesee River; and it is also found on the hills round Short Creek; but we have seen none since we passed Cincinnati.

63   Half a mile east of Indian Kentucky, we saw stones of the gun-flint kind, in the road. The surface is chalky, orange, or red. These form between the limestone, a regular stratum which spreads over a large tract of country. Like the strata in Washington county, it is visible in both sides of every little valley that we crossed. The texture is excellent; and these give fire with the steel equal to the imported flints; but the cracks, or lines of division, are numerous. Though these stones are silicious, the singularity of their situation, induced the celebrated SAUSSURE to ask, if calcareous earth, in any circumstances, can be transmuted into flint? Certainly not; but silex in solution appears to displace a large* portion of that earth, and to combine with the residue so silently as even in many cases to preserve the original form† of the stone. In vegetable petrifactions this earth is so accurately insinuated, that the sap vessels remain visible; and even the colouring matter of the wood is retained, as we observe in the Irish hone.

Notwithstanding its hardness, much of this earth is annually held in solution to supply the demands of ve-

tures of the plant; for *whorls* of five leaves, a few inches apart, surround the purple stalk, in some individuals to the height of six feet.

The former specific names are exceptionable. *Walteri* only refers to a book; and *Carolinensis* to one small district in which this vegetable is indigenous. Botanists, perhaps, have not sufficiently considered the impropriety of imposing such names on species which are scattered over extensive regions.

* Wiegleb found gun-flint 80 per cent. of silica.

† De Cazozy and Macquart have observed the transition of the Gypsum of Cracovia to the state of calcedony.—Dorthes has proved that the quartz in cockscombs at Passy owed its origin [shape] to plaster. CHAPTAL.

getation ;* and Professor Davy has even shewn that the hollow stalked grasses derive firmness from this essential ingredient.

As we approached the banks of *Indian Kentucky,* hearing shrill screams over our heads, we looked up, and first saw the parroquet. These birds, which are about the size of wild pigeons, are sometimes seen on the Miami.†

This *Creek* now scarcely flows, though it has a channel wide enough for a heavy mill stream. Indeed, most of those through this country are very shallow,—bottomed on horizontal lime rock ; and in some places, this stone has been whirled up by the water into heaps. The cavities thus formed are now ponds. It is remarkable that where horizontal rocks lie near the surface, the streams diminish greatly in drowths, whether these strata are calcareous or aluminous.

The north-west side of the Ohio was a wilderness after the adjacent parts of Virginia and Kentucky were settled; and the streams of these states were consequently named before many on the opposite side of the river were known to the white people. To such creeks with the word *Indian* prefixed, the appellation of the southern branches are transferred ; and thus we have Indian Short Creek, Indian Wheeling, and Indian Kentucky, which denote that Virginia Short Creek, Virginia Wheeling, and Kentucky River, join the Ohio in those respective neighbourhoods.

On ascending the hill from this creek, we travelled several miles on a winding ridge, in many places only

---

* It was long since discovered that silica (the earth of flints) was contained in vegetables : but it was commonly considered extraneous or accidental until professor Davy showed that many plants, without it, could not "support a healthy vegetation. From parcels of the following kinds of *Corn,* weighing two pounds each, Schrœder obtained of this earth the annexed number of grains respectively :—Wheat, 13.2 ; Rye, 15 6 ; Barley, 66.7 ; Oats, 144.2 ; and from the same quantity of rye-straw 152 grains.

† Drake says on the Sciota.

about the width of a turnpike, with gulphs on each side
awfully profound.   I estimate these hills at 500 or 600
feet above the Ohio River; and on all parts below the
limestone strata, which appears on their sides, the soil
is extremely fertile.

This country, in general, is wretchedly cultivated;
very little wheat appears, and corn constitutes their
staff of life.   But even this is greatly neglected ; and
wherever moderate marks of industry were observed,
we felt pleasure from the novelty.   We have never
before seen so much difference in the growth of corn;
some being scarcely six inches high, and some four or
five feet.

On the hill side which bounds the flats on the Ohio
above *Madison,* I saw for the first time, a horse strip-
ping bark.   I had long since understood, that such
practices prevailed in new parts of our south-western
states, where these animals receive no food from their
owners in winter; but we think it remarkable that bark
should be preferred to grass.   The nettle tree, *(Celtis
occidentalis)* here called hack-berry, which grows in
abundance over all these hills, is the favorite ; though
sugar-maple and some others do not escape.   He had
stripped the butt to the height of three feet.

We had not seen the *Ohio* since we left *Rising Sun,*
until we arrived on these flats, though we have chiefly
kept within a few miles.   *Vevay,* noted for its vine-
yards and *Swiss* inhabitants, is situate on the banks of
the river, but our road led to the right.

This morning the sun shone faintly through the thick-
ening veil of clouds, and soon disappeared.   Moderate
rain without wind succeeded ; and having travelled through it a long time, just before sunset, as
the sky was brightening in the west, we arrived at
Madison, wet and fatigued.   Here we met the members of the CONVENTION, who had come from the eastern part of the state, now on their return home. *Corydon,* the seat of government, is forty miles below this
village, which place they left this morning.
                                              36 miles

7 mo. 1.—MADISON is the seat of justice for *Jeffer-son* county. It is situate on an upper flat of the Ohio, and back, a few hundred yards from the river. It consists of sixty or seventy houses, the principal number of which appear new. Indeed the larger part of the improvements which we have seen in this territory is of very recent date. Many of these houses are small and of hewn logs.

The jail is about twelve feet square, of the same materials; and, in aspect as well as in strength, forms a great contrast to those gloomy piles which older communities have erected in their own defence. With surprise we had also remarked one of similar appearance at *Boone Court-house,* in *Kentucky;* and though these buildings neither shine much in topographical description, nor add to the beauty of these villages, yet posterity, from such specimens will learn with interest the simplicity of new founded empires; for in a few years these will be only *remembered.*

From the great number of small houses, and an apparent want of regularity in the streets, the aspect of this village is not imposing. With these impressions my companion asked one of the convention how long this *little town* had been laid out? Whether the dignity of the ex-member was offended by such approach,—or whether he thought his country undervalued,—I leave for his biographers to determine; but assuming all the majesty of repulsive greatness, he exclaimed "I hope you don't call this *a little town.*" It is true my friend had seen some cities, if not characters rather greater, but we think this a thriving place, and from its situation on the river, will rapidly augment in wealth and population.

We were pleased, however, with the affability and politeness of some of the gentlemen; and M. from *Wayne county,* informed me that a cave, near Corydon, contains a great quantity of Glauber's salt, amongst which nitre is intermixed. It is in high repute as a cathartic medicine. The quarter section, which includes the cave, has been lately secured by an individual.

It has long since been ascertained that abundance of *nitre* is found in the limestone caves of this country, but it appears to be mixed in unusual portions, not only with this sulphate of soda, but also with the common salt. Hams, cured with that from Kenhawa, requires no particular application of nitre ; and in redness and in flavor resemble those in New-York, where an ounce of this mineral is appropriated to each.

This morning I noticed on a hand bill " the best *qualitied* cut nails" advertised. This expression is a good match for that of " a well *faculized* person," so common in the eastern part of New-York state. No doubt both phrases are very convenient to those who are unused to better language.

The peach trees, near this town were finely loaded with fruit, but those on the hills have been more injured by frost.

65 The laborious operation of ascending the heights from the river, we performed, four miles west of Madison, but we believe the hills are not so high as those in the neighborhood of Pittsburgh. However, since we arrived in this territory, we have been compelled to trace many a long line, greatly diverging from the plane of the horizon.

On reaching the summit, we travelled one or more miles over wet clayey land, similar to what we noticed yesterday on the heights. This plain gradually slopes at last, towards the *Muskakituck* branch of the *White River,* which we crossed nine miles west of Madison, there flowing to the north-west. It is a common mill stream in size, bordered by handsome flats, and apparently comes from the Ohio, which is only four miles distant. I am assured that it heads within two or three miles of that river ; and probably some of its branches have a greater proximity, but the circuit cannot be less than three hundred miles before its waters effect a junction.

Oats are in blossom, but wheat and rye are almost fit for the sickle.

The sides of the road where the soil is calcareous, are nearly destitute of grass. It has been a dry season, but we have no cause to believe that these vegetables ever obtained possession. We cannot solely refer this deficiency to climate, though its appearance is remarkable.

Eleven miles west of Madison, we passed through a land of swales or drains, in the bottom of which limestone lies under a shallow coat of earth. Beneath this rock the water finds a subterranean passage. In some places the arch is broken ; the cavity of the rock then appears four or five feet deep ; and the stream along the bottom, alternately brightens into day, and glides beneath the vault, sheltered from the vicissitudes of this upper world. In some of these *sinks* or broken arches, no water was visible.

New Lexington is seventeen miles west of Madison. It consists of forty houses, a few of which are handsome brick or frame buildings ; but a great proportion are scattered back from the road, formed of hewn logs with a *cobbed* roof, one story high and one room on a floor. On their appearance I can pass no encomiums, though the whole has very recently sprung from the woods.*

At this place the sign of the *Lexington Bank* was displayed by nine swindlers; several of them are now imprisoned.

We were told that salt was manufactured near this place from water completely saturated with that mineral, but which is very limited in quantity. In order to obtain a better supply, a shaft was sunk about one hundred feet. At this depth brine appeared, similar in

* Predicting from past movements, in a few years these villages will not be recognized from my descriptions; and these sketches, though imperfect, will then interest by shewing the march of improvement.

quality to what was procured before, and some of it was driven up to the surface by a wind which roared through caverns in the rocks. However, the water soon subsided; and though the proprietors have penetrated to the depth of more than seven hundred feet, the labour has not been crowned with success. The last two hundred feet cost $1500. The boring was performed by machinery moved by a horse: The salt which is made here, sells for two dollars a bushel, but the quantity is not equal to the demand. .

Near this village we met a large drove of cattle, some of which we were told came from the *Missouri*. The great population and consequent demand for beef in Baltimore and in the cities to the northeast, not only attract the drovers from a vast distance, which would bring them on this line, but the ruggedness of the mountains in Virginia appears to turn the principal current of travelling as high up as Brownsville on the Monongahela.

Another branch of the *Muskakituck* flows on the north east side of this village.

At the *Pigeon Roost,* eight miles from Lexington, twenty-three women and children were massacred in the late war. It appears that the settlement was composed of several families near akin, who resided in houses contiguous to each other. The men who had given some offence to the Indians, were then all absent in the militia near Louisville, except one old man. On the last of the week, about two hours before sun set, while the women were ironing their clothes and the children were playing round the doors, the savages rushed to the attack. In this awful extremity, the old man endeavoured to protect them, till his gun-lock was broken by a ball. He then escaped, but the rest all perished. No part of this frontier, during the war exhibited such a scene of slaughter.

Adjacent to New-Lexington on the west, we saw the last of the limestone; and five miles further on our road,

66

clay slate is uncovered by a brook which flows to the
northwest. The soil, through a space of twenty miles
from this village to the Knobs, like the level country
over which we have passed, is a loam inclining to a stiff
clay, and moderately fertile. The timber is large,—chiefly beech intermixed with oak, poplar,* and sweet
gum ;† but to us the country is not inviting. There is
scarcely one clearing of older date than last season.
These are scattering, and in places we traversed inter-
vals of forest five miles wide. At the brook that runs
northerly at the foot of the Knobs, a soft clay slate appears in the bank, and no stone in all this distance was
observable on the soil.

We were informed at New-Lexington, that we should
find no accommodations for our horses east of the *Knobs.*
It was then past twelve o'clock, and we departed at
the close of a heavy shower, on a brisker gait than we
had usually travelled. But the uncertainty of lodgings,
distant thunder in the west, dark clouds that concealed the sun, and the thick branches of a tall forest, conspired to begloom our path.

My nerves had thrilled at the name of *the Knobs ;* **67**
for these are supposed by the celebrated VOLNEY to
constitute the west bank of a vast lake, which once covered all the upper country of the Ohio, and from
which waters, successively were deposited, the sand,
the shells, and the vegetables which have stratified that
region with sand rocks, lime-stone and coal. We were
therefore about to enter a scene peculiarly interesting.
But these heights would interest without the aids of
philosophy. As we approached the summit, the prospect assumed the features of sublimity. From the
north, northerly round to the southeast, the line of the
horizon was as smooth as if ruled by a pencil ; but wild
mountain heads projected in the opposite direction.
This landscape though obscured by the rain, was rendered more awfully grand by the thunder and lightning
which now flashed and rolled over us.

* Tulip poplar. † Liquidambar styraciflua.

These heights are several hundred feet above the country to the eastward. Observing some rocks not far below the summit, I alighted in the shower to examine them. I was induced to do this because their formation must have a powerful bearing on the theory of that writer, for whose talents I had conceived much respect, and who has been styled " a genius of the first order in physical geography." These rocks were of two kinds, calcareous and silicious ; and as both are of the secondary class, the inference is conclusively hostile to his hypothesis.

The sides of these hills are deeply gullied, and the peninsulated points appear like ribs attached to the vertebræ. Some stand separate, or detached from the main mass, conically shaped ; and high up the sides of one, a horizontal stratum of rocks projects, which has the appearance of limestone. The wearing of water on these piles in some distant age, must therefore have been very extraordinary.

Chestnut grows near the base, and chestnut-oak on the peaks : but as we leave these, and advance westward where the soil is less exposed to the wasting action of winds and rains, the timber becomes nearly as thrifty as on the plains below ; and papaw and spice-wood, as usual, constitute the principal underbrush.

In the channel of a brook which flows southerly one or two miles west of the ascent, we saw many chrys68 tallized stones, varying much in size and nearly spherical in the general form, though the surface is protuberant and irregular. These are usually hollow, break easily, and small chrystals cover the internal surface. I arrange them with the most recent of the secondary class of stones, as in one, a lump of limestone composed of shells, was found embedded.

In the cabinet of specimens in mineralogy at Pittsburgh, if my recollection is distinct, there is a broken shell of this kind, which had been a prolate spheroid, twelve or fifteen inches long, eight or ten inches wide, and less than an inch in thickness. One part of the cavity is apparently coated with verdigrise. I have seen none here equal to that specimen in size.

This day we travelled nearly forty miles, and about dark arrived at our lodgings, excessively fatigued. This was occasioned by our hurrying over the last twenty-three miles, without stopping to procure refreshment.

On asking for supper we were told that the water in the well, on account of the rain was unfit for use. As we did not comprehend the reason why a moderate shower should be so injurious, I only notice the fact at present, and add that butter-milk ill supplied the place of more stimulating food which our exhausted condition required.

7 *mo.* 2.—This house was fortified during the war, and several families occupied it as a garrison. Log-houses like this are readily converted into such fortifications by taking off the upper part down to the joists, and then building it up again with logs two or three feet longer. Such projections on every side are intended to give the besieged an opportunity to fire down on the enemy, if he should attempt to force the door, or set fire to the building; but we are told that no instance of Indians making such attack is known. We had observed houses of this description, soon after our landing in the state, and we have noticed more or less every day since.

This fortress had an appendage (and I believe it is generally so, when neighbours unite together) consisting of a picket fence which encloses the yard and extends the limits of safety. The construction is as follows;— Planks three or four inches thick and twelve or fifteen feet long are placed edge to edge in a trench which has been previously dug, and the earth then rammed closely round them. These are difficult to scale, and impenetrable to small arms.

Cooped up in such lodgments, our frontier citizens

have generally weathered the storm of war ; and when necessity compelled them to venture out, the men have gone armed in a body. On my remarking how unhappily they must have lived in such times of alarm, our host replied, "We enjoyed ourselves much better than you imagine, perhaps as well as we do now,—we were so kind and friendly to one another." These words of the old man were impressive ; and I rode on reflecting, from how much real pleasure we are debarred by the jarring interests of this world.

Our progress this morning was unusually slow, in consequence of the excess of yesterday ; and our horses convinced us that they were suffering from sore feet. The circumstance in itself is a trifle, and will cease to interest us as soon as they recover ; but the *lesson* ought not to be forgotten. At Circleville, we saw men from Dutchess county (N. Y.) who had been under the necessity of changing horses, once or twice, on the road ; and another such a day's ride would compel us to a similar measure. He who wishes to avoid being left to the mercy of strangers (if mercy there be) should preserve an easy and regular gait through the day ; and at whatever time his hackney shews unequivocal symptoms of fatigue, stop. In this exhausted condition, a small excess is hurtful, and a repetition often ruinous. A horse of common constitution, accidents excepted, will perform the circuit of the United States, if well fed and moderately used.

Salem, where we stopped to breakfast, is a new village of thirty or forty houses. A small but handsome brick court-house for *Washington county*, built on arches, is one of the principal ornaments of the place.

One mile and a half north-easterly from this village, a monthly meeting is held by a number of *Friends* who are settled in this vicinity.

At breakfast I was exposed to the infection of an eruptive fever, which, however, to me has never been a subject of much alarm ; but my friend J. S. shewed such anxiety hat I left the house with half a meal. To have a disease of such uncertain termination in a strange land, is not desirable ; but the bearing of one event on another, and consequently, what will finally be best, is not given us to know.

The uncertain tenure of our lives, at all times, ought also to mitigate our apprehensions of apparent danger. We walk in the midst of deaths ; and with the dawn of each day the possibility returns, that those connexions which are inexpressibly dear to us will be dissolved before night.

On the west side of this village, *Blue River*, which is here a small mill-stream, flows in a southerly direction. The banks contain horizontal strata of limestone, which is literally *composed* of shells.

The country westward of *the Knobs*, [or rather the summit level | though not hilly, is varied in surface ; and has a looser soil than the low district to the east. Ferruginous sandstone, the stalagmites before noticed, excellent gun flints, and abundance of limestone are found. The two first kinds, in places, considerably encumber the soil. The flint varies much in colour ; lumps three or four inches in diameter are embedded in the limerocks ; and this sort in texture resembles the imported flint. **69**

We noticed many wells which were dug, in the bottom of *limestone sinks* ; and generally the inhabitants obtain durable water with little labour. It is worthy of remark, that this elevated region preserves the same singular feature as the country round New-Lexington, which is several hundred feet below it ; for, in no other district that I have seen would it be advisable to dig for water in a sink.

Many of the settlers in this quarter are Carolinians; and some told us (probably with a reference to their native land) that " this is a miserably cold country."

Our host, where we fed our horses, had been bitten

by a *copper-head* some months ago, and was scarcely
recovered.   It was said, when we were in the state of
Ohio, that the poison of this reptile, lingers a long time
in tne system, and eventually proves destructive to
the constitution.   The evil appears magnified ; but the
opinion is common, that these are not less dangerous
than the rattle snake ; and we know they are much more
difficult to exterminate.   The dry hills of the Ohio
country seem to be their favorite residence.   We think
however, that snakes are less numerous, even now, than
on the eastern side of the mountains.

About 5 o'clock we arrived at J. Lindley's for whom
I had an introductory letter.   His kind invitation to
stay with him a day, we willingly accepted.

This distinguished Friend removed from North Carolina about five years ago ; and with a few others fixed his abode in the wilderness.   During the late war,
this little community formed the frontier ; but its members appear not to have suffered either from fear or injury.   He has frequently explored the lands beyond
the borders of the settlement in the time of that commotion, and never considered either himself or his
companions in danger.   Indeed there was small cause.
No instance of Indian hostility towards this society is
known ; so firm and inviolate has been the peace which
tne ancestors of these savages established with William Penn, and so faithfully is the memory of his vir-
tues transmitted from sire to son.

The wilderness, however, has now become thickly
populated ; and a monthly meeting is held a half a mile
from his house ; but we learn that no other meeting of
Friends is established further westward.

26 miles.

7 *mo.* 3.—We admired the refreshing coolness of
last evening.   We are assured that in summer, the
heat of the day like what we experience is rarely oppressive; and seldom protracted beyond sunset.   On

the eastern side of the mountains, in this latitude, it is often uncomfortable till midnight.

In our country, the rainy clouds in their approach, seldom vary from between the west and south-west points ; but the lower currents of the atmosphere frequently carry the scud in every direction. Here we are told that both rain and snow arrive chiefly from the south-west; and that winds from the east of north or south are seldom known.

This statement supports the opinion that we have passed beyond the influence of the great Lakes. Winds are often deflected for their original courses by the sinuosities of the shore; and from this cause we sometimes find them blow in opposite directions.

The surface of the land in this neighbourhood is uneven ; but the elevations scarcely merit the name of hills; and much of it appears to be *cellared*. This feature is strong and perhaps peculiar to the western country. Nearly all the brooks are more or less subterranean. In places, the arch is broken for small distances, and the stream visible ; but *Lost River*, to the north of this place, wholly disappears for seven miles; and though this NATURAL BRIDGE is destitute of the sublime scenery of *Cedar Creek* it stands unrivalled in width.

Many of the brooks may be traced by a line of sinks. These in heavy rains become ponds, in consequence of the narrowness of the channel* through the rocks—into some of which the current boils from below, while others receive the torrents that collect on the land ; and in all, the water not undergoing the process of filtration,— partakes of all the impurities of the surface. To this cause I ascribe the state of the well which we noticed in the evening after we ascended *the Knobs*.

But we have reason to suspect that this water, even

---

* Our friend, who has a mill on a large spring, finds great difficulty in forming a pond, on account of fissures in the limestone that surrounds it.

when limpid is prejudicial to the health of strangers?
In us, it uniformly induced a sense of weight in the
stomach, and others have made similar complaints.
We discontinued its use.

It is probable that the *Salt Petre caves** in Kentucky
are on the same level with those near New-Lexington ;
but these around us, as I have remarked, are in a different stratum, notwithstanding the sameness of appearance. We are informed that one cavern in that
state has been explored for ten miles ; and without dis-
missing all doubts of this statement, we may be allowed to remark that *Lost River* proves that some in this
vicinity are surprisingly extensive. 1 observed a sink of
one or two acres which was only a few feet in depth, and
evidently occasioned by the falling of the cavern roof.

We rarely observe any natural cavity in the land
which would hold water except in two cases. The first
consists of the basins of lakes, which are generally on a
large scale, and formed either by the irregular projection of primitive rocks, or by the unequal deposition of
alluvial matter. The second case comprises those cavities of small extent which were produced by a depression of the friable earth. Of these we observe that their
formation belongs to a period since " the dry land appeared ;" and such are chiefly confined to districts that
embosom limestone. Perhaps the only exception to
making this remark general, will be found, where primitive rocks loosened by some convulsion of nature, have
promiscuously fallen together and then been covered by
earth.

T   The cavities of calcareous regions belong to two
306 classes. The first will embrace depressions of the surface where the earth has sunk into caverns, through
small apertures in the roof, and hence assuming the

---

* Cramer in noticing Harden's Creek in that state, 112 miles by
water below Louisville and southeasterly from this place, remarks that " *Sinking Creek*, a b anch of that stream, after head-
ing in three springs and running several miles, sinks, and runs a-
bout four or five miles under ground before it appears again."

shape of a funnel. These appear wherever limestone in great quantities is present, without any regard to the primitive or secondary formation. The second class obtains where the earth over beds of gypsum has gradu- **70** ally settled. The solution of that salt in five hundred times its weight of cold water, removes all obscurity from this point; but the cause of caverns in common limestone is more difficult to elucidate.

It is not probable that this earth remained in its pulverulent form while the masses around it hardened into rock; and that afterwards it was removed by water. United with different acids, however, it varies exceedingly in its degrees of solubility. Though carbonic acid **71** renders it an insoluble precipitate in water, yet the same agent in excess completes its solution; and vegetable matter fermenting in confined situations might furnish the supply.

The nitric and muriatic acids combining with lime also preserve it in solution; and by displacing the carbonic acid may have taken possession in latter periods. Neither should the combination of sulphuric acid be overlooked. Perhaps all these agents, in different places, have assisted in forming the caverns which abound in this rock; and some circumstances render it probable that the process of excavation is continued.

The *hard water*, so common in limestone districts, proves that the rocks through which these currents flow are wasting by solution. The impregnating material is chiefly plaster; but nitrates and muriates of lime, **72** which only exist in a liquid state, are sometimes discovered; and perhaps have been recently formed. The carbonic acid which is found disengaged in the earth under the name of *damp*, and which is also emitted by some fountains, supports this idea; but without such decomposition, clearly shows that water with this addition may become a solvent of limestone.

This view will be less imperfect, when we consider that *new sinks* frequently appear in such regions. The earth on those spots had been settled and compact for

thousands of years ; and its sudden depression evinces
a recent breach in the cavern roof.

It will be obvious that the depth of the cavern will
greatly assist in determining the *figure of the sink*.   In
the lower parts of Pennsylvania, where the quantity of
earth over the aperture is very considerable, it generally assumes the form of an inverted cone.   Here where
the cavern is near the surface, the longitudinal breaches in the roof are more apparent, and that figure is rarely observed.

73   The limestone in this neighbourhood is composed of
small shells which differ from all that I have noticed
to the eastward.   One stone, from the minuteness of
these remains, resembled a mass of mustard seed.—
The cement was ochre.

74   *Half-Moon Spring*,* which we visited this morning,
is a curiosity.   The *aperture* of the fountain is thirty
feet deep, and three rods in diameter; but the *basin* is
more extensive.   The name is derived from its semicircular figure.   Uniting with the current of J. Lindley's mill spring, half a mile to the northward, it forms
Lick Creek, a beautiful stream.

The *Section* [or square mile] that includes this fountain is public property ; being *Lot No.* 16. which *in
each township throughout the territory, is appropriated
for the use of Schools*.   Leases of such lands have been
granted only for short periods ; and in consequence its
value for water works, probably will long remain unre-
alized.   Though the fall of its current is small, yet by
raising *a curb*, it might doubtless be converted into a
valuable mill seat ; and the firm and level surface round
it would favor such an undertaking.

East of New-Lexington we had found limestone in
the bottom of swales, which formed an arch for *subterranean brooks*.   The late heavy rain has unfolded the

* This spring is forty miles west of Louisville.

cause of this singular appearance. As soon as the cavity is filled, the surplus wåter bursts from the sink-holes, forming ponds where the sink is deep, but flowing over where the sides are low. Thus we have a double brook; and the upper current, sweeping away the leaves has also channelled out the land.

Coal is found two miles from J. Lindley's, but of its quantity' and quality but little can be said at present. Salt springs* of value, on the New Purchase, north of this place, have been partially examined; but as the Government of the United States reserve the lands which include such, if known before the sale, individuals who explore, deem it prudent to be silent on these subjects. After the sales much more may be learned of the fossil treasures of this country.

The inhabitants of this neighbourhood preserve much simplicity of dress, and like members of the same family, feel an interest in each others welfare, in the inverse ratio of the parade exhibited. Such manners are characteristic of new settlements; and notwithstanding the privations to which this period is subject, those who have risen to independence not unfrequently recall in memory these days as the happiest in life.

Apparel, however, should vary with the state of society. To wear that of which we are neither proud nor ashamed is the best rule that can be given; and who departs from this maxim has a mind directed to improper objects.

Our horses had been put to pasture where the grass was chiefly *timothy*, yet *salivation* was induced. The cause of this disease has been hitherto unexplained, though it would be difficult to enumerate all the opinions on this subject. Several of these, however, are ab-

---

* On the map in range 1 west, Township, 6 north the reader may find marked a *Salt Lick*. J. Lindley to whose kindness I am indebted for much valuable information. says in his letter of 2 mo. 2. 1818, that they are at work at this lick, and that the prospect is encouraging

solute crudities; and much objection will attend the best that have been assigned.

It appears that thirty years ago, this malady was unknown in the United States. Near Philadelphia, it was first observed about the time that clover and plaster were generally introduced ; and to these it was naturally ascribed.   To this theory the present case will completely fix a negative ; and in our county where horses suffer much from this disease, plastered clover, in fields recently *laid down*, does not induce it.   On the reverse, in white clover pastures, which have never received a sprinkle of that manure, the salivation has been distressing.

By some, the *Lobelia inflata* or wild tobacco, has been charged as the cause; by others, the *Euphorbia maculata*, or spotted spurge ; but both plants are indigenous, and must have occupied the old fields near the sea coast almost a century before this disease was known.   Others have spoken of the venom of spiders.   The question, where were they forty years ago? will instantly occur; neither would this hypothesis explain why the grass of one field will salivate profusely, while *that* in another field not two yards distant, may be eaten with impunity. Nor can we learn why these plants or animals should be more venomous after a shower ; yet this phenomenon is very observable.   If it be said that the insects have sheltered in the grass, we should reflect that a better shelter might often be found across the fence, and that the insects would venture forth on the return of fair weather ; but for several days much acrimony is apparent.

The same objection will arise against ascribing it to *dews*. We have not been able to discover why these should not descend alike on the adjoining fields where a single fence constitutes all the partition ; yet I have noticed at *Cayuga*, that horses in new fields are generaly exempt ; and the same remark applies to meadows annually mowed.

In the afternoon we visited T. Lindley, whose inter-

esting family we shall remember. It is now the middle
of wheat harvest, and only this concern deprives us of
his company to the Wabash. He has appropriated a
field of several acres to the culture of tobacco, and the
prospect is encouraging.

Lands partially improved rate at twelve dollars an
acre.

Sugar maple is found throughout all the Ohio country; and from it *sugar* is generally made in quantities
sufficient for home consumption. We have seen little
of this article from New-Orleans since we left Pittsburgh. There the retail price is from twenty-three to
twenty-five cents a pound.

It appears that *Kanhawa Salt,* with few exceptions,
supplies at least all the country above the falls of Ohio.
Near the river the current price has been six dollars a
barrel. In the manufacture much slovenliness is evident, and we presume that no pains are taken to separate the ochreous matter which floats in the water, for
the whole mass is tinged of a dirty red. The snow-
white salt of Montezuma is obtained from water equally impure.

The *parroquet* commits depredations on the wheat
in harvest, but it is a bird of uncommon beauty. The
head is red, the neck yellow, and the body a light
green.

In the evening we returned with J. L. to our former
lodgings.

In this neighbourhood an earth resembling *bole* is employed as a red dye for cotton. It is squeezed through
a linen bag into an alkaline solution; and requires the
same time as indigo to perfect the colour.

The trees, in this neighbourhood, are chiefly *beech* and
sugar-maple; but the quantity of timber to the acre,
varies considerably in different places. The *papaw*
forms the underbrush, and by closely shading the ground
with its broad leaves, nearly excludes the herbage.

Iron ore is found in many parts of this country. It is mentioned, that two furnaces* will soon be erected, at the respective distances of eight and sixteen miles west of this place.

7 mo. 4.—ABOUT nine o'clock this morning, we took leave of our kind friends, and proceeded on our journey. Three or four miles west of J. Lindley's, the land is hilly ; and near the summit, a *reddish sand rock* overlays the *limestone.* It may be noticed, though such appearances are not uncommon, that on the hills above the limestone level, there are no *sinks ;* but on descending the western side to that level, these depressions are visible. Strata, however, are not so regular in this district as towards Pittsburgh.

After a ride of ten miles, we arrived at the *French Licks.* This place is a reservation, lately owned by the United States, but now transferred to Indiana. I observed three *sulphur springs,†* one of which was more strongly impregnated than any that I have seen. We thought these waters were slightly tinctured with salt and iron.

From the base of a high bank of limestone that bounds this vale on the west, a large spring of fresh water breaks forth, and flows eastward between the other fountains. As we paused on the north bank of this stream, our horses immediately strained down their heads, and began to lick the ground. We now perceived that the stones had a whitish coat, like frost ; and which, on tasting, we discovered to be *common salt,* apparently free from impurities. This recalled the remark of H. DAVY, that " rock salt almost always occurs

* J. Lindley, in a letter of 2 mo. 2, 1818, says, " The furnaces talked of when thou wast here, have not been built."

† Several others are found in the adjoining woods. On our return I filled a bottle with this water, which at that time was limpid ; but in a few hours it became milky and the fetid smell was lost. It is well known to chemists that hydrogen is a solvent of sulphur, and that the appearance here noticed, results from the escape of that gas. The mineral no longer soluble, floats in the water.

with red sandstone and gypsum." The sandstone, in its proper colour, is found on the spot; and though we have no proof of the presence of gypsum, sulphur springs* in New-York are one of its indications.

The celebrated SAUSSURE had previously enquired, why salt mines† are found near mountains of gypsum? Perhaps the answer to be given, will be, that both are confined to regions of secondary formation. No strata of gypsum are known of an older date than limestone which contains shells; and in this remark salt may be included.

The coincidence, however, is curious; and prevails in our country as well as on the eastern side of the Atlantic. Saussure could not have been acquainted with this fact when he wrote; but the western district of New-York is now equally famous for its salt springs and its quarries of plaster.

Such springs are properly ascribed to water which has fallen in rain, and which by soaking through saline earth, or by flowing over salt rocks, is gradually wasting the mine. Indeed, it is probable that in regions of secondary formation, many fountains, now perfectly sweet, were originally brackish. This opinion is strongly supported by the fact, that the salt springs of the present day, have been commonly found to ooze through coverings of mud, in low, marshy situations without any visible outlet; and though Onondaga may furnish an exception, yet it is well known that subterranean waters, sometimes acquire new outlets by earthquakes.

This place is the favorite residence of the parroquet, flocks of which were continually flying round. These birds seem to delight in screaming.

* Though sulphurated hydrogen is not a constituent of gypsum, it abounds in all the best *plaster stone* of Cayuga. Water, in which this mineral is diffused, soon becomes sulphurous.

† " To examine the reason of the singular connexion observed between mines of salt, or salt springs, and mountains of gypsum." See his AGENDA.

We observed that the stream from these *Licks* soon becomes of a pale whitish blue, like a mixture of milk and water; and we had previously noticed, that Lick creek, and its other branches had acquired the same colour. To these appearances, probably, we owe the names of White water, White river, Blue river, &c.

Westward, the country is still more rough and hilly, and much of the soil is encumbered by sand rocks. This district resembles the roughest of the sandstone region north of Pittsburgh. Fine springs issue from the hills; and once more we enjoyed the luxury of pure cold water.

Near the top of a hill two miles westward, over which our road led, the inhabitants procure *whetstones,* which, it is said, are *equal* in quality to the *Turkey oil-stone.* The grit is extremely fine and sharp.

From the position of this quarry, on the top of a high ridge, I conjectured that the sand had not been deposited by water, but collected by the wind, previous to its petrification; but whether the horizontal arrangement will form a sufficient objection to this view, must be left undetermined.

Six miles west of the Lick, the land is less rugged, and some tracts are handsome.

We came to *Lick creek,* ten miles west of these Licks. Swelled by the late rains, it was too deep to ford, though only three or four rods wide, and we passed it in a ferry boat. At this place it flows to the north-west.

As the last gleamings of day were departing, we arrived at Schultz's, near the *Driftwood Branch of White River.*

Though we have been several days on the frontiers, we find some change of manners at every remove. To-night our horses, with many others, were turned loose, in a yard, to a great trough, bountifully replenished with Indian corn; and though oats is far better adapted to their habits, and though their treatment has always been a subject of solicitude, we felt much satisfaction in effecting our escape from the dark shades of a thick forest.

26 miles.

7 *mo.* 5.—THIS tavern is a recent establishment. The proprietor formerly from Pennsylvania, but latterly from Seneca County in New-York, has adopted the eastern mode of clearing land, and at once lays it open to the day. The pleasantness of the prospect, the safety of the cattle and the excellence of the crop,—which now promises to exceed by one half every other that we have seen in the country,—will strongly recommend this method to his neighbours; but we fear there will be more admirers than imitators.

At this place, we saw *the under jaw of a Mammoth,* in which the teeth remain. Though large, it is not one of the largest. It was found in the channel of the river nearly opposite to the house.

Since the discovery of the Mammoth, on the coast of Siberia, in the year 1808, conjecture respecting its figure is confined within narrow limits; while the place of its abode is involved in much obscurity. The situation in which it had lain, cased in ice, for thousands of years, shews that it floated thither. This inference is clear and regular; and perhaps the best evidence, that these quadrupeds belonged to our continent, is not furnished by the circumstance that their remains have been discovered at the Big bone Lick, but that there were strong inducements for them to frequent it.

Currents of water have swept over this country in a period comparatively recent; and the establishment of this fact has a tendency to weaken our faith in the opinion that New-York was once the residence of this creature. The bones discovered near Springfield, N. J. by my ingenious friend C. KINSEY, under a covering of six feet of solid earth, shew at least that great changes have taken place in the surface, since the deposition of these remains; and perhaps it will be difficult to account for this inhumation* in any way so plausibly as by a reference to that deluge, which has left its traces throughout our land long since the existence of air-breathing animals.

Corn, on the west branch of White River, now sells at twenty-five cents a bushel.

About sunrise we resumed our journey. Weakened by disease, I was indulged with a walk to the river, while my companions were preparing the horses, whither they were soon to follow.

Last evening we had heard the noise of *falls* at the distance of a mile or two over the hills; and on approaching, I found the water to pitch down about four feet over a level sand rock, extending straight across the river. The thick woods on the opposite shore, the clear sky, the smooth expanse of water, the foam of the cascade, and the unbroken quiet, formed one of the sweetest scenes of solitude.

Avoiding the force of the stream, small fish in great numbers had come in close with the shore; and eager to ascend the little currents from ledge to ledge, were so crowded together that I could take them up by hand-fulls.

On these banks I first saw the red trumpet flower† growing indigenously.

---

* Large bones (probably of this creature) have been found near the great western canal in the town of Manlius. One of the contractors in a letter to me of 5 mo. 15, 1818, says, "For the embankment across a swamp, I have taken earth from a small hill. At a depth varying from eight to twelve feet, we found *muscle shells* in abundance, with bones of some large animal. One half of a tooth weighed 2 lbs 6 oz"

Dr Drake remarks, that "on the upper table on which Cincinnati is built, a joint of the back bone of one of these species was found at the depth of twelve feet from the surface."

We have no reason to believe that these remains, in either case, would be buried at such depths in the common order of nature.

† Bignonia radicans. On our return I found this plant in Madison county. (Ohio) but the size was diminutive.

Yesterday we were joined by a genteel Kentuckian, who was also proceeding to Vincennes. He was from Shelbyville; and had attempted to travel the upper road, which leads more directly west from Cincinnati. That route, however, he found to be impassable from the quantities of fallen timber and under-brush; and after advancing nearly forty miles was compelled to retrace his steps.

Our company arriving, we forded the river a few rods above the falls. The level sand rock is uncovered two thirds of the distance over, except by water; and the remaining third seems *paved* with muscle shells of a large size. The breadth of this beautiful stream we estimated at 150 yards. The upland adjoining it is good, and the hills retiring, admit flats of moderate extent, which are thickly timbered.

After ascending the hill, which may be 100 feet high, we passed through open oak woods into an extensive plain or *prairie.* Here such are called *barrens,* but improperly, for the soil is very fertile.

These openings present a striking contrast to the eastern parts of the continent, which were shaded by forests; and the cause has become a subject of general speculation. The thrifty growth of timber, which is found through this country in many places, proves, that though the woodlands decrease as we advance westward, the cause ought not to be attributed to climate. Indeed we have never seen, to the eastward, more timber on the same extent of ground than many tracts in this vicinity exhibit, if we except groves of white pine. Our search must therefore be confined to the soil, and to circumstances entirely incidental.

To me it is evident that the immediate causes of these wastes are fire and inundation; but the *predisponent* cause (if physicians will allow the expression) is either an impenetrable hard-pan, or a level rock. At page 98 I have noticed the wet prairies. The same rock, extending under the drier parts, confines the roots, and intercepts the supply of moisture that subsoils generally contribute. The trees, thus stunted admit amongst them a luxuriant herbage ; in autumn it is speedily dried by the sun and wind, and the underbrush perishes in the annual conflagration. Near the borders sufficient evidence of this was often before us in the stools of oak, with shoots from one to six feet in height, which were blasted by recent fires.

These tracts are generally situate near the height of land. On the bordering ridges, the timber attains a moderate size, and the adjoining declivities also produces it of the usual height ; but trees, encircled by these wastes, are uniformly stunted.

In all the wells which we saw in these plains, a hard **77** slate rock was found at the depth of a few feet.

The soil is various. Clay is not uncommon ; in some places sand predominates ; but a fertile loam will give the general character.

These lands may be subdued at a small expence. Near all that we have seen, materials for fencing, at present may easily be procured, and a strong team, with a good plough, would readily overturn the tea plant and the hazle. I saw not one stone on the surface.

Water may be procured in wells of a moderate depth ; but in some, the quality is injured by foreign matters. In one, copperas is so abundant as greatly to discolour clothes in washing ; and the proprietor assured me it would make a good dye.

Several habitations have been lately erected ; but we saw no improvement which induced us to believe that the occupants had much capital.

T Over these plains I saw the dodder *(Cuscuta)* for **307** many yards round, entangling the herbage. This singular vegetable germinates in the soil, and ascending a few inches, takes hold of the first plant it can reach. The root then perishes, and it becomes *parasitic*. On breaking the stem, I have observed the pith to contract, which brought the epidermis together and closed the wound. What I broke to-day, however, was rigid; and perhaps this contraction only happens at an earlier period of its growth. It is extremely injurious to flax. This circumstance has claimed some attention of the farmer; and strange as it may seem, some have believed that the dust of flour mixed with flaxseed in a bag would infallibly produce it.

In the more clayey parts of these prairies, we saw heaps of earth as large as a bushel, which are inhabited by a little animal of the mole kind. We found none of the proprietors abroad, and we were not prepared for invasion. Their name, in this quarter, is gopher.*

As we were descending from the prairie, I observed a halt in the front of our company; and on riding forward, found our Kentucky friend engaged in destroying a large rattle-snake. This was the first venomous reptile we had seen on the journey, except two that lay dead in the road. I believe we have not seen half a dozen snakes of any kind.

Having travelled sixteen miles we took breakfast at Liverpool, [now *Washington*] a village of three houses. Our landlord was from Kentucky; and it appears that state has furnished much of the population of this district.

Here the peach-trees were loaded with fruit. We had previously observed that west of the Knobs, the frosts had not been injurious; but fruit trees between these points are scarce.

Throughout all this western country, it is the fashion amongst the middle or lower classes to salute us by the name of "*stranger.*" The term may often be strict-

---

* Perhaps *gauffre.* "Only two species [of *Diplostoma.*] are known as yet, and they have been discovered and ascertained by Mr. Bradbury. Both are found in the Missouri Territory. They burrow under ground and live on roots; and are called *gauffre* by the French settlers." F. RAFINESQUE. 78

ly proper, and it is seldom, if ever, accompanied by rudeness; yet the practice is so ungraceful, that we shall enter our protest against it, the authority of Walter Scott to the contrary notwithstanding.

A good tract of woodland extends three miles to *the West Fork of White River.* This stream in size and appearance resembles the other branches. Rapids of equal height, also are formed by a sand rock which occupies the whole bottom of the river, and at both places the direction is straight across. On this rock we forded.

No hills appear between Schultz's and Vincennes, excepting those that bound the flats on the rivers. It is seventeen miles from the West Fork to that turn, and much of the eastern part of that distance is prairie. Several miles east of the Wabash, we entered woodlands with a more diversified surface.

Observing a plumb tree, filled with large red flowers twelve feet high, I turned from the road to take a fairer view, and with surprise beheld a rose bush resting its vine-like stem on the branches to that height. The blossoms are in clusters; and as the colour varies with age the appearance is beautiful. I have seen this shrub almost every day since we crossed the Sciota, and believe it might be trained to the height of twenty feet.

Two miles from Vincennes we descended into the prairie that spreads round that town. Here the prospect over level land became extensive; low hills appeared in the horizon, while in the intermediate ground, the academy, rising above the range of buildings, imparted a cast of grandeur to the scene. Backward on our left, two mounds of extraordinary size, rose from the hill at the edge of the prairie. These seem to overlook the country, and resembled in this respect the monuments of the ancient Greeks.

> Around both urns we pil'd a noble tomb,
> —————————that all
> Who live, and who shall yet be born, may view
> Thy record, even from the distant waves.
>
> COWPER'S HOMER.

These remains of antiquity shew that this plain has been the seat of wealth and power; and though it is now only the frontier town of a new race, it will probably long retain a superiority over the towns and cities of this country.

After sun set we took lodgings in this ancient capital of *the West*. 36 miles.

7 *mo.* 6.—VINCENNES stands on the east bank of the Wabash, a beautiful river, 300 yards in breadth. The site is a sandy plain resting on gravel. No flat, subject to inundation, intervenes; and a margin of rounded stones gradually slopes to the water.

This town embraces a great extent of ground; but large gardens, near most of the houses, leave it but small claims to compactness. It is decorated with a few good buildings of frame and brick; but there are many of logs and plaster, on which we can bestow no commendations.

Every valuable or elegant improvement is recent: for although this place has been settled almost a century by the French, we have remarked that the mode of business first adopted by new settlers, long continues to operate; and the history of this town may be cited as an example. A few hunters associated with Indians were the first white inhabitants; and though after the lapse of a few years several Canadian families arrived; and though they retained much of the national politeness, it appears that the cabin bounded their views in architecture, and corn purchased of the natives has frequently preserved their existence.

This primitive indolence, though lessened in appearance by the influx of a northern population, is still conspicuous; and I suspect in some measure contagious. Several inclosures are filled with Jimson* as high as the fences; and without this notice, a view of the town would be incomplete.

But perhaps a traveller never commits greater injustice than in generalizing his remarks; for the

* i. e. Jamestown weed: the thorn apple (*Datura stramonium.*)

meritorious and the unworthy will be found in all districts, and in all communities. Neither am I unapprise d that in reviewing these inhabitants, there are many considerations to soften the severity of criticism.

The precepts of charity require that man should be judged by his own moral principles. And, the point at which he stops in one state of society, may be censurable, while in another state, to have advanced to that point, may be merit of the first degree.

Separated from the civilized world by immense forests, this people were estranged to its comforts, its ambition, and, doubtless, to much of its crime. Avarice had small opportunity to amass treasure, and the love of splendour could be very partially gratified. If, then, we consider that the two main-springs of action in civilized society were wanting, we shall cease to wonder at this result.

But, in addition, they were a conquered people. The British kept a garrison in their town for a number of years; and since the Anglo-Americans arrived, they have often been exposed to Indian hostilities. Indeed when we consider the paralizing effects of such a state, and that partially it has continued till the present time, our censures should be sparingly pronounced.

At the time of determining the streets, no correct idea could have been formed, of the increase of population and of consequence that await this town. A want of sufficient room in some has accordingly been the result; but this inconvenience, in a few years, will be more sensibly felt. Paving has not been commenced; and though the soil is sandy, these avenues are occasionally incommoded by mud. The houses are built on different squares, but are more extended along the river. The number we should estimate between 200 and 300.

This plain is very fertile. Although the sand is clear or white, the " finely divided matter" is so abundant as to give a black colour to the mass. In such gardens as are well cultivated, the vegetation is luxuriant. Drouths are slightly felt. The soil is so absorbent, and the loose substratum admits the ascent of moisture so freely, that though rain had been withheld eleven weeks, we saw small traces of such extreme.

Modern geographers have assigned *fine grass* to this plain. Such an idea is easily acquired by inference ; because a rich soil, like this to the north east would produce fine grass,—but the error is striking. Indeed, sufficient proof might be educed to shew that on this spot none ever vegetated. The herbage chiefly consists of perennial weeds with spaces of *naked earth* between, which coarse wild grass, probably once occupied.

On the bank of the river I found several petrifactions. One of these in grit and colour resembled the white part of the Irish hone. The tree that gave it shape had been six inches in diameter, and this fragment contained one fifth of the circumference. The bark had been removed. The surface left by that covering retained its smoothness ; and the different annual growths were distinctly visible.

About 10 o'clock we commenced our journey up the river towards Fort Harrison. Near the town I counted seven small mounds. Adjoining these a bank and ditch remain which once belonged to a small fortress or store house, probably erected since the arrival of Europeans. All this bank of the river is beyond the reach of inundation.

We soon passed into woodland. *Fort Knox* once stood on this bank, two miles above the town ; but the site is now only discoverable by excavations, remnants of old chimnies, and hewn timber scattered over the ground. The soil, though dry and gravelly, produced, wherever the trees had been thinned by the axe, briars* of luxuriant growth ; and the blackberry was now ripe.

From a bank a little further up the river, a thick stra-

* Rubus villosus.

tum of sandstone projects.   It contains mica, like that at Pittsburgh which is formed into grindstones.

Yesterday, seven miles east of Vincennes, I noticed *mica slate*, and at that town several waggon loads of this stone were lying in a heap ; but I could not learn whence it was brought.   From its appearance on the south shore of Lake Erie, and in all the principal ridges of the Allegany, it is probable that the secondary strata, throughout the Ohio country, rest on this rock ; but whether it projects in places through these strata,— or whether the small quantities which I observed were brought by the great northern deluge from the ridge that divides the waters of the Ohio and St. Lawrence— can only be determined by the position of these masses.

The stems of the *Trumpet-flower* at White River were diminutive ; but here these plants had climbed up many of the trees to the tops ; and the large reddish blossoms extending beyond the branches, presented objects uncommonly novel and beautiful.

[A just medium between cool reserve and colloquial freedom, in recording travels, is a *desideratum*.   It is true, our interest in the welfare of the traveller increases as he unfolds his pleasures and his sufferings; but still there is an insipid triteness, and a minuteness of detail that we wish not to hear.   We care not whether he loves fat meat or lean ; carries a cane, or walks with his hands in his pockets.   Such facts are of no value. It must be confessed, however, that the temptation to egotistic prolixity is great; and, aware of this danger, I should be deterred from retaining the following paragraph, did it not convey instruction which ought not to be withheld.]

Since we ascended the Knobs, my health had been gradually declining.   My stomach was the seat of the disease. Paroxysms of that distressing sensation, which physicians have denominated *anxiety*, had daily increased ; and my friend J. S. had marked the change with silent apprehension. On descending into the *first flats* of the river, it returned with violence, and I entreated my companions to prepare an emetic without delay; but the proposal was rejected, for the air was replete with putrid vapour, the sky overcast, and the ground wet with the late rain. In this comfortless extremity, without the means of preparation, I applied dry pearlash to my tongue till the skin was abraded, taking it rather in agony than with hope. The relief, however, was sudden : the *fomes* of fever was neutralized, and my recovery seemed like enchantment.

[Repeated doses of this alkali in a few days completed the cure; and since, I have frequently witnessed its efficacy on others. Its action is chiefly chemical. In acidity of the first passages it is invaluable ; in dysentery it has ranked as a specific ; and though no medicine deserve this encomium, yet it has speedily afforded relief in numerous cases of that dreadful disease.

A lump, the size of a hazelnut, dissolved in half a gill of water, is a small dose for an adult; but when there is much acid, more pearlash will be necessary to neutralize it ; and in such cases twice that quantity may be taken with safety, if the solution be sufficiently diluted.]

Eight miles above Vincennes, we passed from the woodland flats into the south end of the prairie that extends up to Shakertown. Old driftwood and weeds encumbered the soil, which was black and very fertile; but we could not believe that human beings could frequent it in summer and enjoy health ; yet we saw huts that were inhabited on the border towards the river.

As we advanced, the prospect became more inviting; and we discovered what we had not before learned, that *these celebrated prairies are the upper or second flats on the river.* The surface is undulated ; and at once we assent to the opinion, that it owes its form to some preternatural deluge. The back channel, or *bayou*, through which the water flows when the currents of the creeks are checked by the river floods, unquestionably had the

same origin. The level part of this channel is several
rods wide, and in many places it was covered by standing water; yet we saw no spot that appeared miry, and
the cattle, which were feeding in considerable numbers,
passed over without difficulty. The sides of the bayou
slope so gradually; that except in the lines of driftwood
no traces of inundation are visible.

The advantages that these *natural canals* afford in
times of flood have not been overlooked; and boats often pass up the country at the distance of one or two
miles from the river.

The path, which in places scarcely served to direct
us, led along the eastern side of the bayou; and after
riding a few miles, we gained a beautiful ridge on which
we stopped to refresh our horses. Hard wild grass
scarcely one foot high, thinly scattered among weeds,
constituted the pasturage. Were we to judge only
from this appearance we should not fix the estimate of
its fertility very high; but Indian corn of a most luxuriant growth, as high as the fences, presented a remarkable contrast; and the looseness and blackness of the
soil on that eminence, which for ages has been above
the river floods, excited our admiration.

To the west, the land rises from the bayou for a considerable distance; and the summit, crowned with
trees, hid the river from our view. On the east side
of this prairie, several farms appear which were probably located for the convenience of timber, as we saw
none where the proprietors had ventured far out into
the plain. This tract is from one to three miles wide,
and ten or twelve miles in length; and the novelty,
beauty, and extent of the prospect had a very sensible
effect on our spirits.

The wind met us, on entering this prairie, and continued so regular as to remind me of the current from
a fanning-mill. Like the clouds that move in the superior regions of the atmosphere, it was exempt from
the flaws and whirls that prevail amongst hills and
vallies.

Shakertown, the residence of the Shakers, consists of eight or ten houses of hewn logs, situate on a ridge west of the bayou, eighteen miles above Vincennes. The site is moderately elevated. As we approached, the blackness of the soil, and the luxuriance of vegetation, was peculiarly attractive; but much water was standing on the low grounds to the east; and a mill-pond on *Busseron Creek*, of considerable extent to the west, must suffuse the whole village with unwholesome exhalations. In addition, the first flats of the Wabash, extending one mile west from the creek, are frequently overflowed by the river.

The number of inhabitants is estimated at two hundred, who live in four families.

Pondering on the evils of this mortal life, some have doubted whether it was given in wrath or in mercy;[*] and though we are not authorised to assert, that this sect has been influenced by dark-sided views of our nature, yet marriage is prohibited. From dancing, as an act of devotion, their name is derived. Like several other sects, they conform to great plainness in apparel, but their garb is peculiar. In language they are also very distinguishable. It appears that all complimentary phrases are discarded; but they never use the second person singular in conversation, or say *yes* or *no*, substituting for the latter terms *yea* and *nay*; and tho' I contend with no man about his religious principles,—believing that in every nation he that worketh righteousness is accepted, yet I could not resist the impression, that they had mistaken the antiquated style of King James the first for the original language of the Scriptures.

In their dealings they are esteemed as very honest and exemplary. Until within a few months they entertained travellers without any compensation; but the influx has become so great that they have found it necessary to depart from that practice.

* Jefferson's Notes.

The *estate* at this place consists of about 1300 acres. The *mills*, which they have erected, are a great accommodation to this part of the country, and to these they have added *carding machines.*

A field of sixty acres of *wheat* on the north side of this village, has just been reapt, and put up in shock, The crop is excellent.

Indigo and *cotton*, to the extent of a few acres, are cultivated; and the plants appeared in a thriving state. The products* are wholly designed for home consumption. It is not pretended that these articles would afford a profit on exportation; but it is deemed economical to raise a sufficiency for this numerous family. The price of Tennessee cotton would be enhanced by the carriage hither, and the profits of this cotton would be reduced by its transportation to a market. The same reasoning will apply to the indigo with this additional circumstance: it is only macerated, and the fabrics to be coloured are then introduced. Much labour in preparing it is consequently saved.

These people settled here before the late war; but after their estate was ravaged by the troops who went with Hopkins on his expedition, they sought refuge amongst their own sect in Ohio and in Kentucky, and only returned last summer. They have a fine young or har of grafted apple trees; and their *nursery* is co side ed as the best in the country.

Their *neat cattle* are numerous. Their flock of *sheep* consists of some hundreds, and a shepherd with his dog and gun is employed as a guard.

Sweet potatoes grow remarkably well in this black sand. The *common potatoe* flourishes most in a rich soil, watered by frequent showers; but though the late drouth has been unfavourable, the appearance of this plant is much finer than some of our travellers had induced us to expect.

* About 150 lbs. of clean cotton is produced on an acre.

Water is procured from a *well* between twenty and thirty feet deep. In digging they found the sand coarser as they descended, until it terminated in gravel so loose, that to prevent the sides from falling, it became necessary to work in the hollow trunk of a buttonwood,* which they introduced; and which settling as the gravel was removed, ensured their safety, and now forms the wall of the well. It ought to be repeated, however, that wood soaking in water always injures the quality.

The extensive flat, between Busseron Creek and the River, abounds with the *Pecan*,* a species of hickory. The nut is superior in delicacy of flavour, and the shell is so soft as to yield to common teeth. The Indians, as well as the white inhabitants, have gathered it in great quantities; a market is found for it in every considerable village of this country; and at the falls of the Ohio, the current price has been four dollars a bushel, or twenty-five cents a quart.

On our arrival, we found a young man of genteel appearance, from Kentucky. His intention had been to explore the country up the river, but he concluded to direct his course to the Missouri, giving it as a reason that *farmers in this territory must perform their own labour.*

After procuring some refreshment, we resumed our journey,—turning eastward, and nearly at right angles to the river, intending to visit M. Hoggatt, to whom we had been directed by our friends at Lick Creek. He resides on a farm belonging to the Shakers, at the distance of seven miles.

The configuration of this district is so different from the regions to the east, only excepting some small tracts near the borders of the Sciota, that we seem to have arrived in a new world. Wherever the surface of the ground has been broken, *the blackness* and *depth of the* 81 *soil* excite our admiration. Neither is there any thing

* Platanus occidentalis. The sycamore.

* Pronounced Pek-kawn.

delusive in this appearance, for *the growth of the crops*
fully equals any expectation we could form.

Three miles from Shakertown, we passed a field
which contained the harvest of two seasons. Last autumn the Indian corn had been cut near the ground, and
put into well banded shocks. Wheat was then sown
amongst them ; it had produced a fine crop, and this
was now also standing in shocks,—a clear inference
that provisions are plenty.

Plants which are not found in the eastern parts of the
United States are very numerous ; perhaps three fourths
of the herbage is of this description. I noticed three
species of *Helianthus?* one of which is a remarkable
plant. It grows six feet high with a disk nearly three inches in diameter, and the leaves much resemble the fern.
Observing it first near the Sciota, before the stalk had a-
risen, I even believed it to be one of this curious assemblage. Nature, like water poured on a plain, though
spreading into varieties in every direction, is partial to
particular forms ; and perhaps this partiality is evinced
in nothing more than in *fern leaves.*

A small though beautiful species of *Hollyhock* is
scattered over the prairie. Its blossoms are a fine
red. At first sight, I considered it an exotic ; but it
may be a native, for it is found in the wildest situations
among the groves.

From this prairie we ascended a ridge,—not steep,
and of a moderate elevation,—thinly shaded by small
trees. The sand continues, but a diminution of fertility is immediately discernible, though the district eastward may be called a tract of good land, It is composed of some ridges of that description with intervening
vales. Beyond, the prospect opened into a clayey prairie of great extent, which is nearly destitute of Inhabitants.

We shall not be surprised if many situations in this
district prove unhealthy. The streams have low banks

and in heavy rains, spread wide through the vallies, but the water may be easily led off, whenever it shall be undertaken with spirit, and in such business the scraper would be eminently useful.

As we advanced across the prairie, we saw horses, neat cattle and swine, scattered over it in considerable numbers, and moving about in different directions. Though we had seen much of such openings, our relish of the novelty was unsated; and these feelings were not diminished, when we saw across this great but uncultivated plain,—on the remote border of the civilized world, and where only log cabins have appeared legitimate—a spacious brick mansion in front of the woodlands. This evinces a spirit of improvement highly commendable.

In several places *the land was gullied,* and afforded an opportunity to observe that the black soil is nearly two feet deep; and that it rests on a substratum of yellowish clay. If this part was more remote from the sandy prairies, it would rank higher in the estimation of farmers.

In the evening we arrived at our intended lodgings, where we met a cordial welcome. Hospitality is a strong characteristic of southern manners; and our friend, to an enlightened mind, has added the sympathies acquired by travel.

This, and two other families who live adjacent, constitute all of the society of *Friends* now known to be residents near this river,   25 miles.

7 *mo.* 7.—LAST night we had a heavy storm. In the evening the wind and scud were easterly, but the approach of thunder and lightning from the west, proved that the upper currents of the atmosphere move from that quarter. This morning was overcast, with an east wind,—evincing that counter currents similar to those on the east side of the Allegany Mountains prevail even here.

Our friend has resided between two and three years on this farm. On his first removal from North Carolina, he fixed his abode at Blue River ; but came hither to explore *the lands of the New Purchase* previous to the sale. These lands have excited much attention, but various circumstances have conspired to prevent the surveys from being completed.

It will be recollected, that the expedition to *Tippecanoe* resulted from the dissatisfaction of the Indians, to the treaty in which their title to this tract became extinguished ; that hostilities on their part commenced in the spring of 1812 ; and that after the defeat of Proctor,and the death of Tecumseh at Moravian town in Upper Canada, the Indians sued for peace. The treaty that followed, however, did not restore tranquillity. A Potawattamie chief, reposing confidence in that arrangement, proceeded to Vincennes ; but the next morning he was found dead in the street, into which he had been dragged, and his skull fractured apparently by clubs. On this occasion it was remarked, that though Indians often kill each other, their weapons are the knife and the tomahawk. The perpetrators of this outrage remained undiscovered. The chief was buried with the honours of war; but the light in which the Indians viewed the transaction was soon disclosed by the murder of several white settlers. After this retaliation, though hostilities were discontinued, yet perfect cordiality was not restored till the treaty at Fort Harrison in the present season. One of the surveyors who had been deterred by these unfavourable circumstances from fulfilling his contract,is now out with a company.

These last acts of violence happened since our friend arrived at this place, and several of his neighbours were sufferers. The case of one young man is too extraordinary to be omitted. Riding out to hunt cattle, he passed near Indians in ambush, who shot him through the body, and he fell from his horse. As the savages advanced to scalp him, he recovered from the shock ; ran with his utmost speed, warmly pursued ; and in the moment of extremity when his strength and breath failed him, his horse, which had loitered behind, came up on full gallop and allowed him to remount. He effected his escape, recovered from his wound, and is now living.

This farm consists of 1000 acres. The soil contains little sand, and is consequently more favourable to some crops than the Prairies near the river. We are told that *timothy* flourishes; but *a drowth,* the longest known in many years, which only ceased a few days ago,—and *the army worm,* which has ravaged the meadows,—prevent us from forming a proper judgment from our own observation. By the same creature, the corn has perished twice this season.

These animals, which have committed similar depredations in the eastern part of Ohio, bear some resemblance to the grub-worm; and are regarded as periodical. The name is derived from their moving by myriads in one direction. Some fields and meadows have been saved by deep furrows, in which logs were constantly drawn by horses, so long as these devourers continued to approach. In this manner thousands on thousands have been destroyed.

Wood, for fuel and for fences, is an object of such **82** importance to the farmer, that none is yet found willing to forego that convenience, and to seat himself out in the prairie. On this account, a stranger is liable to err in judging of the population, for we find the eastern border of this tract thickly inhabited.

To satisfy the *claims of the old French settlers,* the United States directed to be set apart, all the lands bounded on the west by the Wabash River; on the south by the White River; on the east by the West branch; and on the north by the north bounds of the Old Purchase. Four hundred acres was assigned to each person entitled to a donation. The land has never been surveyed by order of the government, consequently it has never been regularly performed; and the *maps* of this territory within these boundaries are generally blank.

All lands held in this quarter are therefore under
French* grants. In locating, it was necessary to begin
at the general boundary, or at some corner of lands,
the lines of which would lead thither ; but no course
was given, and the claimant settled the point with his
surveyor as he deemed most to his interest. These
claims have been the source of considerable speculation ;
but the principal part is now located ; and it is expected there will be a large surplus of land, soon to be surveyed by the United States.

Many of these tracts will be destitute of timber fences.   In some parts of the *Grand Prairie*, which extends from the Wabash towards the Mississippi, we are
informed that ditches are advantageously constructed.
The sods are placed on the edges in two parallel rows,
with the turf outward ; the loose earth from both trenches
is employed for filling ; and the strong roots of the wild
grass on vegetating, bind the parts firmly together.

It appears that this prairie has not been ravaged by
fire for some years ; and in various parts, but more especially near the eastern border, shrubs and young trees
begin to shade the soil.   Their scattered situations, with
the injuries received from cattle, give them a stunted
aspect.   From these circumstances it will be difficult to
judge what quality of timber this prairie would produce ;
but where it terminates on the east in a stately wood
of honey locust, sugar maple, blue and white ash, I can
perceive no change of soil.   Neither have I discovered
any marks of an impervious subsoil ; and must ascribe
the destruction of the ancient forest, with the wastes
below Meadville, to conflagration.

This opinion may be explained by a few observations.
Near some part of every prairie that we have seen, whether clayey or sandy, there are trees of diminutive size ;
and though not always distant from each other, the sun

* I have since learned that some militia claims were located
in this tract   The residue is directed to be sold on the 1st. of
9th mo. 1819.

and air has such access that the dampness which prevails in forests, is generally unknown. The leaves and herbage, consequently become highly combustible; and the flame driven by brisk winds, will enlarge the boundaries of the prairie. Several instances of this have been before us. The small timber has been destroyed, and many large trees have been partly burnt. The cause why this prairie extends close to the tall wood on the east, will doubtless be found in these circumstances; for though *windfalls* would let in the sun and air, and be attended by a similar diminution of moisture, we recollect no such tracts in the Western Country.

The *Columbo Root* grows here in great abundance.

In winter when hay and corn have been scarce, some farmers in this district have driven their cattle towards the White River. The woods shelter them from the winds; and abound with grass, bearing the name of that season, which is evergreen, two or three feet in height, and extremely nutritious. In spring, the droves return home literally fat. This advantage, however will be temporary.

Every district, marked by small differences of soil and climate, has plants and animals peculiar. This remark which occurred at P. 113, is well exemplified by these wastes, and we have already learned the names of several new quadrupeds.

The *prairie wolf* is half the size of the common wolf, and it is believed to be *specifically* distinct. It is confined to the prairies, and burrows in the sandy earth. The colour is grey. The legs are short, flat, broad, and stronger in proportion than the common wolf. It has not been known to injure domestic animals; but when sheep are more generally introduced, it will doubtless acquire new habits.

Its motion is slow; and when discovered out in the prairie far from its burrow, is easily run down by horsemen. One was pursued, and so much exhausted in a mile, that the men leapt from their horses, and dispatched it with clubs.

The *gopher* has been mentioned.

The *prairie squirrel* in size and colour nearly resembles the grey squirrel, but the legs are shorter. It is only found in these districts and burrows like the prairie wolf.

It was suggested by some men of observation that, as these creatures are only found in the prairies, such land must have been in this state since the creation. But I cannot perceive that this conclusion is necessarily implied. We have no facts to shew that land destitute of timber is essential to their existence ; we only know that their manners at present are best adapted to such scenes. Indeed we have strong reasons for doubting the correctness of this inference. We have no evidence of original prairies, except those that were formed by excess of moisture. We have no evidence of dry prairies, before conflagrations became regular : in other words, before the arrival of human beings on this continent. The persimmon, the tea plant, and every other tree that can bear the annual bearing, shoot up in abundance ; and if such were undisturbed by fire, by cattle and by culture, these wastes in fifty years would be shaded by forests ;—not lofty indeed, but such as sand resting on gravel would nourish and support.

The grey squirrel, the ground squirrel, and the flying squirrel, are found native, but do not appear to be numerous. To this list should be added the fox squirrel of the southern states.

The deer, the elk, the wolf, and the bear, inhabit the woods. The panther has been rarely discovered, but the wild cat is numerous.

In the brown rabbit, which has frequently bounded across our path, I recognized an old acquaintance, and with it associated the remembrance of early days. This quadruped appears to be very numerous.

7 mo. 8—THE weather of both yesterday and to-day, has been unfavourable to travelling, as showers have been frequent, though the wind and scud are from the east. This circumstance, with the unaffected kindness of our friends, has induced us to remain stationary.

At Vincennes I observed a curious fly-flapper. The construction is simple, and in hot weather the fresh air that attends its motion, is scarcely less agreeable than relief from these troublesome insects. Its position is over the centre of the table.

Two strips of lath three feet long, with a hole in the lower end of each to receive a gudgeon, are first prepared. A broad board with a gudgeon so placed in each end, that one edge shall always preponderate, is then connected with the strips. To that edge a piece of linen one foot wide is fastened; and a handle, eighteen inches long, projects from the opposite edge. The upper ends of the laths are then nailed at the ceiling, and a small cord attached to the handle, communicates motion to the instrument.

A joint in the laths near the ceiling would afford the convenience of elevating or removing it at pleasure.

The privileges granted to the Canadian Volunteers have occasioned severe strictures on the general government; and in travelling one hundred and fifty miles, we have conversed with but few persons who have not expressed dissatisfaction. We are told that the whole of the New Purchase, excepting fractions* and public

---

* A *fraction* is a tract of land where rivers or oblique boundaries have prevented the *section* from being completed. It may consist of any quantity less than a section.

The law of Congress which authorized these donations, directed that the Canadian claimants should locate by sections and quarter sections. Fractions not having been mentioned, and as many of these are very valuable, and include nearly all the lands adjoining the river, the Register of the Land Office with propriety reserved them till the day of public sale.

Lot number sixteen in every township, as in other parts of this territory, is appropriated for the use of schools. A tract has also been reserved round fort Harrison. We knew of no other reservation, though possibly some may be made on account of minerals.

reservations, is spread before them; more than three months have been allowed them to locate their claims without interruption; and to select the most valuable lots and mill seats, from three millions of acres of the best land, ever offered for sale by the United States.

It has been the policy of governments, however, to reward such persons as from principles of attachment have come over from the enemy; and in the present case, they were native citizens of the United States. Many of them left all their possessions behind. Perhaps those who scan the measures of government with candour, would have been satisfied, if the actual sufferers had been put in possession of property so generously bestowed. But a transfer of claims was inconsiderately permitted; certain expence met them in the onset; the office for adjusting their claims, was three hundred miles from the place where the principal number resided; many difficulties had arisen at the end of this long journey; and as cash to the necessitous is tempting, very few will receive one fifth of the value of these donations.

No blame can attach to those who have purchased in a fair market; but some idea of this speculation may be formed from one statement. The right of a private for three hundred and twenty acres, was bought for one hundred and seventeen dollars and fifty cents, and was sold for five thousand dollars. The choicest lots near Fort Harrison have been estimated at fifteen dollars an acre.

A small cotton wood tree stands opposite to the window where I am writing; dark excrescences on its branches like those which appear on this species in the western parts of New-York. It is well known that these blemishes are produced by the irritation of insects;— first by a puncture when the egg is deposited, and afterwards by the growth and motion of the worm. To procure this food, the *parroquets* have been busily employed, at times, through the day; but though they have become so familiar; and though they excel all the birds of this country in beauty of plumage,—their scream is so discordant, and their fierceness of disposition so apparent, as to preclude every sensation of attachment.

These birds build their nests in hollow trees. The strength of their necks is remarkable; and we are assured that when both wings and feet are tied they can climb trees by striking their bills into the bark.

Birds are not so numerous in the Ohio country as in New-York and Pennsylvania. The *prairie hen*, probably a species of the genus TETRAO, is a native. The *tetrao tympanus*, or drumming pheasant of Pennsylvania, called the partridge in New-York is also an inhabitant. The partridge of Pennsylvania called the quail in New-York is very numerous. But this confusion of names is to be regretted ; and in both states the application is improper; for the pheasant of Europe belongs to the same genus as our dung-hill fowls, and the partridge of England is a distinct species from all those of that name in our country.

The *large black bird* (Gracula purpurea,) frequents the principal streams ; and small brownish black-birds, probably of the same species as those that infest the marshes of the Seneca river, are very numerous, and equally predatory.

The *meadow lark*, the *kildee*, and the *land plover* inhabit the prairies. The last has been called the *rain bird*, from its notes being more frequently heard in the calm that precedes changes of the atmosphere. But the mildness of the air may inspire its song, and the stillness allow it to hover more easily over the fields where it loves to wander. From elevations in the air where it is scarcely visible, its note is heard to a great distance like a long shrill sigh. Who hears it in youth will hardly outlive the recollection.

We had been taught to expect that *turkies** were very numerous, but we have been disappointed, for certain-

---

* At that time, it appears that these fowls were hatching or secreted with their young. In the ADDITIONAL NOTICES, a different account will be given.

ly we have not seen half a dozen full grown in all the Western Country.

The *turkey buzzard*, or carrion vulture, is gregarious, but we have seen no large flocks. It is less shy than any other undomesticated bird of its size. When searching for food, it moves in circles so elevated as almost to elude the sight. There is reason to believe that the effluvia of dead bodies, by being specifically lighter than common air, is arranged at a certain height in the atmosphere. On reaching this stratum they more readily discover whence the stream ascends.

The *red headed woodpecker* is seen, but not in such destructive numbers as at Cayuga.

The *little yellow bird* sometimes moves in flocks, and complaint is made of its devouring flax-seed.

To the foregoing list of the birds of this country, may be added the *crane*, the *crow*, the *blue-jay*, and the *red winged starling*.

We learn that *mountain rice* is cultivated by one person, and it has succeeded well. The product varies from thirty to sixty bushels to the acre in the rough ; but it may diminish to one third of these quantities by hulling. This is the best sort ; but it requires more attention and culture than the water rice, as the hoe must be introduced to destroy the weeds, which amongst the latter, the process of flooding completely effects. The latter kind would also grow in this climate, if the land could be regularly laid under water.

Our friend has a handsome little *nursery* of thrifty apple-trees which he raised from *suckers** procured in

* Although it is a current opinion amongst nursery men, that suckers produce suckers in abundance, the emigrant may dismiss all apprehensions on this subject. I have a considerable number of trees, budded on such stocks; several of which now bear apples; and from none of them have I perceived a sucker. I do not assert that these are more exempt than seedling stocks, and nurseries on a large scale could not be conveniently supplied in this manner; but no farmer should be discouraged from raising his own tock.

his neighbours' orchards. He intends to transplant them when he locates a farm. In new countries, where it is difficult to obtain young trees, the emigrant would do well to adopt this method.

7 *mo.* 9.—M. H. having agreed to attend us in exploring the lands up the river, and as maps are necessary, and the creeks unusually swelled by the late rains,—which would retard if not prevent our progress in that direction,—this morning, he and I departed for Vincennes. Our course was south by west, and the distance twenty miles.

This road being back from the river, presented some new objects. Having passed the beautiful wood which I mentioned, including an extensive sugar camp, the trees as we advanced appeared of less and less magnitude, till our path led through oaks of small stature into the prairie.

As the surface of the land is moderately undulated, these openings are interrupted at small distances by *plains*, which differ from the prairies in being dry ground, and in supporting flat-topped oaks thirty or forty feet high, between which are interspersed oak stools. The growth of former years having perished by the annual burning, the young shoots of this season have sprung up in abundance. These are chiefly the white oak, the swamp white oak, and the true black jack.

To the annual conflagrations may be ascribed in part, the scarcity of *snakes* in this district; but the deficiency of hills and quarries to afford them shelter in winter, must remain as the principal cause.

Of these reptiles are enumerated the rattlesnake and the viper. Some garter snakes are found; and I learn that the water snake and black racer will complete the list. The copper head, so common through the wooded country to the eastward, is said to be unknown.

At the end of seven miles we came to *Marie's Creek.* The channel was nearly filled by muddy water, and with difficulty we forded. It is a lazy stream scarcely two rods wide.

During the late war, a neighbouring hunter having started a deer, near the banks of this creek, cautiously approached the root of an old tree, and was earnestly looking through a thick underbrush for his game, when he descried two Indians passing in file at a small distance, Instinctively he shrunk back—raised his rifle, but paused—it was a perilous moment. He knew not their numbers ; and as he was undiscovered, he determined to be still. In a few minutes he heard the report of a gun ; and my friend pointed down the stream to the spot, where at that instant, they killed and scalped a young man who was gathering grapes. A short time before, in full health, he had left his father's dwelling.

The rage and anguish of the parent was excessive. We soon passed by his house ; and the most melancholy reflections arose on my mind. *War*, at best, is a dismal picture. Famine, slaughter and rapine, crowd the pages of its history ; but the keen anguish that invades the domestic circle is unnoticed. To his country, a soldier, or a citizen has perished ; to his family, a father, a husband, a son, or a brother.

South of the creek, oak, not very thrifty, constitutes the principal timber. This tract extends within seven or eight miles of Vincennes ; and with the more open lands to the north, forms a border to the Shakertown prairie. The soil is but moderately fertile. The inhabitants are few, scattered, and in some places we passed on for miles without seeing a house.

Below, the country is more inviting. Beech, sugar maple, honey locust and some black walnut, forms a tall forest ; and a luxuriant growth of herbage overspreads the ground. This woodland extends to the river,—separating the Vincennes prairie from that of Shakertown, —retains a great degree of moisture, like the beech and maple lands to the eastward,—and appears well adapted to the cultivation of grasses. The soil is a strong clayey loam.

Lands partially improved, in this district, rate from twelve to fourteen dollars an acre.

In Vincennes, N. EWING and J. BADOLLET of the *Land-Office, for* whom I had introductory letters, received me with frankness. The former is a native of Lancaster county, Pennsylvania; and the latter of Geneva, in Europe. The friendship of their old neighbour, the celebrated A. GALLATIN, procured them these appointments about nine years ago ; and the high rank which they deservedly hold in public estimation, proves the wisdom of his choice.

In the evening, having acceded to the kind invitation of N. E. to go to his house, which is four miles southeasterly from Vincennes, we took the opportunity to ride to the top of the second mound before noted, and which is near the side of the road. The prospect was extensive and delightful. Excepting a ridge of moderate elevation up the river, where the woodland extends over into the Illinois Territory, there is nothing within the range of the eye that merits the name of a hill.

This *pyramid* was the largest I had ever approached. We estimated the diameter at one hundred and fifty feet, and probably it will exceed forty in height on the west side. As it stands on the slope of the hill, the acclivity on the east side is much less ; and though steep, we ascended it on horseback.

We observe the same singularity of construction as in those to the eastward. The surface is sand, which the adjoining hills may have furnished ; but the interior part is clay, and notwithstanding the greatness of the labour, it must have been brought from a distance. In it, human bones have been discovered. We therefore suppose it was not raised in one age ; and the transportation of the latter material, probably, formed a part of the funeral ceremonies.

At the distance of a furlong to the south, a mound of equal magnitude appears nearly in a right line with

the two which I have noticed. All these are separated
from the prairie by a swamp that lies along the base of
the hill.

This swamp or bog resembles nothing that we have
seen in the western country. A pole may be thrust per-
pendicularly downwards to the depth of twenty feet;
and as it extends to the borders of the White River,
twenty miles below, our intelligent friend conjectures
that it was an ancient channel of the Wabash.

In adopting this opinion, however, I refer to a period
before the formation of the sandy prairies. The vast
quantities of sand and gravel that overwhelmed the river plains, appears to have filled this channel north-
easterly from Vincennes, for a considerable distance
downwards ; and to have turned the river to the south-
west ; but I consider this deluge to have been long anterior to the mounds.

Our road now led through a country variegated by
low hills, chiefly shaded with oak. The soil near the
prairies is sandy ; but as we receded we found it inclining to a clayey loam ; and beech, &c. appears through
the woods.

The mansion of our friend is of brick, handsomely
situated on a ridge which commands a pleasant prospect
of his farm. His daily practice is to ride to Vincennes,
and in the evening to return. This exercise doubtless
contributes to health ; and the bustle of a town contrasted with this charming but sequestered spot, must
increase the relish for domestic enjoyment.

7 mo. 10.—THE antiquities of this country interest
every intelligent mind ; and curiosity seems more awake
because history has shed no light on the subject. N. E.
informed me, that nine miles above its mouth, the Wabash is wearing away a bank which contains great quantities of the bones of different quadrupeds, and hence
it is termed *the Bone Bank.* At the same place, under
a covering of clay and sand twelve feet deep, vessels
of various kinds are found stratified with ashes. Some

of these are large and shaped like a Dutch stew-pot; others are spherical bottles with long necks. Like the fragments found in other parts of the western country, these contain pounded muscle shells. The cement, however, has become very feeble; the parts crumble at the touch, and in every flood the river effects some removal.

Though the ordinance of Congress, under which all the governments north west of the Ohio were organized, expressly declares that no persons, except in punishment for crimes, shall be held in bondage; and though that ordinance has remained unrepealed; yet *slaves* were considered to be so convenient, that the territorial legislature authorized their introduction. For this purpose, indentures were employed. The negro was directed to sign an article, binding himself to serve his master for some specified term of years; refusal could avail nothing, and compliance was termed *voluntary servitude.* I learn, however, from various sources, that it is now generally understood that these *articles* must be declared nugatory whenever a legal investigation shall be made.

In this affair originated a powerful opposition; and for several years past, the territory has been divided into two active parties. Those who were opposed to this innovation, however, soon became the majority; and the members of the late Convention, acting agreeably to the directions of Congress, put the question at rest forever, by excluding the principle of slavery from the state constitution.

After breakfast we returned to Vincennes. The hills that border the prairie on the east, are chiefly composed of sand; and the inequalities of the surface, which are very considerable, show the violent agitation of the deluge that whirled it hither.

Having procured the necessary maps by the very liberal accommodation of the Register, we continued our journey.

We had been invited by B. Parke, a distinguished citizen, to visit him on our return. This we now performed with much satisfaction. He resided in a spacious brick building, erected by the late Governor Harrison, situate at the north end of the town, and which adds much to the appearance of the place. The ground in front is level; but the slope towards the river is easy, and admits of delightful gardens. At this time the *tomatoes* were full grown and abundant; and the *black morella*, which loaded the branches furnished an agreeable repast; but the *Chickasaw plumbs*, with one solitary exception, had all ripened and disappeared. This fruit is delicious, and the tree a great bearer, but suckers appear to spring up around it as far as the roots extend.

Here I discovered that the *worm* which *destroys the inner bark round the root of the peach tree*, is an active inhabitant; and that the *Curculio* destroys much of the fruit.

In conformity to an engagement made last evening, we travelled seven miles further to J. M. M'Donald's, a friendly, hospitable man, where we abode for the night. He has been much in the service of the United States as a surveyor; and was employed to run the *West Bounds* of this territory; north from Vincennes, when it was first discovered that the Wabash River, for more than forty miles, meanders on or west of that meridian.

In his field he pointed out to me a grass, of which I had heard much, known through all the western country by the name of *nimble Will*. It is much esteemed for pasture, especially in Kentucky. I cannot give very strong testimony, however, in its favour, as I have always seen it thin on the ground. In the western parts of New-York, where it also grows indigenously, it scarcely withstands the encroachment of other grasses.

We have been led to believe from seeing so many persons who had marched to Tippecanoe, that the whole military strength of this district was engaged in that

* Solanum lycopersicum.

expedition. Amongst these our hospitable friend may be numbered.

7 *mo.* 11.—WE departed about sunrise, and soon passed into the same road that we traversed two days ago.

Marie's Creek, which has been dignified with the appellation of *a river* on some maps, was now reduced to a light mill-stream; and I think it would be easy to jump across it with a pole. Not far below the surface, sand rock in horizontal strata appeared in the south bank.

About 9 o'clock we arrived, and found my old companions in anxious waiting. In our absence they had explored the country in the neighbourhood of Shaker-town, and had returned yesterday, expecting to meet us.

At 2 o'clock in the afternoon, accompanied by our kind friend M. H. we commenced our journey for *Fort Harrison.* Our road led northwesterly through prairies principally composed of clay, though very fertile, and interspersed with fine farms. It is remarkable that though some parts of these tracts are wet, and now, even covered with water; yet the bog or quagmire is unknown, and there is no danger of being swamped.

Near *Busseron Creek* we passed through a fine tract of woodland, as level and as fertile as the prairie.

At the end of seven miles, we crossed that creek at a *mill,* below which, the water had laid bare a slaty rock in horizontal strata.

We then passed through *barrens* (so called,) which produced corn of uncommon luxuriance. The prospect soon became more interesting. To the left spread an undulated plain of dark fertile sand, thinly timbered by oaks without underbrush; and on our right the scene was variegated with lawns and groves. The low ground is wet prairie, or that kind which is occasioned by the collection and subsequent evaporation of water. Every little knoll of only two feet in height supports a grove. These are termed *islands* by the inhabitants, and not improperly, as floods must frequently surround them.

At the distance of three miles we came out into the *Gill Prairie*, where the extent and beauty of the scene, and the luxuriance of the corn excited our admiration, but the driftwood was deposited in lines, above the level of no inconsiderable part of this fine tract. Indeed we have seen none except the Vincennes prairie that is free from *bayous*. These in times of flood, convert the parts adjoining the river literally into islands; and nearly all communication with the back settlements must be intercepted. In places the channel is excavated, forming when the current subsides, shallow ponds or marshes. These, however, are not miry, and cattle pass over without inconvenience. This bayou, ten miles in length, receives its waters from *Turtle Creek*.

We were now within the limits of *the New Purchase*, and consequently none of the few inhabitants who have fixed here can have titles to the land except through the intervention of Canadian claimants. A cabin and a few acres of corn, constitute the principal improvements.

At Turtle Creek, the woodland commences. Immediately we observed the irregularities of the surface to be greatly increased ; and a clayey loam, which the river alluvions have never reached, producing beech and sugar maple, indicated a total change of soil.

Of the trees in this country we make the general remark, that the trunk, and more especially the branches, are larger than those of the same kinds to the eastward, and stand from each other at greater distances.

83 From a bluff two miles above Turtle Creek, we had a most charming prospect of *La Motte Prairie*, west of the river in the Illinois Territory; and the beams of

the sun, nearly setting, imparted a yellow tinge to the distant woods that encircle this plain. The bluff is upwards of one hundred feet high, and the river flows at its base. The ground declines to the east; the regularity of the descent is remarkably beautiful; and the herbage, like that throughout all this tract of woodland, is very luxuriant.

One man and his family have fixed their residence on this interesting spot, and have cleared a small farm. *Possession* has been deemed of so much consequence in many parts of the United States, and such indulgence has been granted to those persons who have formed *the frontier* in time of war, that even now these settlers anticipate important advantages. Among neighbours, who fear to do each other wrong, such hopes might be realized; but amongst speculators, who will be found here on the day of sale, from all parts of the Union, we can hardly believe that their little claims will obtain much respect.

Our route still led through woodlands. We had five miles further to travel, and the approach of evening induced us to mend our pace; but it became dark before we arrived at *Tarman's,* where we lodged.

20 miles this afternoon.

7 mo. 12.—This person, with his family, resided here before the late war. A small *prairie* of 200 or 300 acres, known by his name, and bordered by thick woods, except towards the river, chiefly contains the improvements. Last spring they removed from the prairie to a new cabin in the woodlands, near the road. The upper story of this building projects for the purpose of defence; and may serve as a memorial, of the apprehensions which overspread the white settlers, before the late treaty with the Indians at Fort Harrison.

A short time before the approach of those persons who came with Hopkins, this family, fearful of the Indians, abandoned their dwelling and retired down the river. In the hurry of removal many articles were necessarily left behind. When the band arrived, they wasted every thing that could be found; and the sons told me that their hogs and neat cattle were wantonly shot down, and left untouched where they fell.

Near the edge of this prairie, I observed some small *mounds.* These are the first I have noticed above the Vincennes Prairie.

I have mentioned the wood house of the eastern states, and the spring house of the middle states, but omitted to notice in its proper place *the smoke house* of Virginia. At least by some, the erroneous opinion has been adopted, that pork cannot be preserved in pickle during the summer heat of this climate. Whether the prevalence of this notion has caused the southern farmer to convert his pork into *bacon;* or whether custom has rendered the flavour most agreeable I leave undetermined; but certain it is that the smoke house is considered an appendage of great value. Our host faithfully practises this branch of rural economy; and in an open log building, we saw nearly one thousand weight of ham, flitch, and shoulder, which was undergoing this process. We presumed that the animals had been recently killed.

Several springs appear in the north side of the bank on which this dwelling is situate. The subsoil is principally sand or sand stone ; and throughout this western country, as in other places, we remark that wherever water comes filtered through this substance, the quality is excellent.

After breakfast we continued our journey. Several families have fixed their abode one or two miles further north ; and so much confidence has been felt in the right of possession that *a saw mill* has been erected in the present season on a small creek. We should be gratified hereafter to learn, that such industry and enterprize have been respected.

In this neighbourhood we passed *a coal mine,* which

has been recently opened, though the work has been but partially performed. The stratum is laid bare to the depth of four or five feet. As the excavation is made in the channel of a small brook, the torrent, by removing the loose earth, doubtless led to this discovery. All the strata of this fossil that we have seen in the western country has appeared near the surface ; and it would not surprise me, if it should be brought forth in a thousand places where the shovel and the pickaxe have never yet been employed.

Last evening between Turtle Creek and the Bluff, we travelled some distance on the first flats of the River ; and in our progress through twelve miles of woods this morning, the same thing occurred. These flats, like the uplands adjoining on the east, are well sheltered with thrifty timber. Overshadowed by woods for such a length of way, we almost forgot our proximity to natural meadows ; and so different are these two kinds of land, that a stranger would as soon expect to find a prairie in the forests of New-York.

In these woods our intelligent friend pointed out to us the ground, on which the escort and drivers of some provision waggons, intended for the relief of Fort Harrison, were attacked during the late war. The Indians lay in ambush on both sides of a bank over which the road led, and when the waggons gained that position, commenced their fire. Only two of the poor fellows escaped. The foremost driver cut loose one of his horses, and after a precipitate flight of more than twenty miles, reached Fort Harrison. The other was a private who concealed himself under the side of a log. From this insecure retreat, continually expecting death, and sometimes almost trodden over, he beheld with horror the butchery of his comrades. After all was *still*, the Indians discharged their guns into the casks of liquor, and cut the waggons to pieces.

Prairies (I am told) are seldom found opposite on both sides of the river. The Wabash has closely traced the west side of this forest ; and directly over in the Illinois Territory, the valley is occupied by *Union* and *Walnut Creek Prairiés.* From these facts it appears, that the same irregularity, prevails in regard to hills and table land, that I have noticed in the eastern part of the Ohio country.

The pecan is only found on the first flats, and appears to be confined within the limits of common floods. It is a stately tree. We saw some three feet in diameter, and nearly one hundred feet in height. The leaf consists of fifteen leaflets : fourteen in pairs, and one terminal.

I have often been surprised at the confused ideas that botanists have exhibited, when treating of this vegetable, and of the species with which it is allied. Though *the outer shells of the walnuts have no determinate opening* like the hickories ; and though *the inner shells are perforated* while that of the latter is smooth—yet one *genus* has been made to include them ; and so much has that ESSENTIAL CHARACTER, and even *specific differences* been overlooked, that *the butternut, the shell bark,* and *the pecan,* have been arranged as only varieties of the same species. We believe no two *genera* of the same NATURAL ASSEMBLAGE* are more distinct.

The timber of the first flats comprises, in addition to the *pecan,* the *bitternut,* the *river nut,* and the *shell bark hickory.* The *butternut,* and, in some places, the *black walnut.* At the river, the *water maple ;* where it is swampy, the *red maple ;* and in the drier parts, the *ash-leaved,* and the *sugar maple.* To these should be added, the *button wood* or *sycamore,* the *ash,* the *elm,* and the *cotton wood.* The last tree sometimes attains

---

*Since writing the above I have observed with much satisfaction, in a late periodical work that C. S. RAFINESQUE, an accurate and distinguished naturalist, has placed the *hickories* in a new genus, *Hiccorius.* Of the old genus *Juglans* eleven species were enumerated, and a majority of these were *hickories.*

a diameter of four feet, and preserves its thickness of trunk to a remarkable height.

The soil of these flats is remarkably fertile ; but mud, left on the herbage by the freshets, causes much of it to putrify ; and the exhalations are very offensive.

A channel, which receives the surplus water of many thousand square miles, must be very unequally supplied ; and during heavy rains it is evident, that

   ————innumerable streams
  Tumultuous roar ; and far above its banks
  The river lift ————

Accordingly, near the northern border of this great tract of woodland, the *flood marks* on the trees were higher than we could reach on horseback.

These marks consist of annular spaces on the bark from which the moss has been removed. We conjecture this happens during floods in the latter part of winter. The ice, forming in the night, encloses the moss; and as the thaw commences at the tree, when the water subsides, the moss will be torn off by the ice in its fall.

On entering *the Prairie* we found it a low strip of land ; and like the south end of the Shakertown Prairie, entirely within the reach of common floods. Whenever the river rises over its banks the road must therefore be impassable. This tract, five miles long, and averaging about one mile in width, is bounded on the north by *the narrows*, where the woodlands from the river and from the hills, approach within ten rods. A heavy current sweeps through in times of flood.

This Prairie is considered to be of small value from its being so subject to inundation ; and no inhabitants are found near its borders. Its name is derived from *Prairie Creek*, a light stream which flows through it **84** from the eastward. A small mound appears on its north bank.

Our friend in leading us towards the woods near the north east corner, directed our attention to the **dry**

ground on which we were riding. In a few minutes
we came to a fine brook which has its sources in the
hills ; but which on reaching the plain is immediately
lost in the sands over which we had passed. We
found several cases of this kind, but observed one
serious inconvenience : as these currents have never
formed a channel to the river, the water in heavy rains,
spreads over the prairie, and in some places coats the
herbage with mud.

These hills are about one hundred feet higher than
the prairies.

Leaving that stream we travelled to the north along
the hill side, through the woods, and soon came out into
Honey Creek Prairie. We were delighted with the
prospect. As we traversed this extensive tract, we
contrasted the granite hills in the east with this soil
which requires no manure ; and nothing but moderate
culture to produce an overwhelming plenty* ; we thought
of the thousands who had toiled and pined on barrens,
while this land for ages had been a range for wild
beasts; and indulged, in fancy, a view of farm houses on
the numerous and elegant sites that have emerged from
this plain.

We explored this Prairie about noon, in clear sunshine. The weather was warm, but not sultry. We
found the most inconvenience from the green-headed
horse fly, which were numerous and active. Excepting
this instance, we have suffered very little from such
insects ; and indeed much less than we expected. It
is an erroneous notion that warm climates produce
them in greatest abundance ; the sultry summers of
northern regions have a full share ; and perhaps in no
country are they more distressing than in Lapland.

*We are assured that when corn (maize) is very excellent, the
whole crop is rarely harvested After securing what is deemed
sufficient, the live stock is turned into the field in the winter to
consume the remainder. We do not believe, however, that this
practice will be of long continuance.

It having become necessary to procure some refreshment, our experienced guide led us into the woodland on the east; and after ascending the hill, directed our course to a new cabin, which was occupied by two families. On entering we were furnished with seats, but the beds were all spread on the floor. In one corner a woman lay in a burning fever. She complained of much pain in her side, and many involuntary moans escaped while her husband supported her head. They were strangers,—young,—probably indigent; and no physician could be found nearer than Fort Harrison.

It was a case of real distress, and the circumstances were discouraging. However, we left medicine with directions.

This family were lately from the state of Ohio. They had arrived in a boat, fixed their residence on the prairie, and drank the warm water from a brook. Apprehensive of disease, they had only left the borders of the river within a few days past, and were received into this cabin as tenants.

[We were much gratified to learn in three or four days that she was likely to recover. Unquestionably many of these emigrants suffer from want of suitable food, and of medicine, and from the want of comfortable lodgings, and of proper attendance.]

The summit of this hill appears to be an extensive tract of table land. The soil is fertile, and produces thrifty timber, but contains little sand except in knolls. This remark will apply to the country in general; and as it perfectly accords with what I have observed in the western parts of New-York; and as some rocks of *granite* are also scattered here, doubtless this land has been overwhelmed by the same deluge. I allude not to inundations produced by extraordinary rains, but to a preternatural flood which swept over the highest hills, and which, to my view, was occasioned by *exterior attraction.*

In descending from the hill, the prospect through the trees had the brightness of a great lake in calm weath-

er.   The low angle at which the sky appears across the
prairie, was the cause of this optical deception.

85   Through this prairie, on the sloping sides of the ridgy
knolls, we frequently observed irregular hollows, several rods in diameter, and a few feet in depth, which
would hold water, had the soil been clayey and compact.
The origin ought not to be ascribed to a depression of
the surface, but to the unequal deposition of sand and
gravel in the time of that extraordinary flood.   The
sides are neither so steep, nor the depth so great but the
plough may readily pass through, and we feel confident
that wheat would flourish in the bottom.   The *Ceanothus
americanus*, or tea plant, which only grows on dry
banks to the eastward, and which also appears on the
driest parts of this land, is found in that situation ; so
loose and so little retentive of water, is the soil.   Indeed we are assured that within an hour or two after
heavy rains, the ploughman may resume his labour without inconvenience.

This species of Ceanothus is completely naturalized to
the prairies.   Burnt down to the ground every season it
has relinquished the habit of a shrub; and conforming to
the vicisitudes of its situation, the same stalks that grew
this spring to the height of six or eight inches, are now
loaded with flowers.

We now directed our course to the westward ; and
at the distance of two or three miles, passed into the
woods that shelter *Honey creek*.   It is worthy of remark
that wherever the streams overflow and deposit a clayey
sediment, we find thrifty timber ; and indeed the dry
land adjoining, —which is the same as the prairie soil —
commonly retains more or less oak.   This fact I consider as an additional proof that these wastes are occasioned
by fire.   As it can only approach from one side, the
chance for the flame to be driven through the trees, is
considerably diminished.

As a continuation of the first remark, it may be noticed, that bayous rarely (if ever) deposit any sediment ;

and in the lower parts of the prairies that are overflowed by the river, we observed the naked sand.

Honey creek is a considerable mill stream. The *prairie* to which it gives a name is computed to be eight miles long, and from one to five wide ; but I suspect the latter estimate is large. It is a beautiful tract of land. By the creek it is separated on the north from the *Terre Haute** (i. e. High land) *Prairie ;* and on the west or north west, from the *Little Prairie.*

On crossing this creek we passed ten or fifteen rods (as we had done on the opposite shore) through a thrifty wood of *beech, sugar maple, white* and *blue oak, black walnut, honey locust,* and *nettle tree;* and then came out into the *Little Prairie.* This contains about eight hundred acres. On it. our friend had made some improvements ; and this was our chief motive in departing from the direct road to Fort Harrison. It is separated from the Terre Haute Prairie by woodland which extends from the river to Honey creek, joining it s me distance above where we forded. The timber on the drier parts of this strip is chiefly *black oak.* The ravages of fire amongst it has been very considerable ; and in this part, the prairie, was visibly gaining on the woods.

We now passed along through the western part of the *Terre Haute Prairie;* and in the calm evening of one of the finest days in summer, the shadows of the oaks lengthening over the plain. Novelty still lent its charm ; and even after we arrived at our lodgings, four miles south of the fort, we were delighted with the prospect of lawns and of distant woods.

This establishment, is not a tavern, but travellers are occasionally entertained. The house was erected in the present season. A few acres of corn are enclosed ; but the proprietor of those improvements

---

* Vulgarly pronounced Tar Holt.

has no claim to the soil but the *right of possession.* This site which is about fifty feet above the prairie to the eastward, commands one of the most extensive prospects that we have seen in the country.

Notwit. st.nding its elevatio , and its pro imity to the woods that shelter it on the west, we observed the same *black sand* that appeared in other parts of these sin u- lar tracts; and where a small excavation has been made for a cellar, I perceived no change at a less depth than two feet. In some of the lower parts of the prairies, I learn that it is even found at the depth of five feet.

7 *mo.* 13.— EARLY this morning we resumed our jour- ney. A few families live near our landlord, but two miles to the north there is a very considerable encamp- ment. Many of these emigrants are from the state of New-York. It is said that *fevers* are prevalent amongst them; and last night a man from the neighbourhood of Genesee river, died. We stopt a few minutes to visit *N. Kirk*, lately from the state of Ohio, with whom our companion D. S. was acquainted. His wife has an intermittent fever.

These notices may seem minute, but the apology will be obvious and ample. The *report* of a traveller which may influence the emigrant, ought to embrace " the truth and the whole truth;" and the profit and the per- il, the bane and the antidote should be set in order be- fore him.

I observed the *Columbo* growing near the borders of these woods, with stalks about six feet in height.

Beyond this encampment to the north, we passed a field containing two hundred acres of corn, which made a very fine appearance, and is the principal crop. The enclosing of this tract with oak rails, was the labour of a company; and each man occupies land in proportion to the length of fence he erected. The w ole has been lately covered by a *Canadian claim;* and though in.

strictness these occupants might be considered as intruders, their case has excited sympathy and called forth some expressions of dissatisfaction with the claimant.

The cabins along the road, from these improvements to the Fort, are numerous; the immediate vicinity of this station has assumed the aspect of a considerable village, and once more we were surrounded by " the busy hum of men."

Fort Harrison stands within a few rods of the river, on a bank which, though not steep, is beyond the reach of floods. It is garrisoned by a detachment from the army of the United States. It was built in the autumn of 1811, by the late govenor *Harrison* and the troops under his command, who halted for that purpose on their march to *Tippecanoe.*

The pernicious effects of spirituous liquors were sadly exemplified a few weeks ago near this place. After the treaty, whiskey was liberally dealt out to the Indians ; and in the frenzy of intoxication, one killed his fellow. To terminate this feud, and to prevent retaliation, it became necessary by their custom, that the murderer should be dispatched by his own brother, and the horrid task was accordingly performed.

About 10 o'clock we resumed our traverse of the country. Directing our course to the northeast through the prairies, we crossed over high broad ridges which might be laid into beautiful farms. The fertility of these lands has been noticed. Such elevations we would expect to be exempt from mud in all seasons, nor do we believe that any unwholesome exhalation would approach.

At the distance of one mile and a half, we came to *Otter Creek* which is a fine mill stream. One mile above the ford is an excellent mill seat, which has just been located by R. Markle, and which he intended soon to occupy.

This prairie is thirteen miles long. The surface declines to the eastward, and becomes so low near the creek, that the water flows thro' in times of flood, forming a bayou which communicates with Honey creek. From the ford, the course of Otter creek is nearly northwest, and just before its junction with the river, the Terre Haute Prairie terminates.

Agreeably to previous observation, Otter creek is sheltered by woodland, and the trees appear on each side as far as the clayey sediment extends.

Spring Creek Prairie lies to the north of this stream: It is about four miles from north to south, and nearly two from east to west. We have seen no tract of this extent equally delightful. One glance takes in the whole opening; and the eye, undazzled by distant prospects that fade into ether, rests with pleasure on woods distinctly visible.

The woods on the northern boundary, chiefly consist of beech, sugar maple and oak, spread over *uplands*, which terminate the prairies on the east side of the river. Along the south border of this tract, *Spring Creek*, a light mill stream, meanders. Its sources are among the hills, and being fed by durable fountains, it suffers less diminution in summer, than many of the larger streams to the south.

We believe that this prairie will be salubrious. From the exhalations of the river, it is sheltered by high lands on the west, which are crowned with oak. No streams sink into its sands. These, with the soakings of the country to the eastward, are intercepted by *Lost Run*, which flows southerly towards Otter Creek; and it appears that no bayou in times of flood, divides it.

The latter circumstance merits consideration. The surface of this prairie, like that of Terre Haute, slopes from the sides towards the middle, and exhibits a depression throughout its whole length. This is in the same line with the bayou from Otter Creek; and if

Spring Creek, instead of its short course, formed a channel for the surplus water of a large district, it would doubtless pass through. Indeed I am not convinced that this does not happen, in extraordinary floods.

On the north side of this stream, we traversed the open woods along the base of the hill. This, we were told, was the route of the army to Tippecanoe ; and we saw *timothy* of fine growth, probably from seed which was scattered at that time.

On the banks of a small brook of pure water, which flows from the hill, we took our noontide repast. We were then six or eight miles beyond the limits of the civilized world ; and no white settlers of any description, are known above Fort Harrison.

Gun flints, similar to those which we noticed near Indian Kentucky, are found in the channels of the brook. I have seen none which give more fire with steel.

In moist places, the common wild nettle *(Urtica divaricata)* occupies much of the soil. Its sting, which was doubtless designed for a defence, is severe to horses ; and one of our hacknies was so irritable as to lie down under the rider.

On the west side of Spring Creek, where it turns north, we found an opening of many acres. Beyond it, towards the river, the land is a sandy plain, above the reach of floods, and thinly covered with oak of moderate size. We consider this an eligible site for a village. The Wabash flows at its base ; the descent to the water is short and easy ; and the communication with the country, will pobably be at all times uninterrupted.*

*The following remark appeared in a Vincennes newspaper, in 1817. " It should not be *forgotten* by those who *know*, nor should it *remain untold* to those who do not know, that there are

Near this plain, the *strawberry plant* grows in abundance ; but the season for gathering the fruit, in this climate, had long since past.

Some idea of the fertility of the woodlands that surround these prairies, may be obtained from the growth of the *Ambrosia trifida,* which we frequently observed. In no other region have I seen it, except on the first flats of rivers.

This day's journey was productive of much satisfaction. We had proposed to encamp ; but unprovided with *punk,** and unsuccessful in all our attempts to kindle fire, we were compelled to return to our former lodgings, more than ten miles from the district in which we wished to spend to-morrow. No traveller in new countries should be destitute of a tinder-box.

7 mo. 14.—From our lodgings, the prospect of this great prairie is delightful. The night was cool, and the morning dripping with dew. The sun at rising, was obscured by a dense cloud of fog which settled near the border of the prairie ; and on enquiry, we learned that a brook† flowed from the hills at that place, and was lost in the sands.

We now proceeded eastward across the Prairie. Knolls or ridges of several acres, lying in a north and south direction, appear through these wastes ; and evince a commotion to which we cannot conceive any river flood to be subject. In the bayou towards the middle of this tract, our horses waded through much standing water.

few places on the Wabash, where high land approaches it so as to afford at all seasons of the year, easy access to the river."

*Punk is a fungus, which extends its sponge like fibres through the decaying wood. The *maples* and *hickories* are the only trees in which we have seen it perfect.

†Lost Creek, for which see the Map.

Near the eastern border of the Prairie we saw a field of corn, the seed of which had been dropt in every third or fourth furrow, and the sod consequently turned down upon it. We consider it a strong proof of the lightness and warmth of the soil. From seed corn treated in such manner in our cool and moist climate, no return could be expected. One precaution, however, is necessary. The inverted soil must be rolled or trodden closely down ; for if the *plumule* unfolds within the cavity, it will be unable to pierce the soil, and must perish.

Crops, in the first season that the prairies are ploughed, exhibit but little of that luxuriance of vegetation, which in succeeding years is so remarkable. This is imputed to the hardness of the wild grass roots, which consist chiefly of the *woody fibre*, absorb even when buried a part of the nutriment contained in the soil, and yield very slowly to decay.

Several families have erected huts in the edge of the woodlands. The inducement has been the convenience of timber and fire wood, a supply of water, and land adjoining ready cleared. But we consider the situation unhealthy. The brooks that descend from the hills, having no channel or outlet to the river, spread, when swelled by heavy rains, and deposit all the impurities that were whirled along by the torrent. The herbage had been coated with mud, and the smell at this time was very offensive.

Changing our course to the north, we crossed Otter Creek at the old ford, and bearing to the east side of Spring Creek Prairie, we passed through groves and thickets that form its border in that direction. This tract is very little elevated above the prairie, and from its soil and productions, belongs to the class of *barrens*. We saw some openings of several acres, moist, and which might form productive meadows. These spaces were beautifully chequered with the meadow sweet, a species of *Spirea* which is herbaceous.

At the distance of two or three miles from Spring Creek Prairie, we came to a rectangular opening of thirty or forty acres which greatly resembled an old field. It is enclosed by black oaks of good size. The surface is handsomely level, and the soil has marks of fertility; but near the north west corner, where a tree had torn up the subsoil, I found a whitish sand, with scarcely any traces of that black fertilizing matter, which so strongly marks the river prairies.

We had intended to visit *Raccoon Creek*, the mouth of which forms one point in the north bounds of the *New Purchase*, being desirous to see the extensive forests of black walnut, which are on the upper parts of that stream; but there was a prospect of rain, and the day was too far advanced. It was therefore determined to explore the lands adjacent to Spring Creek. For this purpose, directing our course westwardly through moist prairies, which are separated by thin groves of stunted oak, we came to *Lost Run*. At this time I judged its current to be as heavy as Spring Creek; but its channel indicated a stream of inferior magnitude; and our intelligent friend informed us, that in severe drowths it ceases to flow. Its banks were thickly covered with pea-vine, as it is here called; but I think it nearer allied to the bean. The aspect of this plant is pleasing, the blossom blue, and the vegetation luxuriant.

Near the north east corner of Spring Creek Prairie, we found a grove of sugar maple on land that declines towards the Creek. Wherever this tree flouishes, the soil is favorable to the production of *timothy*; and, in all places that we have seen, contains no inconsiderable portion of clay. Here a farm might be located that would embrace sandy prairie, fine meadows, a durable stream, good timber, and an extensive sugar camp.

In the woods on the south bank of Spring Creek, we found the remains of wigwams, erected by the Indians, on their hunting expeditions. Some were evidently designed as winter habitations. Of these, dry leaves interlaced with small poles, formed the walls; and the work displayed much skill and neatness.

We have seen no serpent in travelling four days, except a small garter snake, which was coiled on a leaf two feet from the ground.

In traversing such delightful regions, the mind acquires a degree of cheerfulness that rarely attends it in the deep gloom of the forest. But on reverting to the long toils and privations that beset the inhabitant of the wilderness, —and on contrasting the lightness of labour to possess these ancient abodes—a feeling more intense must pervade the patriot. The dark days of his country are past. In fancy, must he view the current of population breaking from the mountains, full, broad, resistless; and the vast and long deserted plains of the Mississippi, fill with life, with intellect, and with elegance.

END OF THE DIARY. 87

ADDITIONAL NOTICES

OF THE

WESTERN COUNTRY.

" THE State of Indiana is bounded on the north
by a parallel latitude, ten miles north of the southern
extremity of Lake Michigan ; on the south by the Ohio
river ; on the east by a meridian passing through the
mouth of the Great Miami; and on the west by the Vincennes meridian, until, in coming south, it intersects
the Wabash, and then by that river to its confluence
with the Ohio."

Of the first settlement made at Vincennes by the
French, it is difficult to find two accounts that agree.
The old French *records* were destroyed by fire ; and all
that has descended to us on this subject, appears to be
traditional. Two of my correspondents have furnished
the subjoined paragraphs. Both accounts are too interesting to be omitted ; and the difference of the dates
shows the uncertainty of the reports in circulation at
Vincennes, though I think the chronology of the first
should be preferred.

" About the year 1690 the French traders first visited
Vincennes, at that time a town of the Piankeshaw Indians, called Cippecaughke. Of these the former obtained wives, and raised families.

" In the year 1734 several French families emigrated from Canada and settled at this place. The first governor, or commandant, was M. St. Vincent, after whom the town is now called. In the year 1763 the country was ceded to the British who held it till the year 1778, when the fort was taken by the American Gen. George Clark. The United States confirmed the French in their possessions ; and a donation of a tract of country round *the Post,* was made to the inhabitants."

" About the year 1702, a party of French from Canada, descended the Wabash river, and established *posts* in several places on its banks. The party was commanded by Capt. St. Vincennes who made this his principal place of deposit, which went for a long time by no other name than *the Post.*

" The French of this place, took an active part on our side in the war that separated us from Great Britain ; but not until they saw an adequate force to assist them in maintaining their standing. In *Ramsay's Life of Washington,* it is stated, that a Spanish merchant of this place, gave information to the Americans, of the situation and strength of the British forces that were stationed here, and that Col. Clark easily obtained possession by his directions. This Spanish merchant, as he is there called, is the venerable Col. Vigo, who resides about three miles south east of Vincennes. He is an ornament to the country and a warm friend to our government."

" In the Indian wars that ended in 1794, the people of this place, though not active, defended themselves against the Indians. The latter, however, were not very hostile towards the French, but killed the Anglo-Americans without mercy wherever they could be found.

" In our last war, the French were as much engaged against the Indians as any other inhabitants of the frontier."

Vincennes, from its antiquity, and from having long been the capital of the Western Country, merits a more particular description than could be included in the Diary. The manuscripts that now lie before me on this subject are voluminous; part of which have been supplied by my correspondents, and part have been procured from other sources.

In the following account of the houses in this town, I place the fullest confidence, as the writer was so obliging as to examine every part of it, on receiving my request for information.

" There are eight brick houses, ninety-three frame houses, and one hundred and fifty French houses—in all, two hundred and fifty-one. These are exclusive of barns, stables, and old uninhabited houses, which I think are equal to the number of French houses, and make the whole number of buildings about four hundred. On the commons east of the town, there are many cellars and old chimney places, which lead me to suppose that Vincennes has decreased in the number of buildings."

Some idea of the *commerce, manufactures,* and *importance* of this place, may be obtained from the following List, which is dated 1st of 1 mo. 1818.

"18 Stores of Merchandise;(*a*)
  6 Taverns,(*b*)
  4 Groceries,
  4 Black-Smiths' Shops;
  2 Gun Smiths' do.
  3 Shoemakers' do.
  3 Saddlers' do.
  4 Tailors' do.
  2 Cabinet Makers,
  3 Hat Factories,
  1 Silver Smith,
  1 Tin Factory,
  1 Chair Maker,
  1 Tobacconist,
  1 Tannery.

  1 Apothecary;
  2 Printing Offices,(*c*)
  7 Lawyers,
  7 Physicians,
  1 Limner,
  Chapel,
  Academy,(*e*)
  Post Office,
  Bank,(*f*)
  U. S. Land Office,
  Court House,(*g*)
  Jail,(*h*)
  2 Market Houses,
    and a
  Livery Stable.

*(a)*This note will comprise all my remarks on the commerce of the Wabash.

We learned at Vincennes that the merchants only accepted cash in pay for goods. At that time, the surplus productions of the soil were too small to have formed any regular channel to distant markets. I am not able to state that it is even now accomplished, but all kinds of *produce* are in brisk demand for cash. The chief part of these purchases are doubtless to supply the immediate wants of the new settlers; but cash has been offered for large quantities of grain at several places near the river.

In the 2d month, 1818, the following prices were current.

	$	Cts.
Wheat, per bushel, was	1	
Corn, do.	0	50
Potatoes, do.	0	37 1-2 to 50
Pork, per cwt.	4	50
Beef, do.	3 to 4	

The reader will recollect, that in 1816, Corn was only 25 cents, and a considerable advance in price, has therefore taken place.

In the prices of *Dry Goods*, there is not much difference between Vincennes and some of the stores in Cayuga county. In respect to *Groceries* on the Ohio River, as well as on the Wabash, the following retail prices are current.

	$	Cts.
Coffee, per pound,	0	37 1-2
When scarce,	0	50
NewOrleans sugar, do.	0	25
Loaf sugar, do. (on the Ohio river,)	0	37 1-2
do. do. do. (at Vincennes,)	0	50
Young Hyson, do.	1	50
Brandy, per gallon,	6	00
Madeira Wine, do. first quality, (at Vincennes,)	8	00
Common Rum, do. —	4	00
Iron, per pound, retail,	0	16
Ham, do do.	0	25

Together with *Salmon* and *Herring*, *Shad* are sometimes brought from New Orleans, and retailed at 25 cents a pound, or 62 1-2 cents each. *Mackerel* 25 cents a piece. *White fish* are brought from the neighbourhood of Detroit.

Since *the Kanhawa works have been monopolized,* salt* has greatly advanced in price along the Ohio. When we were at Vincennes; it was said that a large quantity could be bought at $5, but $6 was the common price. Now it is sold at $10 a barrel, and retailed from $2, to $2 50 a bushel. Salt from the Salines near *Shawanee Town,* at $1 50 a bushel. Last autumn at Fort Harrison, it was sold for $15 a barrel,—a scarcity having been occasioned by unusual floods in the river.

Common *boards* sell at $1 50 per 100 feet, Plank at $2.

The amount of *merchandise* in Vincennes two years ago, was estimated at one hundred thousand dollars.

The merchants of that town procure New Orleans goods at Louisville.

Beer and *Porter* are brought from the breweries in Cincinnati.

The current charge for transportation of goods from Pittsburgh† to Vincennes is *per cwt.* $ 1 00
when boats are scarce 1 25
from Vincennes to Pittsburgh 3 00
  do. to New Orleans 1 00
 to do. from do. 4 00

---

* Salt at Cincinnati, in 12 mo. 1818, was selling at $3 per bushel of 50 lbs. and at Vevay, it was sold at $3 50. Salt is sold according to the marks made on the barrels at the Kanhawa works; and on account of the leakage of brine, a loss of weight is commonly sustained.

† The transportation from Pittsburgh to Louisville is from 40 to 50 cents per cwt. when the amount of freight is considerable.

(h) An innkeeper, in a Vincennes paper of " Feb. 6,
1818," offers to accommodate his customers on the
following terms, viz:

	$	Cts.
" Breakfast, - - - -		25
Dinner, - - - -		25
Supper, - - - -		25
Lodging, - - - -		12 1-2
Horse to corn and hay one night,		37 1-2
One horse feed, - - -		12 1-2

This agrees well with our experience of *tavern
bills*, though in some places the charges were higher.
For instance, a horse at oats and hay one night was 50
cents. But oats are scarce in Indiana, and
horses are fed on corn, which is shovelled out
to them without measure. The common practice is to
charge 12 1-2 cents for *a feed* ; that is, as much as
the horse can consume, be it more or less.

In some good houses in the state of Ohio, the fixed
price was 75 cents for every thing that a traveller needs
for one night, including his horse. But in that state,
sometimes we meet with extortioners.

—— ——

(c) The following *Newspapers* were published in Indiana in 2d *mo.* 1818. These were all *weekly.*

" The Western Sun,	Vincennes,	E. Stout, Editor
Indiana Centinel,	do.	S. Dillworth.
Indiana Register,	Vevay	J. F. Dufour.
Indiana Republican,	Madison,	J. Lodge.
Dearborn Gazette,	Lawrenceburg,	B. Brown.
Indiana Gazette,	Corydon,	A. Brandon.
Indiana Herald,	do.	R. W. Nelson.
Plain Dealer,	Brookville,	B. F. Morris.

" The above offices, except the Western Sun, have
all been established since the constitution of this state
was formed."

N. B. We learn that the Herald is discontinued at Corydon, and the INDIANIAN, by the same Editor, is now published at Jeffersonville.

(d)" This was built by the French Roman Catholics, and in their own style. It is sixty-six feet in length, about twenty-two feet wide, and nine feet from the ground to the eaves. It has a kind of steeple, about eight feet high, with a small bell."

" The Roman Catholics, at present, have no pastor, and no other religious society is established. Itinerants of all sorts preach here occasionally, and have nearly the same audience."

(e)" The *Academy* stands east of the town. It can be seen a considerable distance in every direction, and makes a very handsome appearance. It was erected in 1807. The walls are brick ; the length is sixty-five feet the width forty-four feet, and the height three stories. It was designed for eighteen rooms. Ten thousand dollars have been expended, and it stands unfinished. The fund consists of land, twenty-five miles south of this place. The Legislature authorized the sale of a part of this tract, and appointed twenty-one trustees to govern the Institution ;" but the hopes of its founders have not been realized. " Only a common school has been kept in it. [March 24, 1817."]

" Two large *Schools* are now kept in this town."

" A *Library* was established in 1817, which now consists of more than 700 volumes. The annual contribution is two dollars on each share."

*(f)*This institution was chartered on the 10th of September, 1814, and the capital has been increased to $ 1,500,000. Nathaniel Ewing, President ; Isaac Blackford, Cashier.

A power is vested in the Directors to establish branches, so as not to exceed one to every three counties ; and one has lately been located at Brookville.

On the " 29th of November, 1817, a dividend was

declared by the Directors at the rate of twelve per cents
per annum, for the last six months on amount of stock
paid in."

The charter of the Farmers' and Mechanics' Bank
of *Madison,* also bears the date of September 10, 1814,
The capital is $500,000, John Paul, President, and
John Sering, Cashier. A branch has been fixed at
Lawrenceburgh, Thomas Porter, Cashier.

(g) "This is a brick building, forty by fifty feet, and
two stories high. It is very handsome and commodious."

(h) The jail is built of logs.

(i) The livery stable is of brick, and very large.

"Above the town, though within sight, they are
building a *steam grist mill* and saw mill. The latter is
so far completed, as to have commenced sawing timber
for itself and the grist mill, on the 1st of January,
1818."

———

Vincennes is situate one hundred and twenty miles
by the road, north-west of *Louisville ;* one hundred and
seventy east of *St. Louis* by the present route ; three
hundred miles south south-west of *Chicago ;* and one
hundred and sixty miles north-east of *Kaskaskias.*

The number of *Inhabitants* at Vincennes has been
estimated at from 1500 to 2000.

"Unimproved *lots* of half an acre, on the principal
streets, sell from five hundred to one thousand dollars.
In the back streets, the prices of lots are from fifty to
one hundred dollars." 7 *mo,* 1817.

To their former intercourse with the Indians, we
trace a singular practice in this town. "As soon as
it becomes dark every store is shut up." My correspondent adds, that "though licentiousness and dissipa-
tion prevail, they also rigidly abstain from opening
them on the sabbath."

Climate is always an interesting subject to the geo-graphical enquirer; and all my correspondents, aware of this circumstance, have been minute in their re-marks. "Accurate observations on the thermometer have been made and registered by Judge PARKE," of whom my obliging friend J. B. BENNETT, procured the following statement. It will be perceived that an ac-count of one month has been inadvertently omitted.

Extremes of Farenheit's Thermometer.

	Deg.		Deg.	
" December 1816,	17	lowest	61	highest
January 1817,	11	below zero	60	
February	5	do.	66	
March	18	- -	70	
April	39	- -	83	
June	52	- -	88	
July	58	-	95	
August	53 1-2	- -	95	
September	40	- -	93	
October	23	- -	80	
November	24	- -	70	
December	2	- -	66	
January 1818,	5	below zero	59	
February [to the 12th.]	16	do.	40"	

As *the seasons* are infinitely irregular, I deem it best to give the views of my correspondents separate and entire. The difference in their statements, may be re-conciled by considering that some have drawn conclu-sions from a long series of observations; and that others have been guided by a few recent facts. A considera-ble difference of temperature is also observable, between the black sandy prairies, and the clayey woodlands.

———

" The *winds* in summer prevail most from south and west; in the winter from the north and east.* East

* I do not consider this to be incompatible with the statement which I received at Lick Creek. The direction of winds thro' the

winds generally produce falling weather. West winds are common with a clear sky.

" The *Summer* is generally dry, especially in the month of August. At such times vegetation is checked, particularly in sandy soils, and the streams diminish considerably. Wells, however, seldom or never fail at Vincennes.

" In winter, the atmosphere is generally clear and cold. The *Snows* are seldom more than three inches deep, and are commonly melted by sunshine. *Sleighing* sometimes continues for two or three weeks.

" *Spring* is attended by much wet and cloudy weather. Vegetation commences about the 20th of March. The *peach* blossoms the last of that month. *Grass* is abundant after the first of April, but young cattle do well in the river bottoms during the whole winter. The *strawberry* ripens the last week in April. *Wheat harvest* commences from the 20th to the 30th of June. *Vernal frosts* have been noticed as late as the first of May, and the earliest *autumnal frosts* about the first of November. To this, however, there are some exceptions. July 18, 1817."

———

" The *depth of our snows* for the last ten years, has not exceeded six inches. The *thickness of the ice*, in the Wabash, is sometimes ten or twelve inches.

vallies of large streams and over elevated plains, in the same neighbourhood, is often very different ; and this circumstance deserves the attention of all those who study METEOROLOGY. The following extract from Cook's last Voyage, will place this subject in a clear and proper point of view :—

" Before we had got up one anchor [in *Awatska Bay*] so violent a gale sprung up from the *north-east*, that we thought proper to moor again, supposing from the position of the entrance of the bay, that the current of wind would in all probability set up the channel. The pinnace was dispatched to examine the passage, and returned with intelligence, that the wind blew violently from the *south-east*, with a great swell setting into the bay."

Ploughing may be commenced by the tenth of March, and carried on with very little subsequent interruption from frost or snow. *Strawberries* ripen about the 15th of May. *White frosts* are sometimes seen in the early part of April, and have been known on the 23d of October. March 30, 1817."

" *Winter* generally sets in about the first of January, and breaks up about the first of March. Last winter the *thickness of the ice* in the Wabash, was eight inches; and this winter [1818] about the same. The *snow* at Princeton has been four inches deep; at Vincennes eight inches deep for five weeks, and at Fort Harrison twelve inches deep."

" *Wheat harvest* is generally about the last of June or first of July. *Strawberries* ripen about the middle of May. In backward seasons, *common fruit trees* are in full bloom about the middle of April, but often earlier. *Vernal frosts* are all over by the first of May, tho' last spring was an exception. *Autumnal frosts* at Vincennes commonly begin about the first of November. Last fall I saw beans, tobacco, and other tender vegetables, unhurt by frosts on the 4th of November; but in the vicinity of Fort Harrison, frosts appear in September. The *snows* at this place are very light. Eight inches has been the deepest which has fallen in many years. Last winter there was little; but we had *sleet*, which made good sleighing for four or five days.

" I have seen more serene weather, during this winter, than in ten winters in your country."

" On the 7th of November I left *Corydon*, and arrived on the 13th. On our way, the snow fell about three inches deep. *The weather* from that time till the 20th, was cold, when it became mild, and continued so till the 10th of January. On the morning of the 18th, the *mercury* stood eleven degrees below zero; the Wabash River closed, and has remained so ever since. [10th February, 1817.]

" The *snow* has not at any time fallen more than three inches, and but three times in all. There is a peculiarity in this climate, and the absence of turbulent winds is remarkable. The old settlers agree, that there has been less snow than usual ; but that the cold has continued longer than at almost any time within their recollection. Yet there has not been five days that a northern man would be uncomfortable at work with his coat off.

" The farmer may be well employed the whole autumn and winter. Prairie lands, in particular, may be broken up with the plough from the first of March until the first of November, and most of his laborious business may be performed in temperate seasons.

" I am told that a great portion of the year is warmer than in the vicinity of Philadelphia, but the nights in summer are much cooler. The mercury is seldom above 94 degrees, although it has been at 98. Wild greens are sometimes procured the first week in March. Peas with common attention are fit for use by the 15th of May, but with care may be produced much earlier."—W. P. B.

I learned, while in that country, that the snow in eight years had not at any time exceeded five inches in depth. In the remarkable snow of 3 mo. 31, 1807, it was about eleven inches; but in Scipio it was two feet.

Except when walking at noon day, we were seldom disagreeably warm, although we wore boots, with coat, vest and pantaloons of fulled cloth ; neither did we find one night in which a blanket was uncomfortable, unless in apartments heated by the afternoon sun.

These observations include a period of ten days near the Wabash river; but we were told that on the praigies it was sometimes very hot*; and indeed this has been sufficiently indicated by the thermometer.

＝＝＝

Near Salem, on the high *table land* at the sources of Blue River, I was assured, that in the winter of 1815–16, the *sleighing* continued for six weeks, though in part of that time the depth of the snow did not exceed one and a half inches. In Cayuga county, steady cold for such a period would be very remarkable : but the south winds, which often occur within the vicinity of the lakes, dissolve snows of common depth, in a few hours. It appears that Indiana is exempt from these sweeping gales, and that the snows are melted by sunshine.

＝＝＝

As a *test* to these remarks, I give the following extracts from Dr. Drake's excellent " *Picture of Cincinnati.*" This town it should be recollected, is situate in a deep reverberating valley of the Ohio ; that part of the waters of this river arrive from the south, while those of the Wabash come from the regions of steady cold in winter ; and though Vincennes is one third of a degree further south, probably the temperature is not higher than at Cincinnati.

The dates of his CALENDAR of FLORA "are the mean terms of several years observation." From this list I can give only a few items, but the whole of his remarks deserve attention.

* M. Birkbeck, however, says, " the heat of this climate is not so oppressive as I expected. I have been using strong exercise through three of the hottest days that have been experienced in four years. On one of these days, I walked with my gun in the Prairie, and travelled on horseback the other two, without great inconvenience. The only sultry night I have experienced proved the prelude to a thunder-storm."

March 5. Commons becoming green.
April 8. Peach tree in full flower.
    18. Lilac ——— ————
    20. Apple tree ———————
    24. Dogwood ——— -———
May 9. Flowering locust in full bloom.
June 4. Cherries beginning to ripen.
       Raspberries ——— ————

From 1806 to 1813 inclusive, the lowest extreme of Farenheit was eleven degrees below 0, and the highest ninety-eight degrees.

"The greatest degree of cold ever observed at this place was on the 8th of January, 1797 ; when, according to Governor Sargent, the mercury fell to eighteen degrees below zero."

"The quantity of snow which falls at Cincinnati is inconsiderable. The deepest that has occurred was perhaps ten inches ; but four is about the ordinary depth, and many are not more than two or three. The ground seldom remains covered longer than two or three days."

"The latest vernal frosts are generally at the close of the first week in May."

"In general, the last of September is the earliest period at which white frost is perceptible in the valley of the Ohio."

———

"The Ohio Countries have been considered much warmer, in the same parallels, than the Atlantic states." This opinion, Dr. Drake has controverted with much ability ; and his independence on this occasion, entitles him to the respect of every friend to natural science. He admits a difference of temperature, but deems this to consist more in the distribution than in the absolute quantity of heat.

I am inclined to believe, however, that this difference

of distribution is in favour of the Western Country. Observations made near Schuylkill and inCincinnati, at sunrise and at 2 P. M. though averaging the same, will give very unequal views of those climates. In the south-eastern part of Pennsylvania, the approach of evening is often attended by an uncomfortable heat, which is frequently protracted until midnight, while on the western side of the mountains a refreshing coolness prevails. Here then, are several hours, of which we have no account, and which would, in summer, considerably affect the thermometrical register. If vegetation is equally advanced at Cincinnati under a lower temperature, the inference is clear that spring is milder than on the western side of the mountains.

In addition to our own observations on the coolness at evening, I select the following notices :

" The dew, in the woody vallies of this country, is so copious in the summer and early autumn, as to be felt before sunset. In the night it sprinkles from the trees like drops of rain ; but in more elevated and open situations, its quantity is much less." DRAKE

" Melting, oppressive, sultry nights are unknown here. A cool breeze always renders the night refreshing." BIRKBECK'S Notes at Cincinnati.

" The nights are more comfortable than they are even in Virginia," CRAMER, on the Climate of Mobile.

The *water* of the Wabash forms a good lather with **89** soap. At Pittsburgh, for washing, the river water was good, but it becomes harder in its descent. At Cincinnati an increase of lime was evident ; and near the mouth of the Wabash, the water, of the Ohio was *hard*.

The reader may observe that limestone is scarce above Pittsburgh, but in parts of Ohio, Kentucky, and Indiana the quantity is immense. It appears, that in this stone there is always more or less gypsum.

The *Wabash* has a gentle current, except at the *Rapids*, twenty three miles below Vincennes. This obstruction, however, is not very difficult, as flat bottomed scows eleven feet wide, have readily ascended. In dry seasons, it is necessary to lighten boats."

" The *Rapids* are occasioned by flat rocks, which extend across the river and might easily be removed."

" *Steam* boats* may navigate this river from four to six months in the year."

The *distance* from Vincennes to the mouth, has been variously represented. It was formerly estimated a one hundred and fifty miles, and in some instances the computation has been reduced to one hundred. It appears to be about one hundred and twenty. Boats frequently go up in six days, but ten days are more commonly required.

The *south wind* which prevails in spring, and which greatly facilitates the ascent of boats, often becomes a head wind in consequence of the winding channel of the river.

" The Wabash is boatable about four hundred and fifty miles. Perogues have been taken out of this river into the Miami of the Lake. In low water the portage is nine miles. This communication is not so much used now as formerly."

Neither the Ohio nor the Wabash can be ascended in times of full flood by common boats. The advantage which has been taken of the bayous on the latter river, has been noticed.

My friend, D. STEER, observed that the navigation of White River must be difficult on account of its crookedness, as a boat, without great exertions and continual care, will cross the current and run a-ground, The Wabash is also remarkable for its serpentine course

---

"* It is expected that a steam boat will be in complete operation on the Wabash, next spring or summer." Letter of 6 mo. 16, 1818.

and from Vincennes to Fort Harrison, which is only reckoned seventy miles by land, it is computed to be one hundred and fifty by water.

" The Wabash is four hundred yards wide at its mouth, three hundred at Vincennes, and two hundred at Fort Harrison. It is fordable in many places."

To avoid accompanying boats in the tardy ascent of this river, many travellers land at *Evansville** which is situate at the mouth of Great Pigeon Creek, and proceed to Vincennes by land. The distance is fifty-six miles. The road is tolerably good in summer, and much used ; but after the autumnal rains, quicksands are frequent in *the barrens* through this country.

Princeton stands on the road between these towns, and is twenty-eight miles from each. It is four miles south of the Potoka river on a handsome elevation. The following list was made in 1 mo. 1818.

" Brick houses, three ; frame houses, ten ; log houses eighty. Total ninety-three. Six stores of merchandise ; three taverns ; three lawyers ; two physicians. There is also a court house, jail, clerk's office, recorder's office, post office, and the following mechanics' shops : blacksmiths, two; cabinet makers, one; gun smiths, one ; shoemakers, two ; taylor, one ; saddlers, two ; hatters, one ; tannery, one ; chairmaker, one."

" The inhabitants are principally *Kentuckians.*"

———

" Instances of *longevity* are frequent. There are now living in Vincennes four Frenchmen, who were at the defeat of General Braddock, and who have lived here between fifty and sixty years. There are, also, two French women between eighty and ninety years old. One person by the name of Mills, died on the Wabash, aged one hundred and fifteen years." 3 mo. 30. 1817.

* "The mouth of Great Pigeon forms one of the best harbours between Pittsburgh and New Orleans."

"A soldier who was with the troops that defeated general Braddock, now resides here. He is a stout healthy man, and able to labour, though near one hundred years old. He has always been temperate." July 1817.

This is not used to invalidate the first statement. Another account says, "last year there were four Frenchmen at Vincennes, who were in Braddock's defeat, and two this year." 1818.

"The *army worm* is periodical. The cut worm and the caterpillar are annual, but their depredations are inconsiderable. The weevil is unknown on the Wabash."

The correctness of Thomas Jefferson's opinion, that the *Bee* is not a native of our continent, has been questioned. I have therefore been particular in my inquiries, and the following statement will be read with interest.

"It appears that the time has been, when the bee was not known in our country. The old French settlers saw none ; and toward the Mississippi, it has not been more than twenty or twenty-five years since it was first discovered. J. M'Donald informs me, that in the Military bounty lands above the junction of the Illinois with the Mississippi, which he surveyed last winter, the bee has not been seen more than fifteen years."

Another correspondent says, " Bees are very plenty in the woods ; and as the Indians here call them " white people's flies," it is believed they are not natives.

"Great quantities of honey have been found in the woods above Fort Harrison. One man found twelve bee-trees in less than half a day." 6 mo. 16. 1818.

"*Pine* grows up the Wabash, and on the knobs of

the Ohio and Silver Creek." It appears, however, to be a scarce article, and even window-sash is made of black walnut.

" *Red cedar*, of good quality, is found up the Wabash."

" I have seen neither the chestnut nor cucumber tree in this country."

==

Wherever the fire ceases to ravage, wild fruits soon become abundant. The plumb, the crab apple, and the persimmon trees appear in the borders of the Prairies ; and the grape-vine should be included in this remark. Near M. Hoggatt's, we judged that a hogshead of hazel nuts might be readily collected. A correspondent confirms these observations.

" This country produces grapes in the greatest abundance. I came down the Wabash eight miles by water. The shores are lined with willows, many eight or nine inches in diameter, and the whole appear to be loaded with grape vines. Hazel nuts are equally plenty. The same may be said of the black walnut and hickory nut, and of the latter there are several kinds. These afford food in abundance for hogs, and they live through the winter in the woods without any other sustenance."—" It is not uncommon for a farmer to kill one hundred hogs and receive six hundred dollars for them, without giving them one ear of corn. I know one man, who sold pork this winter [1818] to the amount of one thousand dollars, without one dollar's cost for food."

" The *Pecan* in the middle is about the size of a white oak acorn, but much longer, and terminates at each end in a point. I think these are more delicious than the small shell bark.

" The *Persimmon* [near Vincennes] is quite plenty. It grows on a large shrub, or small tree. The fruit is about the size of a small peach, and is very delicious. The green fruit is remarkably astringent ; and if eaten, affects the mouth so much, that for some time the person is almost incapable of speaking.

" The *papaw* is another fruit which is unknown in New York.   I have seen some trees of these twenty or twenty-five feet in height.   The fruit is cylindrical, and larger than a turkey egg, ripens late in autumn, and then becomes yellow.   The seeds like those of the persimmon, resemble gourd seed.   The scent and flavour are too luscious to be agreeable to those who are unused to this fruit ; but the disgust soon abates, and we find it highly delicious."

With these fruits, I have been familiar from infancy, but have preferred the language of my correspondent.

━━

" Wherever a high piece of land appears on one side of the River, the opposite shore is low and sunken ; and from Raccoon Creek, fifteen miles above Fort Harrison to the mouth of the river, I believe there is no exception to this remark.

" There is one inconvenience attending this country, exclusive of the overflowing of the Wabash.   All its tributary streams after a heavy shower of rain, rise above the banks ; and overflow the low land adjoining, which on all, is of considerable extent.   In time of high water, it is one of the most difficult countries to travel through, I ever saw.   I have known it for more than four weeks at one time, that no person could get away from Union Prairie, without swimming his horse, or going in a boat."

━━

" The *Buffalo* has totally abandoned our country, but the *Elk* still remains in many places."

" *Raccoons* are in great plenty, and very destructive to corn.

" The *Pole Cat* or *Skunk* are very numerous throughout the country, as well on prairie as on wood land.

" The *Opossum* also inhabits this country in great numbers. Some are as white as snow, and others of a light grey, resembling in colour the grey rabbit.

" The *Porcupine* has been seen in this country, but is very scarce.

" The *Prairie Wolf* is numerous. In size, it is a medium between the red fox and the common grey wolf. The colour is grey. Its ears are sharp and erect like those of the fox. Unless several are in company, it is not destructive to sheep; but it destroys lambs and young pigs. On Christmas day, 1816, thirteen were killed on Fort Harrison Prairie without firing a gun. During the same winter, there were about thirty killed on Union Prairie, by running them down with dogs and horses. It is very resolute when attacked and unable to escape; no dog alone is able to subdue it. In the summer season it is not to be seen; but in winter it frequents the prairies in great numbers.

" The *grey* and the *black wolf* are also natives. Whether these are different species or not, I must leave undetermined."

" I find no *black squirrels* in this country, but it abounds with *grey ones* hardly so large as the black squirrel with you."

———

" The *Pelican*, so common on the Mississippi, also frequents this river, but not in great numbers. I saw the head of one which had been taken near Vincennes. From the point of the bill, which is from seven to ten inches long, a pouch or loose skin extends to the breast, which would contain about ten quarts."

" The *Swan* is sometimes seen on this river."

" The *Crow* appears in great numbers, and are **very** destructive to corn."

" A bird inhabits this country, called the *sandy hill Crane*. Its size is remarkable. When full grown and standing erect (for its legs and neck are very long) it is between five and six feet in height. The colour is nearly that of iron rust. I have seen large flocks on the prairies. It is very wild and noisy. When slightly wounded, no dog can approach it with impunity."

" The *Prairie Hen* is rarely seen in summer ; but in winter, it is more numerous on the prairies than quails are in the state of New York. The size is nearly that of the common domestic hen. It is spotted like the guinea fowl, but the colour is browner, like the pheasant. The tail is shorter and does not spread like that of the pheasant. The difference between the cock and the hen is not greater than in those of the quail ; the male is a little larger, and the stripes on the side of the head are a little brighter than those of the female. It can fly much farther, and with more apparent ease, than either the quail or pheasant. As an article of food, I think it inferior to the dung-hill fowl. It lays about twenty eggs, and brings forth its young in the early part of summer. Though its common food is procured in the woods, it is fond of corn and grain."

" The *Robin* and the *red headed Woodpecker* are numerous."

" On the approach of any large bird the *Parroquets* immediately commence flying round and round in flocks, screaming most hideously. In this way, they escape the hawk."

" The *Hen Hawk* is not very numerous."

" *Wild Turkies* abound in this country. *Wild geese* and *ducks* are also plenty. I have never seen a *loon* in these waters."

" The Wabash abounds with fish of many kinds; which, in the months of April, May and June, may be readily caught with the hook and line."

" The *Gar* or *Bill fish* is more than two feet in length. It is quite slim. The bill is about six inches long, tapering to a point. Its scales are very close, thick, and hard."

" The strength of this fish is great. In a small Creek which flows into the Wabash, I discovered a considerable number, and caught several in my hands; but was absolutely unable to hold one."

" There are three kinds of *Cat-fish :* the Mississippi cat, the mud cat, and the bull head. Some of the first have weighed one hundred and twenty pounds. The mud cat is covered with clouded spots, and is a very homely fish. The head is very wide and flat. Some have weighed one hundred pounds.

" The real *sturgeon* is found in the Wabash, though the size is not large. These have been taken from twenty to sixty pounds weight.

" The *shovel fish* or *flat nose* is another species of sturgeon. It weighs about twenty pounds.

" The *pond pike* is taken in ponds from one to three feet long, but very slim. It is an excellent fish.

" The *river pike* is large and highly esteemed, but scarce.

" The *drum* or *white perch* weighs from one to thirty pounds. It is shaped like the sun fish.

" The *black perch* or *bass* is excellent, and weighs from one to seven pounds.

" The *streaked bass* is scarce.

" The *Buffalo fish* is of the *sucker* kind, and very common. Weight from two to thirty pounds.

" The *rock Mullet* is sometimes seen three feet long. It is slim, and weighs from ten to fifteen pounds.

" The *red horse* is also of the *sucker* kind. It is large and bony, weighing from five to fifteen pounds.

" The *Jack pike* or *pickerel* is an excellent fish, and weighs from six to twenty pounds."

In another communication, I. found the *silver-sides* noticed without any description. " It weighs from three to six pounds."

The *eel* is frequently taken in the Wabash, and weighs from one to three pounds. I was told that no fish was found in these waters of a good quality for pickling ; and the facts, that mackarel are brought over the mountains from Philadelphia, and white fish from Detroit, tend to confirm that statement.

" The *fresh water clam* or *muscle* is so plenty, as to be gathered and burnt for lime. Twenty years ago, I am told, no other kind of lime was procured."

" *Craw fish,* which resembles the *lobster*, is very common in the low lands of this country. It is a size larger than the common crab. It works in the ground, and throws up heaps of earth about six inches high, and hollow within. These little mounds are very numerous, and the surface of the ground resembles a honey comb."

" The *Ground Mole* of this country is nearly as large as the common rat. It is very injurious in gardens. It moves along at the depth of two or three inches under ground, raising a considerable ridge ; and not only loosens the roots of vegetables, but devours them. It is remarkable how fast these little animals can force their way through the earth."

" *Horned cattle* are subject to the *murrain*, which sometimes has been very destructive. It may be prevented by care, and cured by proper applications."

" In the old settled parts of this country, but little fodder is saved ; the wood pastures are exhausted ; and the cattle in spring, become poor, get sickly and die."

" The most common *diseases* are fevers and agues, with some liver complaints. The dysentery is very little known. In my opinion, diseases yield sooner to medicine than in more northern climates."

" The prevailing diseases of this country are *bilious*, which sometimes terminate in malignant typhus. It is quite rare to hear of sickness from November until some time in the summer."

" A list of the *prevailing diseases* in this country is subjoined,

" Typhus, gravior et minor—Bilious, intermittent and remittent fevers. Pleurisy is frequent in spring. Rheumatism and comsumption are very rare, compared with New-York. A wet spring followed by drowth is an unfavourable indication."

From my DIARY of 7 mo. 15. I copy the following paragraphs.

' It ought not to be concealed that at present in this country, there are many sick people ; and we believe that there are many situations, some of which have been noticed, that may properly be denominated *sickly ;* but we could not, with any propriety, extend this remark to the country in general. We know of no person who is sick near this river, but who would have been sick, probably, with the same exposure in any part of the United States. The manner of removing hither, is such, that our surprise is rather excited that so few are diseased. Many are cooped up during the heat of summer for six weeks, exposed to the powerful reflection of the sun from the water, while the roof over their heads is heated like an oven. In addition, they have the smell of bilge water, and the exhalations from the muddy shores. Their daily drink is supplied by the river; its warmth relaxes the tone of the stomach; and the putrid particles which float through it, operate unresisted.

' On landing, their situation is not much better. Huts insufficient to shelter them from storms, or from the chilling damps of the night, become their homes ; and bad water, with provisions not well chosen, and to which the constitution is not habituated, combine to derange the system. When this event happens, and fevers prevail, *the occasional cause* is not removed, and in many cases no proper medicine is administered. Such have been the circumstances of many emigrants from the eastward, and especially of those who were indigent.'

These paragraphs explain the causes of disease which in that summer so remarkably prevailed near the Wabash. Of the sick, the chief part were new comers. In 1815 the same observation was made ; and from the population of Vincennes, and of the district immediately around it, which was estimated at three thousand, " twenty-five persons died, but nineteen of that number were strangers."

In the first settling of Cayuga county, it was remarked that emigrants from the eastward, were more sickly than those who crossed the mountains from the south. The causes of disease could be clearly traced to the marshes of the Seneca river, which was the common thoroughfare in summer, before the present turnpike road was completed.

From what I have observed, a change of climate (where it chiefly consists of a change of temperature) has but a slight influence on a healthy constitution ; and this will appear rational when we consider, that the heat of summer in high latitudes, is frequently as great and as oppressive as is regions far to the south.

But a change of climate is often attended by other changes of greater importance. Excessive and unaccustomed fatigue, uncomfortable lodgings, and inferior diet, are only part of the vicissitudes to which travellers in new countries are exposed. The danger to this class is sometimes increased by inquietude of mind, which prompts the convalescent to exertions beyond his strength ; and a relapse in fevers is frequently fatal.

Having thus brought the danger into view, some remarks on the best means to avoid it, may not be inappropriate.

In the spring of 1817 the late S. R. BROWN, desired my opinion on the question, whether a residence in Indiana would be favourable to the health of emigrants from higher latitudes ? A paper was accordingly prepared under the disadvantages of great haste and much indisposition, and without any corrections, published in his WESTERN GAZETTEER. The advice which it contains, however, I am persuaded is of importance ; and having apprised him that that view of the subject was intended for this work, I shall proceed with the transcription, altering, where I deem it proper. Much of this is intended for emigrants from the eastern states.

Descend the river after the commencement of autumnal frosts. The effect of these in neutralizing or preventing putrid exhalations has been frequently observed ; and the smell from the shores after a flood, in warm weather, is very offensive.

Avoid going in a vessel with a leaky roof. A crowded boat is an inconvenient place to dry wet clothes ; and the expense of being comfortably sheltered, will frequently be less than the damage in furniture, without considering the probable loss of health. To

bend thin boards for a cover is customary, but not sufficient. I have seen no roof of that kind which would
be a shelter from a driving shower of rain. A sick woman said to me near the Wabash, "I ascribe my sickness, in great measure, to one dismal night that I en-
dured on the river. The rain poured through every
part of the roof, and to sit on the bed with my children
under an umbrella was our only refuge."

If, however, to descend in spring is unavoidable,
start as soon as the river is clear of ice. Make no delay; for not only health, but life may depend on a timely
escape from the effluvia of those shores.

If the river be low, and by this or other unavoidable
delays, warm weather should surround the emigrant on
the river, guard against a heated roof over head. Boards
nailed on the inside, or an awning on the out side, will
be important auxiliaries to comfort and to health.

At such time, no river water should be used without
filtering. This operation may be expeditiously performed in a vessel like an upright churn with two bottoms. These are three or four inches apart ; and the
upper, in which many small holes are bored, receives,
in the centre, a tube one inch in diameter, extending
above the vessel, and communicating with the cavity
between the bottoms. After spreading a cloth on the
upper bottom, fill the vessel upward with well washed
sand, and from above let in water downward through
the tube. In a short time it will rise through the sand,
divested of its impurities, and run over at an ear in
sufficient quantities for every culinary purpose. In a
few days the apparatus may need cleansing. As the
filth will be chiefly below, a hole opened in the lower
bottom will allow it to pass off. See Melish's Travels,
vol. 1. p. 159.

If the water have not an agreeable coolness, cider or
strong beer should be mixed with it for drink, as the
warmth without some stimulant will relax the tone of
the stomach, and predispose the system to disease.

But beware of spiritous liquors. If such, however,

are taken, let the quantity be cautiously regulated. Every excess debilitates; and to think of escaping disease, by keeping always in a state of excitement, is desperate folly. When fevers attack such subjects it is commonly fatal. Some men who travel much, and who have neither moral nor religious scruples to dissuade them, totally abstain from *spirits* in unhealthy situations, Rich wholesome* food, guards the stomach much better from infection, nor would I omit in the list of such articles, well cured ham and strong coffee.

Travellers should never change their diet for the worse. The fatiuges of mind and body, in most cases, require that it should be for the better. To live comfortably is true economy. Any additional expense in provisions would form but a small item in a doctor's bill, without taking into view the loss of time, of comfort, or of the expenses of nursing. To lay in a good stock of wholesome provisions should therefore, by no means, be neglected.

On landing, let one of the first objects be to provide a comfortable habitation. Water from brooks should be filtered, but during summer no dependance ought to be placed on this supply. If springs are not convenient, dig wells. Much of the sickness of new countries is induced by bad water.

Let no temptation prevail on the emigrant to go fishing in warm weather. Of the smell of the shores I have spoken. To be wet is imprudent; and to be exposed to the chilling damps of the night, greatly increases the danger. But fresh fish† are unwholesome, except for a

---

* In a medical author I find the following interesting remark: "The predisposing cause of intermittents, is clearly debility, with penury of blood; because the robust, and such as have a generous diet, are most free from this disease."

† "The Roman Catholics, who, during forty days Lent, rigourously abstain from flesh, but indulge freely in a fish diet, are said to be less nourished by it, and to become sensibly thinner and weaker, as HALLER, indeed, tells us he had himself experienced.

slight change of diet. We know of no new settlement that has been healthy, where the inhabitants live chiefly on fresh fish. If, however, fish must be eaten, buy them; any price is cheaper than health; and if fishing must be done, do it in cloudy weather; but at night be comfortably sheltered.

Let no fertility of the river flats be an inducement to cultivate them, until naturalized to the climate; or more properly, recovered from the fatigues attending emigration, for composure of mind is as important as refreshment to the body. When the body is debilitated either by labour or fasting, it is more susceptible of infection, and these exhalations after floods are putrid. Land of an inferior quality, in a dry airy situation will yield greater *neat profits.*

Delay in taking medicine, is often fatal. The patient ought not to wait till he is *down sick*, but if the stomach is disordered, which is the case at the commencement of all fevers, a glass of pearl ash and water may afford relief. The quantity is stated at page 147. If this should prove insufficient, take an emetic, or small doses of emetic tartar, only to nauseate. Should this produce an intermission, with a moist skin and clean tongue, take peruvian bark, or those of dogwood, *(box-wood)* willow, or oak, which have been found eminently useful.

Of alkaline medicines, perhaps pear lash is the best. Its good effect in *cholera morbus, diarrhœa,* &c. have been often experienced; and it is always an excellent preventive. It sweetens the stomach and promotes digestion.

I have one caution more for the emigrant. The water, in places, throughout all the Ohio country, is satur-

"The disorders of the system, the herpetic leprous and scorbutic eruptions to which the *ichthyophagi* are said to be more especially liable, show, we think, with other observations, that fish is neither so easily digested nor assimilated to the human system, as flesh

"Sea fish are more flourishing than those which inhabit the rivers and fresh waters." 　　　　Edin. Encycl. Art. Aliment.

ated with sulphate of lime. This, like the sulphates of soda and magnesia, is cathartic ; and in one ounce doses, is an active medicine. Inconvenience to grown persons from these waters, however, is rarely experienced ; but on small children the effect is considerable, and to those just weaned it has often proved fatal, by inducing *diarrhœa,** which exhausts the patient, for no medicine can give permanent relief while the *occasional cause* is unremoved. This is easily done by refusing water and giving milk. If the disease is far advanced, paregoric may be necessary to diminish the irritability.

From the same cause, the waters in many parts of the Western District of New-York, produce a similar effect. I discovered the benefit of this practice in one of my children, who seemed wasting to a skeleton ; and have since witnessed much of its good effects on others.

The beautiful bluff above *Turtle Creek,* noticed at page 170, now called *Merom,* has become the seat of justice for Sullivan county ; and was selected by commissioners appointed under an act of the Legislature. The agent, who was authorised to sell the lots, makes the following remarks in his advertisement :

" It is situate on the east bank of the River, thirty-five miles above Vincennes, on that elevated ground known by the name of *The Bluff,* the highest bank of the Wabash from its mouth to the north† line of the

---

* Children, accustomed to take all their food in a liquid form, retain after weaning an eagerness for liquids ; and as water is generally at hand, it is substituted for the mild aliment of which they have been deprived. When either the sulphate of lime or of magnesia, is held in solution, these substances operate actively on the delicate fibre, and the peristaltic motion is greatly increased. In proportion to the loss of moisture thus sustained by the system, will be the thirst. With every draught fresh causes of irritation succeed,—the motion of the *lacteals* become inverted,— and emaciation and debility rapidly ensue.

† It should have been written *east line of the state.* In no part of its course does the Wabash approach the north line of the State.

state.   The river washes the base of this high land one mile.   Freestone [sandstone] and a quality of [impure] limestone, appear in the bank in great abundance. Springs in every direction around the town are discovered.

" From the most elevated point of the bluff, the eye can be gratified with the charming view of *La Motte Prairie,* immediately below in front ; and with *Ellison and Union Prairies* on the right and left ; the whole stretching along the river a distance of not less than thirty miles, and all now rapidly settling.   In the rear of this beautiful site, is a flourishing settlement of twenty or thirty farmers, three miles east of the town."

Gill's Prairie, south three miles, has at present a handsome population of industrious farmers.

" A mile and a half from the town, a mill will soon be erected on Turtle Creek by a* Mr. Bennett.—June 27, 1817."

It is with much satisfaction, that we perceive a new name for a new town or village.   Hitherto when the *importations* from Europe or Asia have been insufficient, it has become necessary to borrow from our neighbours, to a degree that is absolutely humiliating ; and perhaps in no part of the United States is this practice carried to the same excess as in *Ohio.*   The following list of names is copied from *Kilbourn's Gazetteer* of that state, published in 1817.

---

* We object to employing the indefinite article in this manner. Though it may seem discourteous to attack in an individual, what fashion has sanctioned, yet we mean no personal rebuke,—entering our protest in general terms against a custom, which in our ears has always been harsh, unnecessary and ungraceful.   If the writer means in this manner to guard against mistaking one person for another, it must at least be conceded, that the attempt is awkward and insufficient ; and as it is understood for a hint that the individual so noticed is obscure, we suggest whether its discontinuance would not be an advancement in good manners.

6	towns or villages of the name of Fairfield,		
5	do	do	Franklin,
5	do	do	Goshen,
10	do	do	Green,
7	do	do	Harrison,
7	do	do	Jackson,
11	do	do	Jefferson,
6	do	do	Liberty,
14	do	do	Madison,
5	do	do	Milford,
5	do	do	Oxford,
5	do	do	Pleasant,
5	do	do	Richland,
7	do	do	Salem,
10	do	do	Springfield,
17	do	do	Union,
11	do	do	Washington,
12	do	do	Wayne.

To persons who find it necessary for them to impose a name, we would suggest, that any thing is more tolerable than the repetitions that now assail us.

Rapp's congregation are settled at *Harmony*, fifty miles below Vincennes. The cultivation of the vine has engaged their attention; but the manufacture of *cloth, nails*, &c. with the production of grain has claimed a share. A *steam Mill* has been erected.

" We have a *law* which requires every military and civil officer to take an oath or affirmation to suppress *duelling* in every shape and form." It will be well if this oath be not considered as words without meaning, for on the opposite side of the Ohio, this atrocious practice is quite in fashion.

" Forty dollars may be collected by a Justice of the Peace."

I noticed the following *vegetables* growing indigenously, near the Wabash, between Vincennes and Fort
Harrison ; but am aware that this list gives a very imperfect view of the BOTANY of that District.

Acer saccharinum	sugar maple
Acer glaucum	river maple
Acer negundo	ash leaved maple
Acer rubrum	soft or red flowering do
Asclepias decumbens	butterfly weed
—— *syriaca*	silk weed, Indian hemp milk weed and others
Annona triloba	papaw
Arum dracontium	many leaved Indian turnip
Asarum canadense	wild ginger
Aralia spinosa	angelica tree
—— *racemosa*	spikenard
Ambrosia trifida	
—— *artimisifolia*	hog or bitter weed
Adiantum pedatum	maiden hair
Bignonia radicans	red trumpet flower
Corylus americana	common hazel
—— *cornuta*	horned.
Celtis occidentalis	nettle tree or hackberry
Cercis canadensis	fish blossom, or Judas tree
Carex, many species	sedge
Cassia marylandica	wild senna
Ceanothus americanus	Jersey tea plant
Cephalanthus occidentalis	button flower
Convallaria multiflora	Solomon's seal
Convolvulus panduratus	wild potatoe
Carduus, several species	thistle
Carpinus americana	horn beam
Circea lutetiana ?	Enchanter's night shade
Collinsonia canadensis	horse weed
Dyospyros virginiana	persimmon
Dirca palustris	leather wood
*Æsculus flava**	stinking buck eye
Evonymus americanus	spindle tree

* This is not abundant. The wood is of small value. Cattle
have been poisoned by the fruit,

Fragaria virginiana	strawberry
Fagus ferruginea	beech
Fraxinus,	white } ash
——	blue } ash
Frasera verticillata	Columbo root
Guilandina dioica	Kentucky coffee tree
Gleditsia triacanthos	honey locust
—— *monosperma ?*	(almost without spines)
Galium, several species	goose grass
Helianthus, several species	Sun flower
Hedera quinquefolia	poison ivy
Hydrangea arborescens	
Impatiens	touch-me-not
Iris virginica	blue flag
Juglans pecan } Hiccorius of Rafinesqe	pecan
— *squamosa*	shell bark
— *ovata*	bitter nut
—	upland pig nut
Juglans cinerea	black walnut
—— *nigra*	butter nut, or white walnut
Jeffersonia diphylla	two leaved Jeffersonia
Laurus sassafras	sassafras
—— *benzoin*	spice wood
Liquidambar styraciflua	sweet gum
Liriodendron tulipifera	tulip poplar, white wood
Lobelia inflata	
Monarda	wild mint
Morus rubra	mulberry
Nyssa integrifolia	gum tree—pepperidge
Platanus occidentalis	button wood
Populus angulata	cotton wood
Pyrus coronaria	crab apple
Potentilla, two species	cinquefoil
Podophyllum peltatum	mandrake, May apple
Polygonum, various species	
Panax quinquefolium	ginseng
Prunus	wild plumb
Quercus nigra	black oak
—— *alba*	white do
—— *rubra*	red do

Quercus prinos v. *palustris* swamp chestnut oak
—— *phellos*   willow leaved
—— *triloba*   true black jack
—— *discolor*   swamp white oak
—— ——   spanish oak
Robinia pseud-acacia   black locust
—— ?   (in the swamp east of Vincennes.)
*Rubus villosus**   black berry
—— *occidentalis*   black raspberry
Rhus glabrum   smooth sumach
—— *typhinum*   stag's horn
—— *radicans*   poison vine
————   another
Smilax rotundifolia   green briar
——   herbaceous
Spirea salicifolia   willow leaved spirea
—— *herbaceous*   meadow sweet
Salix conifera   cone bearing willow
—— *nigra*   black
—— *tristis*   shrub
—— ?   (with linear leaves near Fort Harrison)
Scandix, two species   cicely
Solanum carolinense‡   horse nettle, or Irish plumb
Tilia americana   basswood, or linden
Ulmus   red elm
————   white do
Urtica divaricata   common nettle
—— *pumila*   stingless
——   another
Vitis, two species   grape vine
—— *vulpina*,   fox grape not observed
Verbena, several species   vervain.

* One of these shrubs had grown up near the branches of a **crab**
tree, which prevented the stalk from bending until it had attain-
ed the height of twelve feet. When I observed it, it was finely
loaded with ripe fruit.

† This vegetable grows in the clayey prairies east of Shakertown. Whether a native, or not is uncertain. It is scantily armed with spines; and when it takes possession of a piece of
ground, on account of its deep penetrating roots, is removed with
difficulty.

Dr. DRAKE mentions the *Catalpa* in Indiana as far north as Cincinnati, but I did not observe it.

A plant, which I conjecture to be a species of *Plantago*, abounds in the channels of small streams west of Loghary. It is of a larger growth than the *P. major.* I have not seen it as far west as Madison ; but on our return I observed it in the state of Ohio, between Xenia and Columbus.

A new species of *Viburnum* also grows along these streams. It resembles the *V. dentatum* ; but the bark is scaly like the *Spirea opulifolia,* and has no suckers like the arrow wood.

———

The Potoka discharges its waters into the Wabash, one mile below the mouth of White river. It is navigable for boats. Where the road from Princeton to Vincennes, crosses this stream, the current is dull and deep; but there is a mill-seat just below which is formed by considerable rapids.

———

' *Coal* is found thirty miles below Fort Harrison, in the banks of a small brook. This *mine* we viewed as we went up the river. On the White river, and its branches this fossil is abundant. It is also found in the neighbourhood of Fort Harrison. *Limestone* appears in considerable quantities in the bank of a small creek which empties into the Wabash three miles below that Fort, and in several places further up the river.' Diary of 7 mo. 1816.

"Limestone is found near *Princeton.* It also appears below *York,* on fraction No. 17, of Township 8, north Range 11 west. *Coal* is found west, directly opposite to Fort Harrison, under a bank six feet high. It has also been found under limestone, in the Illinois Territory on

the line between townships No. 8 and 9, north range,
12 west.   1818."

92   I have no doubt that coal, limestone, and sandstone
will be found plentifully in the high woodlands in every
part of that country, when proper search shall be made.
In such soils we have never seen the friable earth very
deep, and solid rock unquestionably forms the founda-
tion of the hills.

' Last autumn, [1817,] the Indians brought twenty-
93 eight pounds of *copper* to Fort Harrison, in one lump.
The metal is so pure, that without any refining, it has
answered all the purposes of imported copper. It is
supposed that the Indians found it about thirty miles
above the mouth of *Raccoon creek*, in Indiana." My
friend J. BENNETT, from whom I received this account,
has kindly furnished me with a specimen, and no doubt
can exist of its excellence. Its malleability I have
well ascertained.

But though it should be proved that they found it at
the place designated, there would be much uncertainty
at present, whether the discovery is of much importance; that is, whether the metal is a native of the
rocky strata which underlay the country, or whether,
like the granite, it has been scattered on the surface.
When the numerous facts which shew that the granite arrived from the north are considered,– and also, the
resemblance of this copper to that on the south shore
of lake Superior,—a conjecture, assigning both to the
same origin, would be plausible.

All the best *lands* near the Wabash river which had
not been reserved by government, or located by Canadian claimants, were sold at auction in the 9 mo. 1816.
Much land of the second or third quality, (and no in-

considerable part of these kinds is very fertile) remained, however, for entry at two dollars an acre payable within four years, by instalments. One fourth within two years, and the remainder in two equal annual payments. This condition is the rule ; and eight per cent interest is added to all payments after such become due, and eight per cent discount is allowed for prompt pay. Thus lands paid for at the time of entry, only cost one dollar and sixty three cents an acre.

To accommodate persons who may be unprepared to make a payment in full —or who may wish to secure a lot while they attempt further discoveries,—lands are permitted to be entered for a certain number of days. This privilege, however, has been frequently abused. Entries have been made for the sum of sixteen dollars, (one twentieth of the purchase money,)—which confers the right to remove within forty days, every valuable timber tree from the premises; and if no other purchaser appears, the term is even lengthened to 90 days.

Last winter (1817-18) from five to ten dollars, was the price of Prairie Lands, and from two to five the price of Wood Lands.

The fertility of *the sandy prairies* near the river is very remarkable. If lime is a constituent of this soil, the portion must be inconsiderable, as acids produce no effervescence. Neither is the vegetable matter in much quantity. The finer parts diminish but little in the fire, and are changed from black to a reddish brown. Hence the fertilizing principle is a mineral earth.

The idea of *soils perpetually fertile,* was not original with H. Davy, though to him we owe the first scientific view of the subject. Vegetable matter soon dissipates, but the primitive earths are imperishable ; and if my conjecture is correct, these prairies will be sources of abundance through distant ages. A field was pointed out to me, which had recently been enclosed from the commons of Vincennes, and which produced corn of extraordinary luxuriance. From the nakedness of this ground it is evident, that a vegetable soil would soon become sterile.

One of my correspondents remarks, " We have a prairie below this place, which has been in cultivation seventy or eighty years, and now produces well."

Lord KAIMS mentions a field near the Clyde, in Scotland, which had annually produced a crop for 101 years, and still retained its fertility. The subjoined extract is from the EDINBURGH ENCYCLOPEDIA. "The lands of *St. Jago,* ⌊Chili⌋ though constantly cultivated for two centuries and a half, without receiving any artificial manure, have suffered no diminution in their amazing produce."

Some of the great Bottom of the Mississippi, between Kaskaskia and Illinois, " has been in cultivation 120 years, and still no deterioration has yet manifested itself." BROWN'S WESTERN GAZETTEER.

———

"I have lately visited Fort Harrison, passing upwards from Vincennes on the Illinois side of the river. After traversing a rich tract of *woodland* four miles, I went five miles through an *arm of the Grand Prairie.* Much of this is too low. Fine *woodland,* three miles wide, separates this from *Ellison Prairie,* which is a rich tract, seven miles long, and averaging three miles in width. Good *Woodland,* but not of the first quality, then extends thirteen miles to *La Motte Prairie.* This is an extraordinary tract, and is eight or nine miles long. I then passed through *woodland* of a good quality ten miles to *Union Prairie,* on which *York village* is located. Here I crossed the river to the Indiana side.

" *Fort Harrison Prairie* is a most delightful tract. It contains, perhaps, 22,000 acres, including the woodland lying between it and the Wabash. This woodland is very fine, and on an inclined plane from the prairie to the bank of the river—which is generally from twenty to thirty feet high for several miles. The woodland on the east of this prairie is an elevated tract with a rich soil. Springs and brooks flowing from it, are numerous.

" This prairie is bounded on the north by Otter Creek, on which Major Markle is building mills." [W. P. B.] These have since been completed. The construction, it is said, is uncommonly excellent ; and that the saw mills are capable of sawing 6000 feet of boards in one day.

———

" The soil of the *prairies* is excellent for both corn and wheat. Of the latter, the crops vary from twenty to forty bushels an acre ; and of the former, from fifty to one hundred bushels. Major Markle for rent alone, besides what he raised himself, has more than 8700 bushels of corn." 11 mo. 1817.

———

The country will be more healthy when *levees* shall be raised across the *bayous,* and longitudinal ditches cut in particular places. The expense of forming a bank six feet high at Otter Creek, would not be a work of extraordinary magnitude for an individual; and a prairie thirteen miles in length would be exempted from inundation. At Honey Creek, the same remark may be made in respect to the construction.

Of the practicability of such measures, we were well convinced, when we were near the Wabash ; but on our return, at *Franklinton,* we saw a lévee which had been raised to that height by the *scraper,* and which has completely rescued a valuable tract from the river floods.

I have noted that *ponds* appear in places through the bayous. The small streams which are lost in the sands, probably after heavy rains supply the water; and the expense of a small canal, which would render the lowest parts of these tracts arable, would be a slight tax for the neighbouring inhabitants. Indeed the proprietors themselves, would be reimbursed in one or two seasons for such expenditure.

If the bayou from *Otter Creek* were closed, the stream which sweeps through *Honey Creek Prairie* would be less formidable. Where two such currents form a junction, the narrow and winding channel, already dammed by the river, is insufficient to discharge the accumulating waters; the torrent at every creek receives an accession of force, and spreads the inundation still wider in its progress to the south.

A Post office has lately been established at Honey Creek, two and a half miles south of the old ford on that stream, in Range 9 West, Township 11 North, Section 25.—Name, *Hoggatt's*— M. Hoggatt, Post Master.

Cant phrases, the true marks of a defective education, are common in the Western Country.

A considerable number is expressed by *a smart chance*; and our hostess at Madison said, there was "a smart chance of yankees" in that village.

Rolling is a term which may be frequently heard in conversations relative to lands. We are not to understand by this word, *a turning round*, but *a diversified surface*.

Slashes, means flat clayey land which retains water on the surface after showers. From this comes the adjective, *slashy*. It is in common use, and like the word *chore* [corruption of *chare*] in the eastern states, is almost an *indispensable*.

Balance is another word which is *twisted* from its proper meaning. This is made to imply the remainder, " The balance (unappropriated residue of land) will be sold at auction."

———

The *Cäne*, which once overspread a large part of Kentucky, is nearly destroyed; but it grows abundantly on the Wabash, and extends from the mouth of that river almost to Vincennes.

———

The *iron-weed*, which I first saw above Pittsburgh, extends on clayey lands all the way to the Wabash. It is a pernicious plant in meadows.

———

The wet Prairies abound with the fern-leaved *Helianthus*, and on our return, we saw thousands of these blossoms turned to the sun.

———

N. Ewing had six kinds of *exotic grapes* in his garden, which flourish; and though receiving little attention, were finely loaded with fruit. That climate is congenial to the vine. Indeed we believe this culture will become very profitable. At Harmony, fifty miles below Vincennes, we understood that twelve acres had already been planted as a vineyard.

———

Various kinds of *esculent vegetables* are taken to Vincennes by the SHAKERS, nearly two weeks earlier than such can be raised in the wood-lands round that town.

94   Six miles west of the French Licks, we saw the semblance of *a corn-stalk,* of very remote antiquity, which was found in that neighbourhood. It apeared that the cavity of this plant (once occupied by the pith) was filled with sand, which became cemented by ferruginous matter. The impressions of the nerves were very distinct. It had been nearly two feet in length, and was raised out of the earth by the root of a falling tree.

———

95   The district from the Knobs to the east branch of White river, is high *table land;* and apparently composed of strata, which were deposited on this part, after the general surface of the Ohio country was formed. There is some reason to believe, however that parts of this great bank were removed before the commencement of petrification. The *White river* flows round it on the north. When we ascended these *heights* on the east, we were in constant expectation, during our progress for some miles, of descending on the western side; so different is this tract from any we had ever traversed. On our return we particularly noticed the ascent and descent of every little ridge, and could discover no general inclination of the surface. No plain, barren, or prairie, is found within its limits.

    We are assured that the Knobs do not appear south of the Ohio. The sides are surprisingly irregular. On a north course from Salem Meeting-house, within three miles, the *descent* appears; but on an east course, the distance to the *edge* is computed at ten miles. From the latter spot, beyond the winding of that vale to the westward, these hills extend to the north-east till the eye is bewildered with the prospect in the distant horizon.

    In this district, *petrifactions* are numerous. In the channel of a brook I found the semblance of a perennial rooted herb, in which the different annual growths were exhibited. It was five inches long by one inch in thickness. The *bark* of the root appears to have been the *mould,* as the internal part was hollow, or filled with chrystals. The *rattles* of a snake, remarkably large, had also been converted into stone.

The *stalagmites,* or dumpling stone, which was noticed in the DIARY, appears confined to this region. We observed it near the border, but not on the plains below. **96**

From the singularity of its figure, from its cavity, and from the numerous petrifactions in this vicinity, I could scarcely resist the impression that the fruit of some species of *Cucurbita* had been the model. Other considerations, however, would be unfavourable ; and it must be confessed that nature has performed many operations in Mineralogy, which continue secrets.

....

The following paragraphs are from *Clarke's Travels in the* HOLY LAND:

"He [Djezzar Pacha] then informed us, that upon Mount Carmel he had found several thousand large balls, and never could discover a cannon to fit them ; but that a peasant had found a field-piece which Buonaparte had concealed previously to his leaving the country, capable of receiving every one of them."

" We supposed that by these balls, Djezzar alluded to mineral concretions of a *spheriodal* form, found in those mountains. As the Turks made use of stones instead of cannon shot, it is probable that Djezzar, who was in great want of ammunition, had determined upon using the *stalagmites* of Carmel for that purpose."

In the eastern parts of Indiana, much of the grain for bread is ground in *horse mills.* I have learned that the proprietor of the mill finds horses ; and takes for *toll,* one fourth of the wheat, and one sixth of the corn or other grain, if not bolted. The floating mills on the Ohio river, take one sixth of the *wheat* and one eighth of the *corn.*

————

97 I submitted with regret to the disappointment of not passing the *west bank of Volney's imaginary Lake,* in another quarter. We are willing to allow a wide range of imagination in geological theories; but in support of such opinions, we do think the reader is entitled to the collection of a few facts. It has, indeed, been fashionable to imagine that every valley which pours a stream through mountainous ridges, was formerly the bed of a lake; and some indulgence for the custom of the age may be allowable. We also admit that such speculations are harmless; but we consider them rather as the first efforts of an excursive fancy, than as the sober deductions of a vigorous understanding.

How our mountains were broken to admit a passage for the rivers, presents a problem of difficult solution. We have discovered no fact to shew that these breaches were produced by the pressure of water; and the remaining masses of the Blue Ridge, for example, are so vast as to preclude the conjecture. We can conceive, indeed, that an earthquake might effect a rupture; but so many rivers have been let forth, without one unnecessary opening, that we reluctantly admit the possibility. When we come to reflect, however, that the surface of the valley is so shaped as to guide the stream across it on a brisk current to the very entrance of the mountain; and that no traces are discoverable, of these waters having ever discharged through any other passage, we are satisfied that such suppositions are unwarrantable.

In Volney's theory, still greater difficulties arise. 1st.–He has not provided sufficient materials for a dam. 2d.–If such dam had been completed it would not explain the appearances of the country to the eastward.

3d.–Neither would it explain the geology of the country, westward.

1st.–– The Knobs do not extend across the valley of the Ohio. Neither do these, to the north, form any obstructions to the White river, which receives the surplus waters of the great plain in which New Lexington is situated.

2d.–The hills in the Ohio country are formed of strata, apparently horizontal, piled up to the height of several hundred feet. Now a pond standing over this vast district, would not produce such appearances. The shell fish, indeed, whose remains chiefly form the limestone, might arrange themselves along the bottom; but no lake in modern times has furnished any support to an opinion that vegetables are retained in its waters as a prelude to the formation of coal; and we want evidence for the belief, that materials for this fossil were collected in this manner at any period since the creation. On the reverse, we do not hesitate to ascribe the arrangement of all extensive strata to tides which like those of the present day, have been caused by *exterior attraction;* and which have swept over the face of every country. In no other way can we rationally account for the conveyance, and regular distribution of sand, over large districts of secondary formation,

3d.––Much of the country westward of the Knobs abound with marine shells; and it would be equally proper to show the origin of the countless millions which appear in that elevated region. This could not be done, however, on his principles; for no land of sufficient height is found either on the borders of the Ohio, or of the Mississippi.

To conclude, every stone that we have examined on the Knobs is of the latest formation; and the whole pile apparently rests on strata, which, extending, form the surface of the lower country. We therefore assign it a more recent date.

98   The subsoil of a country is an important circumstance in regard to its *Waters*. Though the quantity of rain that falls in different parts of a district of equal elevation be equal, yet the inhabitants may be very unequally accommodated with rills and fountains. Where the soil is a hard clay, or a close horizontal rock, the water collecting in torrents, is hurried away to the rivers. Where limestone abounds, there are always caverns in the earth; and the depth of these will affect the depth of wells. Thus the vast quantities of this rock in the northern parts of Kentucky, and in the lower parts of Pennsylvania, cause the waters to sink deep ; while the more recent and thinner formations of Indiana confine it to the surface. Sand, gravel, and granite rock where the strata are inclined or vertical, retain the drippings of the clouds; and these supplies, clarified by filtration, burst forth into fountains durable and salubrious.

We breakfasted at *Loghary* in company with two men from Chenango county, New York ; and as they were exploring with a view to emigration, as well as ourselves, the sitting was considerably protracted. At last, I was left alone in the porch with two of the neighboring loungers, when one expressed his belief that *them fellows were Yankees.* His comrade sneered at the idea of a doubt, and declared he could tell a Yankee blindfold. The meaning of this rudeness was not to be mistaken. With a promptness, therefore, not characteristic, I looked full in his face, and asked, Am I a Yankee ? The abruptness of the question was disconcerting. His reply, which was made with much hesitation, only increased his embarrassment, for he completely failed in his pretentions ; and I presume will be more civil to strangers for the future.

As an apology for the shyness and disrespect, which our northern citizens sometimes experience in the Middle and Western States, it should be remarked

however, that this prejudice has not arisen entirely
without a cause.   The conduct of fugitives from justice and from credit, has been so immoral, in the course
of their retreat through these countries, that the phrase
" a Yankee trick," has become proverbially common.

It is to be much regretted that travellers should throw
off the restraints of decorum.   When this happens a
few times, the sweeping remark that " I never saw a
decent man from that country," immediately follows ;
and the national character becomes tarnished.   It is
such vicious or sportive freaks, performed on the wrong
side of " a narrow frith," that

> " Makes enemies of nations, which had else,
> Like kindred drops, been moulded into one."

There is nothing peculiar, however, in the sufferings
of New England.   Kentucky has been equally *misrep-
resented*, by many of her boatmen, at New Orleans; and
Ireland in all parts of the world.   Indiscriminate censure or approbation of any people is absurd ; because
all nations furnish examples of vice and of virtue ; and
who treats not all strangers according to their merits,
may have merit himself, but it is shaded by a cloud of
prejudice and folly.

━━

In *Scipio*, THE VARIATION OF THE MAGNETIC NEE-   99
DLE is nearly 4 1-2 degrees westerly.   On the transit
line, which was cut through the west part of *Junius*,
it is only 2 degrees 45 minutes.   At Pittsburgh, the
variation is 30 minutes (easterly ?); at *Waynesville,* on
the Little Miami 4 1-2 degrees easterly ; and at Vincennes 6 1-2 deg. easterly.   It thus appears that THE
LINE OF NO VARIATION is not far from Pittsburgh.

It would be satisfactory to know if *a corresponding
line of no variation* is found on the opposite parts of
the globe ?   If the greatest variation prevails in 90 degrees of longitude from such lines ?   And if any regu-

lar difference in the *dip* of the needle is observed in different places ? These questions arise from the hypothesis, that the magnetic pole is within the Earth, and consequently not 90 degrees from the Equator, but I can lay my hand on no work, in this remote region, that can furnish the answers.

If the magnetic meridian constituted the arch of a great circle, from the above *data* the distance of the magnetic pole could be readily ascertained. This, however, is not the case. *That* meridian is a crooked line; and in addition, the needle is not only subject to a diurnal variation, but earthquakes,* it is said, permanently affect its polarity.

The line of no variation is moving eastward. In twenty years we find a difference of nearly 45 minutes; but the view would be more interesting if we had the distance in miles which it has traversed in that period. Observations made in Europe, shew, however, that such a line in that quarter of the globe had a different motion. At London in 1580, the variation was 11 deg. 15 minutes easterly; in 1622, only 6 degrees easterly, and in 1662, the line passed that city to the westward. In 1791, the variation was about 23 degrees 30 minutes, westerly.

A correct chart of the variation in every part of the globe, with the course of its motion, would be an interesting present to the friends of science.

•••••••••••••

In the foregoing remarks, local attraction was not taken into view. Many of the ores of iron affect the needle remarkably, and some are such as have been little suspected. I have seen it settle nearly half a degree from the true course; and after repeated observations,

* Note.—In time of earthquakes, electrical phenomena are frequent. It is well-known that electric shocks destroy magnetism and restore it; that granite which contains iron is magnetic; and that observations and analogy render it probable, that the Earth is chiefly composed of this rock. Will these premises assist in explaining why the direction of the needle, at such times, is varied.

discovered that the error was occasioned by a granite rock, at the distance of more than two rods. On presenting a fragment, the cause of attraction was evident. The *black mica* of these rocks in Cayuga county embosom much iron; and of this, all that I have examined is magnetic.

It appears that ferruginous substances disturb the needle in two ways. Iron, when reduced from the ore, is in all cases obedient to the magnet; and therefore, when a mass is brought within the circle of attraction, the needle is impelled to approach. This action is well exemplified by a man in a skiff, who attempts by a rope to draw towards him a large ship.

In this case, however, the *circle of attraction* is limited; and the needle remains undisturbed by the presence of any quantity of iron, provided it be kept *without* that circle. Thus the surveyor's chain may be brought within eighteen inches of the needle without exciting any motion, for round this magnet the circle is of small diameter.

When other magnets, which lie beyond the attraction of the needle, disturb it, its magnetism ought not to be considered. It has now entered a greater circle than its own, and become obedient to a body beyond its reach, or on which it can act with no corresponding impulse. Thus a gun barrel, or the tire of waggon wheels, which have acquired magnetism by friction, powerfully affect it at the distance of six feet. The greatest distance at which magnetic ores of iron can act, perhaps has not been ascertained; but these circles unquestionably extend to very considerable distances.

....

The Conductors of the Northern Expedition, in the last season [1818] have witnessed extraordinary magnetic phenomena. " In Lat. 74 deg. 30 min. N. Long. 60 deg. 30 min. W. very near the head of Baffin's Bay, the *variation* of the compass, by accurate observations repeatedly made *on board* both ships, was 89 deg. and

the *dip* 84 deg. 30 min.—In Lat. 75 deg. 48 min. N
Long. 61 deg. 30 min. W. the variation was found to
be increased ; for though *on the ice* it was only 88 deg.
13 min. yet *on board ship* it was at one time 95 deg. ;
that is, *the needle pointed,* instead of north, *to the south
of west.*" The difference appears to have been occasioned by local attraction.

---

101 *Notes of a Journey from Fort Harrison to Fort
Wayne.*

45 miles, a small village of the Miamis, on the waters of
  Eel river.
25 do. the second Indian town, also on Eel river.
50 do. to Pipe Creek. Many small creeks water
  this district; but Pipe Creek is a considerable
  stream, and famous for its mill seats. Much
  of these lands are low and wet.
8 do. above Pipe Creek is the Massasinaway town
  of Indians. It is at the junction of this river
  with the Wabash.
50 do. continuing up the Wabash.
13 do. across from the Lower Portage to Fort Wayne.
  Here are some irregular hills, and some marshes.
191 miles, total distance.

  It has been said that the common potatoe dwindles
in the state of Ohio. But on our arrival in the neighbourhood of Granville, the inhabitants of which are
chiefly from the Eastern States, we found it extensively cultivated ; and the vegetation was not less promising
than what we observe in the Western District of New
York. The secret is, the inhabitants of the south are
very partially acquainted with its use. At breakfast
or supper its appearance is extremely rare ; and even
from the dinner table it is often excluded by the sweet
or Carolinian potatoe ; while its value as an article of

food for live stock is unknown or unexperienced. This is so remarkably the case, that on our journey westward through the Ohio country, we do not recollect observing at any place, except Shakertown, one rood under culture with this vegetable. If travellers find no good field of potatoes in that land, these remarks may assist in explaining the cause.

———

The right pronunciation of *names* is as necessary as the right pronunciation of *words*; and believing that many of our untravelled readers would receive it favourably, we have bestowed some attention on this subject. There have been omissions, however, which we will supply in this place.

Wau-bash is the common pronunciation on that river; but in this country we frequently hear the uncouth sound of *Way-bosh.*

Vincennes is pronounced *Vin-cenz* by the most respectable persons in that place.

Pa-ra-rah is a common pronunciation; but it is too great a barbarism to be tolerated. By placing the letters in this manner, *prai-rie,* the proper sounds cannot be mistaken.

In *Levee,* (an embankment) the accent is sometimes placed on the last syllable. It should be *lev-e.*

ADDITIONAL NOTES.

NOTE TO PAGE 3.

THE importance of these springs to the surrounding country will be appreciated by the following statement:

On the smaller spring are erected, a fulling-mill, which in the present season of 1816-17, dressed 15,-000 yards of cloth,—carding-machines which wrought into rolls, last summer, 18,000 pounds of wool,—and a saw-mill (assisted in its motion by a brook turned into the basin of the spring) which sawed 60,000 feet of boards and scantling.

On the larger spring is erected a grist-mill, thirty by forty-four feet, three and a half stories, with two run of stones, and the necessary apparatus. It is stated to be capable of grinding 200 bushels of grain *per* twenty-four hours; and as this stream, with the other, suffers no material diminution in drowths, or increase in heavy rains, and no obstruction from ice in winter, it is the main-stay of the surrounding country in extraordinary seasons. In the present extreme severity of frost, grists arrive from a distance of twenty-five miles in almost every direction. [2 mo. 15, 1817.]

NOTE TO PAGE 4.

" The Chevalier de Lamanon has asserted that the numerous quarries of plaster which are found in the vicinity of Paris are the depositions of an ancient lake." Chaptal, from whom this is quoted, adds, " The wrought iron, *(a)* and the various remains of animals which are found at the bottom of the quarry of Mont Matre, shew that its formation is not very ancient."

The horizontal strata of our quarries, evince that these, also, are depositions; but it would be strangely absurd to assign them a date since the manufacture of iron. No doubt can exist of the fact that this gypsum is coeval with the *Great Ledge,* and older than the gravel hills ; for the beds in many places, not only underlay those elevations, but also underlay considerable bodies of limestone.

It has been already mentioned in this volume, that plaster is dissolved by 500 times its weight of water. Wherever these rocks are exposed to its action, a decrease invariably happens ; and on this process, indeed, the indications to be observed in exploring, are entirely founded.

In consequence of the removal of the gypsum by solution, the incumbent soil acquires* a *peculiar undulation of surface,* which may be occasioned either by the unequal† hardness of the rock, or by the irregularity of the covering. This appearance only occurs where the beds are imperfectly sheltered by a loose subsoil. Beneath limestone or hard-pan, which prevents the transudation of moisture, the rock is found unaltered ; and in one instance it has been discovered in the same state, at the bottom of a swamp.

The *plaster stone* in addition to pure *gypsum* contains much extraneous matter. *Sulphuretted hydrogen*‡ as one constituent has been noticed ;§ and though it would be unwarrantable to assert that all *sulphur springs* originate from plaster beds, yet in this country, we know of no such fountains except in the vicinity of those quarries. This gas is abundant in the stone, but all is absorbed and removed by the water that dissolves the gypsum.

* See page 129.

† It is believed that black plaster is more soluble than that in which the chrystallization is more distinct, as the opake particles more freely admit the moisture.

‡ It is also contained in the black limestone of this country. Round many detached stones which lie buried in a moist or loose subsoil, a black marl is found resembling that of the plaster beds; but these stones diminish too slowly to mineralize fountains in any remarkable degree.

§ See page 135.

A third indication of the presence of plaster is found in *the black earth* which overlays that rock when the subsoil has afforded an imperfect shelter ; but this, like the former, is not unerring. It is discoverable in beds which no longer enclose plaster ; and after penetrating it to the depth of fifteen feet, I have retired from the search, fully convinced that the whole quarry had been wasted by solution. Indeed, in one excavation, gravel appeared at the bottom.

This residuum is a valuable manure for the yellow, clayey loam that covers it, though I know of no instance where it has been regularly applied ; but the proprietor of a field in which it had been thrown up, remarked, that wherever it was mixed with the soil, even in small quantities, the wheat resembled in luxuriance that which springs from a burnt brush heap.

The best of this marl when taken from the earth, is an impalpable paste ; and accords with " the black pyritaceous clay" of Chaptal. The dark colouring matter appears to be *sulphuret of iron* in powder ; and we suspect that its chief fertilizing principle resides in this ingredient. The quantity of *sulphur** is also considerable. This was discovered by projecting it on ignited charcoal in a dark place, when the flames appeared in minute specks. *Carbonate of lime* is proved to be a constituent by its effervescence with acids. The concreted limestone which is found in many places near these quarries, results probably from its solution in water charged with carbonic acid ; and the suggestion is favoured by the presence of ochre in those *conical piles* that *surround many of the springs in the vicinity of East Cayuga.*

We have thus enumerated five ingredients of the *plaster stone*, and we are satisfied that in some specimens, *clay, ochre* and *sand* might also be detected. The value of this mineral as a manure, will therefore depend on the proportion of these substances ; for independent of the gypsum, the effect of which soon

* Independent of what appears in chrystals.

ceases, soils may receive with this stone imperishable and fertilizing additions.

(n) This statement is so remarkable, that we are induced to inquire if some mistake may not have been committed ? In the stony strata of our globe, which **102** enclose animal remains, no vestige of the human* race, with this exception, has been discovered ; and a circumstance so anomalous should be received with caution. In a succeeding note, reasons will be given for believing that since this *formation,* the constitution of nature has undergone an extraordinary change. Indeed, that Philosopher has not asserted in direct terms that wrought iron was *incased in the rock ;* and unless this was clearly ascertained, we must think some other explanation of this appearance may be given, which will be more probable than that the rock was formed since the manufacture of iron.

In the quarries of this country which have not been sufficiently sheltered, the plaster has been so irregularly dissolved that the residue resembles *jambs* or *pillars ;* and the spaces between, contain, near the bottom, black marl pressed down by the yellow subsoil which has fallen, or been washed into the hollow. Now it is evident, that if wrought iron had been left on the surface of that part of the rock which was wasting, it might be found after a long lapse of ages with black marl at the bottom of the quarry.

Further, in considering this assertion a difficulty presents itself which is not easily obviated. As this salt is dissolved by water, its *precipitation,* in the common order of nature, would only happen by diminishing the solvent ; but instead of such diminution, we are told that the waters of that Lake were supplied by three considerable rivers, the *Seine,* the *Loise,* and the *Marne.*

* American Monthly Magazine for May 1818.

NOTE TO PAGE 4.

The first bridge over this water was erected in the summer of 1800, and rested on *bents*, the posts of which were driven deep into the marly bottom. The convenience thus afforded to travellers, however, was of short duration. In the spring of 1806, several thousand acres of ice, loosened from the shores, moved up the lake in a strong gale from the south ; and returned with a force which proved irresistible, and the ferry boat was resumed. Soon after a bridge was erected over the outlet two miles to the north, but this route was not sufficiently inviting. Finding the current of emigration could not be turned in that channel, an incorporated company in the summer of 1813 erected the present bridge with a hope of better success. The posts were driven deeper, and the bents more firmly connected ; but notwithstanding these precautions, and that of placing ice-breakers to the south, it was only saved from destruction the ensuing winter by the intrepidity of JAMES BENNETT, one of the proprietors. The ice in its approach had past the piers, and was forcing the bents, when he descended singly, amidst the crash, with an axe, and going from post to post equalized the pressure till the whole field ceased to move. The railing, which before was beautifully straight, still retains marks of that violence.

NOTE TO PAGE 8.

In considering such astonishing appearances we become satisfied that these ought not to be ascribed to the Earth's attraction simply restoring the waters to a level. We believe, indeed, that the most extraordinary tides swept over this country ; but the ridges which were formed at that period, owe not their arrangement to water. Many are so sharp, even at this day, as barely to admit a foot-path on the summit. Fine earth, 103 sand, gravel, rounded stones, and rocks of great weight are intermixed without order ; and we have frequently observed in these piles, surrounded by different substances, bodies of marl, which have apparently been removed *entire*.*

A belief in the agency of *ice* on this occasion, will appear equally precluded on a careful consideration of these circumstances ; for though we may account in this manner for the transportation† of rocks, yet the different depths at which these ponderous bodies are buried, and the singular arrangement of the mate.ials forming those hills which took place on the spot where they now lie, would leave no support to that conjecture.

We have shewn that *this deluge moved up an inclined plane.* We are convinced that no explanation of such appearances, by referring to convulsions of our elements need be attempted ; that no motion originating within our globe could arrange in this manner the loose bodies on its surface ; and we have therefore not hesitated to ascribe these phenomena to an *Exterior*‡ *Attraction.*

It is well known that ponderous substances in a state of minute division, may be suspended in fluids. The difference in the removal by water, of one cubic foot of sand, and of a sandstone of the same weight will be instantly evident ; and the reason will be found in the principle of common attraction. In small bodies the superficies is great in proportion to the solid

* We do not assert that none of the materials of these ridges have been deposited through water. The perpendicular sect on of a sand hill near Auburn, presents very curious phenomenon equally demonstrating the descent of the sand through that fluid, and the violent commotions of the deluge.

† See Picture of Cincinnati, page 75.　　　‡ See page 180.

§ In the *Cube*, when the side is 1 the superficies is six times as great as the solid content ; when the side is 6 the solid content is equal to the superficies ; and when the side is 12 the solid is double the superficial area.

content. The surrounding fluid comes more immediately in contact, and by proximity of attraction resists the general pressure to the centre. With an increase of magnitude, however, there is not a proportionate increase of surface ; the internal parts are more distant from the contact and the consequent attraction of the fluid ; and inadequately supported, the solid falls to the bottom. With these principles in view, the removal of large rocks by the simple pressure of water will not be admitted. On the principle of a *foreign attraction*, however, the explanation of these appearances is clear and consistent. Every loose substance on the surface of the earth would be lifted or drawn along ; and the rock*(a)* which had been fastened down by gravitation, receiving a new and opposite impulse, would become as obedient as ferruginous sand to the magnet. The particles of clay would keep pace with the coarser materials of the hills ; and the Great Rock of Montezuma estimated at 3000 cubic feet, move along with the sand that supports it. **104**

The *great extent* of this deluge is also favourable to our exposition of the subject. Its traces, indeed, are variable, and in some small districts scarcely perceptible ; but a wide space of country bears unequivocal marks of its progress ; and we feel assured that future observers will extend the limits of these discoveries.

We have read no author of recent date, who has attempted to account for these phenomena except Dr. DRAKE. His remarks are interesting ; but the sphere **105** of his observations was too limited to favour a just conclusion. From him we learn that " these *fragments of primitive rocks are said to be scattered extensively over the state of Ohio, the Indiana Territory, and Kentucky.*" He also remarks, " The older alluvions are composed of sand, gravel, and water worn pebbles, *covered* from two to six feet deep with a bed of yellowish loam. The *upper table* in the town of Cincinnati is of this kind. Vegetable substances, chiefly the decaying remnants of trees, have been found in different parts, at various depths from twenty to thirty feet. The beds

of sand lie in most parts at considerable depths, and
have an obliqe or wave like stratification." S. H. Long
of the Topographical Eugineers in the service of the
United States, has informed that " *detached rocks of
granite are numerous in the country to the south west of
Lake Michigan.*" We observed *granite near the Wabash,* and in Madison county, (Ohio,) on our return.
B. F. Stickney, in a letter to the Secretary of the
Western Emigrant Society, dated, Fort Wayne on the
Maumee, remarks " No excavations having been made,
we can only view the surface. The silex is generally
in the form of *sand* ; but *there are detached rounded
blocks of granite and porphyry* ; and there are a few
*considerable masses of gneis and schistose mica, much
wave worn.*"

This deluge can be also distinctly traced to the eastward. The arrangement of the numerous sand hills in
the vicinity of Albany are referable to the same period ;
though we have not learned whether granite in that district has been discovered. At Ballston similar
phenomena occur. That village, according to Dr.
Meade,* " is surrounded by a range of *undulating* [*sand*]
hills."—" Within seven miles of Ballston is situate the
village of Saratoga. The road from Ballston is chiefly
over a *sandy pine plain.*" Again, " The *transition*
rock is still observed at both sides of the river [near the
Cohos] but soon after, *a range of sand hills commence,
and all traces of the strata are lost for several miles.* till
having passed over these hills which extend to the distance of twenty miles, we arrive in the neighbourhood
of Ballston." Further " The ground at [Ballston and
Saratoga] is principally composed of two or three species of rock of secondary formation, but these *are so
covered with immense beds of sand* that it is difficult to
ascertain the formation." Also, " The surface of the
ground both at Ballston and Saratoga is *covered with large
insulated masses of stone,* commonly called boulders, con-

* Chimerical Analysis of the Mineral Waters of Ballston and
Saratoga.

sisting of large blocks of quartz and rolled masses of other primitive rock. These scattered blocks must have been transmitted from the neighbouring mountains, as *they are not attached to rocks in situ and have no connexion with them. They are found in every country, and prove the action of an extensive flood of water.*"

The country to the south furnishes many proofs in support of our theory. The extensive plain which terminates at Tioga Point, is one vast bed of sand and gravel, elevated far above the reach of river floods ; and the surface is remarkably undulated. Similar appearances occur in many places down the Susquehanna. At the base of the hills southeasterly from Wilkesbarre, a coal mine was covered by loose gravel; and twenty-five miles north-west of Philadelphia, we have frequently ploughed a large bed of loose gravel on the summit of a hill nearly one hundred feet above the Schuylkill. Stones of several species are buried at different depths or scattered over the surface as at Cayuga ; and as a proof that this flood had also a southerly direction in that district, a kind of sand stone which is there very numerous, has only been discovered *native* at the Blue Mountain, distant forty miles in a right line.

The venerable CHARLES THOMPSON, more than thirty 107 years ago observed, that a deluge had overwhelmed that country. His remarks on this subject illustrate our proposition ; though no traces of an old channel of the Delaware below the *Wind Gap* are discoverable ; nor have we found what obstacles prevented the waters of that river from flowing into the Hudson.

" From the best accounts that I have been able to obtain, the place where the Delaware now flows through the Kittatinny mountain, was not its original course, but that it passed through what is now called " the Wind Gap," a place several miles to the westward, and above one hundred feet higher than the present bed of the river. The Wind Gap is almost a mile broad, and

the stones in it such as seem to have been washed
for ages by water running over them. Should this have
been the case, there must have been a large lake behind
that mountain, and by some uncommon swell in the
waters, or by some convulsion of nature, the river must
have opened its way through a different part of the
mountain, and meeting there with less obstruction, carried away with it the opposing mounds of earth, and
deluged the country below with the immense collection
of waters to which this new passage gave vent. There
are still remaining, and daily discovered, innumerable
instances of such a deluge on both sides of the river, after it passed the hills above the falls of Trenton, and
reached the champaign. On the New Jersey* side, all
the country below Crosswick hills seems to have been
overflowed to the distance of from ten to fifteen miles
back from the river, and to have acquired a new soil by
the earth and clay brought down and mixed with the
native sand. The spot on which Philadelphia stands
evidently appears to be *made* ground. The different
strata through which they pass in digging to water, the
acorns, leaves, and sometimes branches, which are
found about twenty feet below the surface all seem to
demonstrate this."*

The celebrated Cuvier has also noticed such removals : " In some countries, we find numerous and *prodigious large blocks of primitive substances* scattered
over the surface of the secondary strata, and separated
by deep vallies from the peaks or ridges where these
blocks must have been derived."

Dr. Drake has suggested that the granite of the
Ohio country arrived from the north. We have shewn
that the *native* stones of this country have been regularly carried in the same direction. We have shewn
that the primitive rocks to the south vary in colour
from those of the same species in this district. We
have believed that ours were detached from strata in

* Indeed, the formation of no inconsiderable part of West
Jersey may be ascribed to the same periods·

Canada, and the observations of M'KENZIE tend to **108**
prove their identity. About one hundred miles east of
Lake Superior, he observed that " the rock is generally
hard, of a *dark blue grey ;*" and at Lake Winipeck
" the north bank is *black and grey rock.*" He had informed us that that country is granitic ; and although
there is much variety of colour in our fragments, a
great proportion would accord with his descriptions.
This is suggested for the use of future observers.

The gravel hills to the south of Lake Ontario have
been briefly noticed ; but a further description may be
proper. Of these astonishing monuments, we have seen
no place that presents them in more interesting forms
than *Montezuma.* The beautiful ridge on which this
village stands, coincides with the magnetic meridian ;
but those to the south, which are more elevated, and
which exhibit greater marks of violence in their arrangement, vary to the left from five to twelve degrees.
We have not observed a greater variation, however,
than two degrees in such as are adjacent.

The shape of these hills is various, but we believe the
principal number may be comprised within two classes.
THE HIGHEST AND MOST ABRUPT appear to contain a
greater proportion of coarse materials. The ascent at
the north end is generally steep ; and the greatest height
and magnitude of the ridge is near that extremity.
From a side view, the epithet of *hog-backed* has been
applied. The descent towards the south is long and
gradual, though the whole distance will rarely equal
two hundred rods. On the north end of several ridges,
the eye may trace the sharpness of the summit continued downward, and turned towards the north east for a
few rods before it terminates ; but this feature is not
general.

It is very rare to find one ridge commence on the
southern slope of another. In some places, two ridges
appear contiguously side by side ; and a shallow channel of two or three rods in width extends the whole
length like the indentures of a melon. Such is the hill

at Dr. CLARKE's.   The spaces of level land between
the ridges, however, are very irregular; and in some
considerable tracts, a solitary eminence appears.   Such
is the hill to the north of Montezuma.   We have seen
several thus situated, not of greater magnitude than
some mounds in the western country; and only distinguishable at first sight by resembling the longitudinal
section of a prolate spheriod.

The height of these ridges is very variable.   We
have not estimated any at one hundred feet above the
surrounding lands; but we think from forty to seventy
feet altitude, would include a great number.

The second class will include those ridges of less
elevation, which are very straight and extend for greater distances than the former.   These eminences are
remarkably picturesque.   On many, the summit is too
sharp for a road; but others are sufficiently broad for
this purpose; and in some places, advantage has been
taken of these *natural turnpikes*.   A case of this kind
occurs to the north of West Cayuga.

The *islands* which are surrounded by the marshes of
Seneca river resemble in every respect the hills on the
adjacent shores.   Some of these rise just above the
surface, as if much of these bodies of earth and gravel
had sunk in deep water.

Very few gravel ridges of much regularity are found
south of the great Western Turnpike.   On the east of
Cayuga bridge several appear in sight; and through two,
it was necessary to cut a passage for the road; but these
terminate at a small distance to the south.   The sand
hills near Auburn, and near the north-west corner of the
Owasco Lake are of this kind, but very irregular.

In considering this subject, it is evident that the first
effects of an exterior attraction would be perceptible on
fluids; and that, in succession to the most extraordinary
tides, detached solids of greater specific gravity than
water, would acquire new motion.   It is clear, however,
that the strata, fastened down by cohesion, would not be

obedient to those impressions. In extending our views to such districts as would furnish the greatest quantity of moveable matter, the craggy mountain, or the wave worn shore, would first be presented to the mind ; and to the south of such collections, we would look for the most unequivocal traces of the deluge ; for although the *primitive rocks* in our county have been removed from afar; and though in several instances, we have seen *native* rocks deposited on heights, far above the strata from which they were taken,—yet it is worthy of remark that all these substances are scattered in the greatest abundance, immediately to the south of their native beds. The sand and gravel of the hills which rise on the borders of Lake Ontario, were doubtless derived from that great basin. One mile south of the Cayuga Lake, sand and gravel are also piled into hills ; and in the village of L'Orient, one ridge, at least, appears of the usual form. This makes an angle of twenty degrees with the meridian. Indeed, in many parts of this district, the difference is greater than at Montezuma.

The impulse by which loose materials were congregated into hills, merits our attention. The manner in which earthy particles collect when agitated on a board, was considered ; but desirous to observe the effects of an exterior attraction, we drew a magnet rapidly over ferruginous sand, scattered evenly on a plain. When paper was interposed to prevent an actual contact, the experiment was successful : —the sand was collected into long ridges, irregularly grouped, and resembling the hills of Ontario in miniature.

Notwithstanding this similarity of arrangement, our pretensions on this subject are humble. We suggest, but we do not insist on this explanation. Indeed, the filaments of iron filings that form near a magnet, appear to be occasioned by the particles becoming magnetized ;* but we have no proof that common earthy matter has been subject to similar impressions.

* A piece of spring tempered steel will not retain as much magnetism as hard steel, soft steel still less, and iron scarcely retains any. ADAMS on Magnetism.

It *is* possible that some of our readers may consider these remarks as presumptuous; and that we endeavour to pry into counsels forbidden to our race. At various tribunals the writer of travels may be arraigned. Although we are confident that such charges would be deemed narrow and illiberal by enlightened minds, yet we respect opinions which are founded in piety. To such readers we would suggest, however, that *ignorance* is neither respectable nor useful. On this dark base the altars of superstition have arisen, and the fires of intolerance have consumed its victims.

Some pious persons have believed, indeed, that any exposition of natural subjects not warranted by the text of MOSES, is reprehensible. But the gloom of such prejudices is passing away; and Revelation receives, instead of contravention, the most ample support from the votaries of science. The account of the Creation is a brief sketch. It contains, notwithstanding all that is necessary for faith and devotion; and we are convinced, that on a liberal interpretation, every seeming inconsistency with modern discoveries may be, reconciled. It was not necessary that Moses should understand the system of the Universe. It was not necessary that he should teach Astronomy; for on it no man's virtue or happiness depended; neither can we think that it would have proved auxiliary to his mission. The same kindness has ever been extended to man, as our Lord shewed to his Disciples near the close of his ministry: " I have yet many things to say, but *you cannot bear them now.*" The dispensation of moral and religious duties, has constantly been adapted to the state and condition of society; and many centuries passed away, before the nations were prepared for the divine precepts of a Saviour.

Some eminent philosophers have been puzzled by the Mosaic account of the deluge. Four and twenty oceans were computed by one writer as necessary to drown the whole earth; and as it could not be known where such a flood had arrived, or whither it had retired, the truth of the Historian was questioned. Others more favourable to religion, supposed it was limited by the neighbourhood of the Euphrates. We have now sufficient evidence that those who received the account as an article of faith, chose their path in wisdom. Indeed we consider the traces of a deluge *over all the Earth* to be demonstrable ; and this passage of scripture, instead of subverting our confidence, has become one of the strongest proofs of divine revelation.

We conclude this part of our essay in the language of one, who stood eminent as a scholar and a christian.

" ———— Has not God
Still *wrought by* MEANS since first he made the world?
And did he not of old *employ his* MEANS
To DROWN IT ? What is his creation less
Than *a capacious reservoir of* MEANS
Formed for his use, and ready at his will."—COWPER.

No part of nature presents appearances more astonishing or inexplicable than the stony strata of our globe. In the period of these formations, we discover an unvarying tendency to petrification ; and the rapidity of this change evinces a state of the elements, unknown in later ages. Substances the most perishable, now form portions of solid rock. The flesh of fishes and of serpents, which in our summers putrify in a few hours, there retain every lineament ; and doubtless will astonish all succeeding generations.

Since that period the order of nature has been reversed. Dissolution has touched* every rock not protected by the ruins of others ; and the mountain is wearing away. The destruction of animals by that flood during which the gravel hills were raised, was unquestionably immense ; yet nothing but the shells† of fish and the bone,

---

* I have noticed the gradual decomposition, or rather dechrystallization of limestone. In various places north-west of the Alleghany Mountains, where the horizontal strata of this rock are uncovered, the sectional fissures are several inches in width,—evincive of its disintegration.

† Shells, even when attached to the living animals, are ch carbonates, of lime.
iefly

of the largest quadrupeds have been undissolved,—and
the latter only when sheltered from the changes *(b)* of
the atmosphere. Of the other myriads not a vestige
remains. In this country, we have discovered the formation of no stone since the deluge, except such as
were cemented* by the solution and deposition of lime
and iron ; and from these have resulted the breccia, the
stalactites and ferruginous sandstones, though silicious infiltrations probably exist.

Much pains have been taken to account for the
formation of rocky strata, which contain marine exu-
viæ ; and imaginary ponds have been assigned to various tracts of country. However, this labour might be
spared, by reflecting that as these remains are found
nearly 9000† feet above the present level of the
ocean, ponds must be unnecessary ; because the waters
have submerged all the boundaries below that height.

On the reverse, if the sea once stood over all parts of
the earth, whither have the waters retired ? No probable solution of this difficulty has been presented ; and
therefore, countenanced by analagous appearances, we
ascribe the elevation of these substances to foreign
attraction ; for whatever may have been the impulse
that raised the gravel hills, it appears to have returned
at different and distant periods of time.

We have noticed the improbability of sands forming
in horizontal strata on the bottom of lakes. It is
deposited, indeed, by the water which whirled it along as
soon as the current becomes checked ; but in this case
the arrangement is not regular, neither would it be found
at great distances from shore. In the sandstone of this
109 country, we have conclusive proof that the materials
fell through a moving flood. In one place, the rock rests
on limestone ; and to the height of a few inches,
abounds with the scallop shell ; but very few are found

* On treating a silicious sandstone of this kind with muriatic
acid, the effervescence was violent.

† KIRWAN, as quoted in the American Monthly Magazine ; but
JEFFERSON says 15,000 feet.

in the upper part of the stratum,—the shells sinking
more speedily than the sand, as their central parts were
further removed from the contact of the fluid. This
quarry is in Lot No. 69, (East Cayuga) on high land,
and sufficiently remote from any stream to preclude the
idea of a current, not preternatural.

We have other objections to the notion that stony
strata were deposited from ponds. No supporting
circumstance occurs at the bottom of our lakes ; no rock
is formed, and no fishes are buried in the mud. On the
reverse, those that die become buoyant, float to
shore, and suffer decomposition. The same remark may
be extended to birds. Yet from the slate of Seneca
Lake, a small bird was taken ; and one near the size of 110
a robin was quarried at Ludlowville. Strong proof
would be necessary to induce our belief that these were
not buried by an overwhelming flood, and preserved
during a state of the elements of which modern ages
have witnessed no parallel. Indeed, no coal,* no salt
rock, no animal petrifaction, of a date within the last
4000 years, have been discovered.

The slate ridges, and even those of limestone which
cross the *Great Ledge* preserve nearly the same course
as the gravel hills ; and on the south side of the Turnpike, are chiefly constituted of these stones, though the
coverings are of later alluvions. We have made no
observation that proves conclusively, that this flood was
so violent in its motion as the last, for no primitive
rock has been discovered amongst its depositions ;
but we have already mentioned that limestone rounded
by rolling, appears in the slate at lake Erie ; and as
none of that species is found to the south, within probable distances, *it* evidently *arrived from the north.*
Limestone is also embedded in the slate of Scipio. In
the former case, it is only a few feet above the level of

* At page 54 is a remark on the conversion of wood into jet,
as a prelude to the production of coal, the correctness of which
may be questioned.

that lake ; but here it is several hundred, and no hills on this side of Ontario are so elevated.

111   Dr. WITHERING has noticed that ferns, now only in-digenous in America, have been impressed on the iron stone of Britain ; and the Abbe LA PLUCHE has ob-
112   served on rocks in France, the impressions of a plant now only native in China. In geological enquiries such facts are important, and evincive of tides and revolu-tions the most extraordinary.

But even in these scenes of desolation the elements ceased not

"To work the will of ALL-SUSTAINING LOVE."

The admixture of soils, the diffusion of clays, with the sifting and arrangement of sand for the various pur-poses of the arts, were effected in those awful periods, and the ores of iron were collected, after the mines of salt and coal were deposited and secured, an inherit-ance to all succeeding generations.

The grand order of our system is to spring, to flour-ish and to die. The period for which many* plants and animals were intended, is past ; and like the individu-als of every race, whole species have perished. The space assigned them has been filled ; new orders arise; and combinations more beautiful are unfolded. The sheep tenants the deserted ranges of the wolf, and the yellow gleams of harvest, succeed the dark foliage of the forest.

(a) The mind of him who has never raised an eye from the ordinary pursuits of life, to contemplate the wonders of nature,---who has seen nothing more active than the flood, or the tempest, in this comparative state of quiescence which the elements have assumed,---and who forgets the immense distance between his own pow-ers and those of his Creator,---may revolt at such pro-

* It is questionable whether the beds of coal are the remains of any vegetable species now in existence.

positions. The narrow mind cannot be instantly expanded. But when from the confined perspective of plains and of mountains, his views are turned to the countless worlds which bespangle the heavens;—when he considers their astonishing magnitudes and velocities,—he may learn, that though mighty was the motion that arranged the hills and the vallies around him, they shrink to a grain on the scale of Creation.

(b) " The horns and tusks of animals, *in a fossil state*, form a considerable article of the interior commerce of Russia. Professor PALLAS informed me, such prodigious quantities of elephant's teeth were discovered on an island which lies to the north of the Samoiede Land, that Caravans come annually laden with them to Petersburgh. The most remarkable circumstance is, that instead of being mineralized, like elephant's tusks found in the south of Europe, they may be wrought with all the facility of the most perfect ivory ; but *this only happens, when they are found in a latitude where the soil is perpetually frozen.* Those dug in the southern parts of Siberia are found either soft or decayed, or mineralized by silicious infiltrations and metaline compounds. If frost alone preserved them, they were frozen in the moment of their deposit." CLARKE's Travels in Russia.

NOTE TO PAGE 8.

My conjecture on the formation of the Ridge Road, was founded on the belief that the waters which have deluged this country, rushed from the northern ocean. The surface of lake Ontario, consequently acquired an extraordinary elevation ; and while this flood was impelled to ascend towards the mountains, the earth's attraction, on the secession of this preternatural impulse, gave the waters an increasing velocity northward, bearing along sand and gravel, which on striking the lake, suffered immediate deposition.

This opinion was supported by observing a ridge more than 150 miles in length, lying nearly at right angles to innumerable ridges, composed of the same materials, and which approach* but never touch it. This appearance was explained by supposing that the gravel hills had been formed by that impulse in its course to the south, and that the waters of the lake had been driven from the shores on its return.

On passing the ridge road to the north every hill disappears, and the surface of the country gradually declines to the banks of the lake. It was conjectured that this tract had been sheltered by the waters of the lake during this extraordinary submersion.

Subsequent observations, however, have weakened our confidence in these deductions. The form of this ridge accords not with the varying appearances of the hills and vallies to the south ; and in one place, it turns on a plain nearly at right angles, and at a very considerable distance from more elevated land. These difficulties we are not prepared to obviate. Yet I am unwilling to renounce the opinion that this ridge and those to the south were arranged by the same astonishing commotion ; and am not without hopes that future discoveries may remove the obstacles that now bar our progress ; believing, however, that impressions have been made on matter, of which the traces are so few and so intermixed with those of other periods, as to elude investigation.

113   Popularly, this ridge is an ancient beach of lake Ontario, and it is supposed that the *dam* has been lowered in latter ages. One writer, indeed, to prove that this disruption is of modern date, avers that no mounds have been found north of that elevation. But the fact is disproved. On the east point between Ironda-

* Such is the appearance as far as I have seen or learned, west of Pultneyville; but eastward towards Sodus, where the ridge becomes more irregular, this feature is not preserved.

quot bay and the lake, there is a mound of considerable magnitude.

This theory is discountenanced on a close inspection. Fine earth intermixed with sand and gravel, is not found in banks driven up by the waves. It cannot settle amidst such conflicting agitations. Yet this ridge in places towards its eastern extremity, is a fine loam intermixed with gravel.

In this part it is very irregular; and may be found thirty rods wide, and apparently twenty feet higher than the ground to the south. It resembles a mass of loose earth which had been suddenly precipitated.

It is too unequal in height to resemble a beach. In one part, it is formed of fine blowing sand, and doubtless this has been raised by the wind; but where small longitudinal inequalities appear (but which are very rarely discoverable,) the height is not preserved; and on one gravel *beach* which only extends a few rods, the depress on near the middle is considerable.

This ridge has not been discovered to the east of Little Sodus. Now, if it had been formed by the waves of Ontario, the beach would extend round both shores of that lake; and this deficiency furnishes the most conclusive proof against that conjecture.

If any thing were yet wanting to shew that the road was formed in some general commotion of nature, the ridge on the south shore of lake Erie would supply that evidence. It extends at least from Coniat creek near the west bounds of Pennsylvania to Huron river,— nearly 120 miles. It is from three to six miles from the lake; and the materials are sand and gravel. This bank is of less magnitude than the ridge near lake Ontario; and the country above it, has also less inclination to the north.

It is remarkable that neither of these ridges approach the outlets of those lakes.

Extracts of Letters relative to the Ridge Road.

" I saw a young man who was on the Ridge Road a few miles east of the Eleven Mile woods. Some men were digging a well directly on the ridge, and he had the curiosity to examine what was thrown out. The first two feet was a sandy loam. Beneath this were gravel and stones of various sizes, blue and rounded like those which roll in water."

" I observed as I approached the ridge (west of Iron-diquot,) that the face of the country on the north side is smooth as far as I could see; and the inhabitants informed me it was the same all the way to Ontario. The ridge itself was chiefly composed of sand, but I saw no gravel, or round stones similar to those which are found on the shores of lakes."

" The height of the ridge above the adjoining lands at this place is about four feet, but in other places it rises to sixteen. It is about six rods wide; but I should estimate its width, a few miles west of the Genesee river, at full twenty rods. Many persons well acquainted with the country on the north side, assure me that it is smooth, and none speak of either hills or knolls."

———

NOTE TO PAGE 10.

114   The manner in which gypsum operates as a manure, perhaps remains to be one of the *desiderata* of chemical philosophy. From the property of sulphuric acid to attract* water from the atmosphere, some have ascribed the increased vigour of the plant to a timely supply thus furnished. But it does not appear that exposure to the weather affects its composition, though it effects its solution; and while the acid is combined,

* In one day three parts of sulphuric acid exposed to the atmosphere are increased in weight one part; and one ounce by twelve month's exposure has been found to gain an addition of six and a quarter.   Dr. Henry.

its attractive powers must be latent. The doctrine has also been rejected on the ground, that all the supply that could be received from this manure, as commonly applied, was too trifling to be taken into view; and that even a larger quantity made no perceptible difference.

Other philosophers believed the effect to be entirely medicinal. Having observed the benefits of common salt and other minerals in the animal economy, the operation of this salt on vegetables, was deemed to be analagous; and accordingly it was classed as a stimulant. The objections. however, which are enumerated below, appear to bear equally against this hypothesis.

Subsequently Professor DAVY suggested, or ascertained, that it formed a part of the plant; and that this portion, though small, was necessary to " a healthy vegetation." It must be admitted that this theory is plausible; yet it appears not to explain every thing connected with the subject; and the following objections, if not invincible, will merit attention.

1. On some soils, where the vegetable matter has been reduced, and the land mellowed by frequent ploughings, not the smallest benefit from this manure has been perceived: but or restoring the vegetable matter, the effect of gypsum is striking.

2. On the same soil from which gypsum produces a luxuriant vegetation, simple culture has an effect similar and not less remarkable.

3. The same result is also produced by rain water in small and frequent applications.

4. Animal substances.

It would be desirable to know, why in all these cases, that mineral is not equally necessary? Or if it be, whence, and in what manner is the supply obtained? The quantity in animal substances is exceedingly minute, and should scarcely be considered in this calculation.

NOTE TO PAGE 20.

I copy the following from Cramer's *Navigator*, as shewing a popular opinion, that similar changes prevail in our western waters. So far as his own observations extended, we may implicitly receive the statement; but the infinite irregularity of our seasons, the inaccuracy of common observers, and the frailty of the memory unassisted by notes, diminish much of the interest which such views are calculated to excite.

" There is reason to believe, that the seasons of high waters and hard winters are again returning to the Western Country, which for twenty years or more, absented themselves to some other clime. The same is observed of the rising of the Mississippi, which depends for its floods altogether on those of the northern rivers. Forty or fifty years ago, it has been observed by an old inhabitant of Louisiana, that the Mississippi began to decrease in its rising, and continued to decrease gradually for twenty years; and these last twenty years, it has been observed by a gentleman of accuracy, to increase yearly, and by such gradual steps as not to be generally noticed ; in consequence the banks have got a considerable population, which is now obliged to retreat half ruined, and abandon totally the fertile farms formed with labour and difficulty. In the risings of the Mississippi in 1811, the inhabitants were much injured ; but in 1813 all have been obliged to fly, except those protected by strong levees, and many of these suffered from the levees giving way. In this year the river at Natchez was higher by about eighteen inches than in 1811 ; and in consequence, the losses have been beyond calculation. Lands are now considered not worth possessing, which three or four years ago were thought to be invaluable."

NOTE TO PAGE 29.

Further westward, the relative elevation of this ridge is probably less than that of any other on the globe, which separates rivers of equal magnitude; and the facilities for intercommunication are extraordinary. From a small lake at the head of the *Muskingum*, it is only one mile to a branch of the *Cayahoga*. In the township of *Ravenna* (five miles square) there are good mill seats on branches of the *Cayahoga*, and of *Big Beaver* or *Mahoning*. A batteaux navigation, with only a portage of four miles, is frequently used between the *Sciota* and *Sandusky*; and one of only five miles is required between the *Great Miami* and the *Auglaise* a branch of the *Maumee*. In times of flood, loaded boats pass between the Wabash and the St. Mary's.

The extracts that follow are from a valuable paper written by S. H. Long of the United States Topographical Engineers:

" In *a flat prairie* there is a small lake, about five miles in length, and from six to thirty yards wide, communicating both with the rivers* Des Planes and Chicago, by means of a kind of canal which has been made partly by the current of the water, and partly by the French and Indians, for the purpose of getting their boats across in that direction in time of high water. The distance from the river Des Planes to Chicago river, by this water course is about nine miles, through the greater part of which there is always more or less water, so that the portage is seldom more than three miles in the driest season—but in a wet season boats pass and repass with facility between the two rivers.

" The Kankankee rises in *a flat marshy country* in the neighborhood of the St. Joseph's of the Lake, and runs a meandering course westwardly, passing the southern extremity of Lake Michigan, at the distance

* " The Illinois is formed by the union of three considerable rivers—the Des Planes, the De Page, and the Kankankee."

of twenty or thirty miles from it. Near the head of
this river is a small creek putting into the St. Joseph's,
through which boats have passed in time of high water
from the St. Joseph's to the Kankankee."

It is greatly to be wished that no narrow jealousies
may prevent the completion of an intercourse, which
Nature has so beneficently commenced.

NOTE TO PAGE 33.

The foregoing account of the titles to those lands was
the best that I procured verbally; but since my return
I received the following statement from a friend who
has long been distinguished in public life for integrity
and talents. He has apprised me that it was sketched
from memory, but believes it to be substantially correct. I feel a satisfaction in giving it, because it
places the subject in a new point of view.

" *The Triangle*" contains about 185,000 acres of
land, and each cost the State of Pennsylvania seventy-
five cents. This land with those north and west of
the Alleghany river and Conewango creek, was offered
for sale under an act of the legislature in 1792, with a
condition of settlement, before in use in the sale of
lands. No person was allowed to locate more than
400 acres, which was to be settled within five years, by
erecting a habitable house, and clearing at least two
acres to every hundred taken up, unless prevented
by the enemies of the United States. The purchase
money was twenty cents an acre, or twenty dollars per
hundred, payable in five years. Titles could be acquired by settlement and subsequent payment; or
by payment when a warrant issued, and subsequent settlement. In either case, payment or settlement must
have been made before a patent could issue, unless the
contingency of prevention should occur.

" Within one or two days after the law had passed, a
surplus of warrants was taken out, to cover the whole

territory offered for sale, and the money paid for them. The restriction of four hundred acres was evaded by obtaining the warrants in *feigned names*, which subsequently in many cases passed at the Land Office. John Nicholson, it is believed, covered the whole "*triangle*" and an immense territory beside, only excepting the Reserves. Descriptive warrants were required, but one called *a leading warrant* was only such in reality, and an indefinite number was designated as adjoining in succession. Nicholson afterwards formed the Population Company for the purpose of perfecting his titles by enlarged resources. The Holland company, the Asylum Company and others, also became original warrant holders to a great extent.

"The Warrantees made very expensive efforts to settle their lands, but on the conditions of purchase it was impossible to secure their titles. In some instances the settlers whom they had sent, claimed for themselves, or removed to other lands to acquire rights by settlement.

"A most distressing scene of litigation ensued. On these motions the questions arose, Was the settlement prevented by enemies of the United States? Should persisting to make settlements after the danger had ceased, be deemed necessary to satisfy the law? Or was a simple interruption or prevention sufficient? The Supreme Court of the State and that of the United States, came to different decisions. The Supreme Court of the State claiming co-ordinate jurisdiction, evictions *alternately* took place under the opposite decisions of the courts. The discouragement resulting from this uncertain state of property, has continued from the year 1800, and is still hardly closed. The progress of the controversy has favoured the claims of the *Warrantees* against the *actual settlers*, as they are called, though at an expense and trouble that success will ill requite. This controversy with that of Wyoming, and *the shingling system** in other parts of the State, has

* The act of locating warrants on the same spot by different

made titles to land so very uncertain, that no inconsiderable part of this State is still a wilderness, while New York and Ohio are well peopled in less favourable situations.

NOTE TO PAGE 60.

A friend has suggested that this statement may excite unfavourable doubtings. On consideration, however, I find no cause to alter the paragraph, unless those fumes are too ponderous to float far. No rational doubt can exist, that smoke is often wafted hither from beyond the Mississippi; and the darkness which has several times overspread this country, aught to be referred to the accumulation of that vapour.

I have seen nothing written on this phenomenon, except by those whose names are subjoined. We have witnessed several dark days in the western parts of New York, but I recollect none since the year 1808. In the autumn of 1807 the darkness was most remarkable. At one o'clock P. M. it became necessary in the house to light candles; and in the field we found it expedient to quit gathering potatoes, as we could not distinguish them from stones. Before evening the north west prevailed, accompanied by rain; and as the darkness dispersed, a new morning seemed to dawn in the west.

Attentive to this phenomenon at the instant, I thought I could not be mistaken respecting the cause. The quantity of smoke that floated in the air was unusual, and the last broken clouds which were visible resembled brass. The south wind blew moderately during the darkness. The north west wind and rain commenced together, and a continual increase of light attended their approach.

persons at different times. The lines of whole surveys often interfere with each other in the most capricious manner. A tenant in possession has frequently defended himself against several ejectments, and has at last been evicted by a prior right."

These facts evince, that the latter wind originated beyond the extent of this vapour, and bore it backwards; and the south wind, constantly rushing in against it, the vast valley of the lakes became the theatre of accumulation.

When we consider the small quantity of soot [concreted smoke] which on glass will obscure the rays of the sun, we shall be satisfied that the cause assigned may be sufficient to produce the effect.

BELKNAP's account of the extraordinary darkness which happened "May 19, 1780" in New Hampshire, strongly supports this theory. On that day the rivers were covered by a sooty scum; and a snow drift became black. Before noon the clouds resembled brass; and one hour after noon, it became necessary to light candles.

BATH, British writer, has attempted to account for the darkness which prevailed at Quebec on the "10th, 15th and 16th of October, 1785." He ascribes it to the rushing of aqueous vapours into fields surrounded by woods, and deems this sufficient to produce thunder, and lightning, and darkness. It can merit no further notice.

The atmosphere is most smoky in Spring and in Autumn. South west winds in fair weather, produce smoke even in winter; but the appearance is rare, or in diminished quantity in summer, notwithstanding the new clearings that are generally burnt in that season; (a) and I know of no instance of its approaching from the north west. The annual burning of the immense prairies to the westward, doubtless furnish the principal part. A correspondent at Vincennes remarked, that almost every night during winter when the ground was bare, *the prairie fires* illuminated some point of the horizon.

The impurities that float in the atmosphere in dry weather, are very considerable. This is evinced by comparing the first rain after a drowth with that which

falls near the end of a long storm ; and in smoky
weather even at Cayuga, linens which are exposed to
the open air, acquire a yellow tinge. The *simoon* only
prevails where the atmosphere is uncleansed by rain.
In our own country where this process is frequent,
poisonous or unwholsome winds are unknown.

....

*(a)*On the 16th of 7 mo. 1818, we had a remarkable
exception to this statement, but which substantially
confirms the principle. A breeze from the north was
so surcharged with smoke that its smell was not only
perceptible, but its pungency affected the eyes. This
phenomenon was preceded by drowth ; and considering that the new clearings to the westward, both on our
side and in Canada, had chiefly produced that vapour,
I felt confident that its duration would be short. In
about four hours the cloud passed away, and appeared
in the east like the approach of twilight. The sun was
so much obscured that opake bodies in its rays scarcely
made a shadow, and the addition of thick clouds would
unquestionably have produced darkness.

━━ ━━

115

NOTE TO PAGE 63.

FROM THE NATIONAL INTELLIGENCER.

In 1811, the first steam boat to navigate the Western
Waters, was launched at Pittsburgh, Pennsylvania.
There are now in full tide of success, on the Mississippi and its tributary streams, *thirty-one* steam boats ;
and thirty more are building, and nearly completeted,
for the same navigation. Allowing each boat three
voyages in a year to New Orleans, at the present rates
of freight and passage, the income of sixty-one boats
is estimated at the enormous sum of $2,556,660 per
annum! What a world of industry, enterprize, activity and productiveness !

NOTE TO PAGE 84.

Perhaps the most remarkable instance of *sliding*, on **116** record, happened on the Genessee river, "in the town of *Nunda*, fifteen miles above *Geneseo*, on the 30th of 6 mo. 1817. In the afternoon half an acre of a high steep hill, twenty or thirty feet back from the shore, fell into that stream ; but "half past ten at "night, the people in the neighborhood were alarmed by " a tremendous noise, accompanied by a jarring of the " houses. Immediately upon going out, they discover- " ed high masses of the mountain tumbling from above " into the river, and dashing the waters to a great " height. About fifteen acres of the surface is sup- " posed to have fallen. The cavity left in the hill is " of a circular form, the best part of which presents a " precipice, nearly perpendicular of 150 feet in height. " The current of the river is completely obstructed, " and a new channel is forming through the opposite " lands."

A letter from a correspondent in Ontario county, confirms this statement, and adds, "The earth so en- tirely filled up the channel, that the stream was not navigable for rafts for a considerable time after."

Are not such removals confined to horizontal strata of secondary formation ?

NOTE TO PAGE 90.

It has been observed that the peach tree is more pro- ductive on hills than in vallies ; and, in respect to ma- ny tracts of country, the remark is incontrovertible. For this effect, several causes may be assigned. In low places, the reflection of the vernal rays from surrounding objects produces a heat which brings on the blossom un- seasonably ; and on the descent of colder currents of the atmosphere, it perishes. But such situations, when injured by moisture, are also more subject to frosts in clear calm nights than the adjacent hills; and this is so remarkably the case in much of the country east of the mountains, that the idea* of a chemical process confined to these spots has been suggested. This view is now countenanced by the discovery that in the formation of *gasses* much *free caloric* is combined; and that an emission of carburetted hydrogen re-commences in such places† on the return of warm weather.

On the reverse, the protrusion of the germ on hills, is retarded by a cooler atmosphere, so long as there is danger from frosts; for, whether we ascribe this diminished temperature to more elevated currents which have not been warmed by reflections from the surface of the earth, and which in horizontal directions break on these heights,—or whether we believe with DARWIN, that air, expanding as it ascends the hill, combines with more caloric,—the effect on vegetables, which impart a portion of their heat, will be the same. To such views of the subject we are indebted for the method of heaping round the trees in winter, ice or snow; and of sheltering it from thaws by a covering of litter. The chillness, thus produced at the root, occasions a delay in germination till the warm season is confirmed.

On this subject, a writer in the ENCYCLOPEDIA BRITANNICA made the following effort:

"We find *by a number of experiments* that humidity is the thing that makes frost fatal to vegetables; and therefore every thing that can occasion humidity in them, exposes them to these injuries; and every thing that can prevent or take off an over proportion of humidity in them, every thing that can dry them, *though*

* Jefferson's Notes.

† The *frigorific mixtures* evince that *caloric*, either *free* or *latent*, is subject to powerful attractions; and that in summer, it may be totally withdrawn from water, which is then converted into ice.

with even an increase of cold, must prevent or preserve them from those injuries."

To doubt is no crime in philosophy ; and reasons for adopting an opinion exactly the reverse I shall proceed to unfold.

If indeed the fruit could be reduced to that state of dryness in which the bud reposes in winter, the scheme might be successful ; for where there is no moisture to expand into ice, no injury from cold has been observed; and the grain of maize, and the seed of cucumbers, which produce two of our most tender plants, may be cited as examples. But drying the surface is totally insufficient while the sap vessels remain filled ; and the plants which spring from these seeds, perish as completely in the green-house as in the open air, when the juices become frozen.

On the reverse, the moisture which covers the plant must shelter it from the freezing air, in the same manner, (though not so completely) as it would be sheltered in the time of a vernal frost, if the whole were six inches under water; and when, at last, the current of air has cooled it to the freezing point, if no part of the latent heat is received by the plants, the ice, at least, will be interposed as a covering.

In controverting this opinion, however, I will not rely on theory alone. During eleven years residence near Cayuga I have never known the peach to be injured by frost on the shore of the lake, though in all the lands at a distance, that fruit has been totally destroyed. In the former case, the humidity of the air was unquestionably greater than on the higher grounds; and one tree which I distinctly remember, and which was remarkably productive in a frosty season, was exposed to the spray of the waves.

Other facts may be employed to throw light on this subject. It has been recorded that apricots have been preserved by the FROST CONDUCTOR, which consists of

a rope of straw wound round the tree, while the lower
end is immersed in a tub filled with water. The name
of this apparatus, however, shews that the inventor
could not have understood the *reason* of its effects;
because straw is a very imperfect conductor of heat;
and frost, being only the result of its absence (a nullity) could not be conducted. The straw, by winding
round the tree only a few times in its descent, must
confine the natural warmth in a very slight degree;
and therefore to the exhalations alone ought we to ascribe all the benefit produced by this contrivance. Indeed, without such appendage, tubs of water are found
to soften* the air of cellars in winter, and to prevent the
more tender vegetables from freezing.

The gravelly flats on the brooks which flow into the
Cayuga lake, which contain but little vegetable matter
to putrify, and which dry up in summer, form excellent
sites for orchards. The trees are more sheltered from
cold winds, and at least not more subject to frosts than
on the higher grounds. Situations near many streams
in the state of Ohio are also favourable to fruit.

Dr. Drake has a remark in point:—"It is a well established fact that in spring, although the fruit of these
vallies [of the rivers] is much more forward than on
dry and elevated situations, it suffers less from frost.
This seems to be owing chiefly to the fogs which"—"arise
from the surface of the river, and must be regarded as
a real transportation of heat."

It was remarked in 1816 near *Marietta,* that peaches
and apples were destroyed on the windward side of

---

* Pope has said
———— " A lake behind,
"Improves the keenness of the northern wind."
In winter, it would *soften its keenness*; in spring or autumn
increas its chillness; and in summer *improve its coolness*. The
climate on our side of both lakes, Erie and Ontario, is more temperate than the region three degrees to the south;—cooler in
summer and less intensely cold in winter.

the Ohio: but such trees as received the exhalations of that river, retained their fruit.

The practice and observations of fruit gardeners, also tend to establish the same principle. The boughs of the pine and of other evergreens, have been successfully employed to shelter fruit trees in spring; and on some favourites even blankets have been occasionally used. Further, it has been observed that crowded orchards and the central parts of untrimmed trees have been most productive in cold seasons. Now it is evident that after rains all these coverings retain the moisture.

We are therefore warranted in rejecting the notion, that trees on hills owe the preservation of their fruit to the dryness of the air. On the reverse, if orchards were peninsulated by ditches, and flooded from warm fountains, or even from brooks in cold nights, much damage would be prevented. Such water, late in spring, would average twenty degrees warmer than the frosty air; and would be constantly reducing the difference of temperature.

The effect of cold water on frozen plants before sunrise is well known. This acts by gradually reducing the irritability which had accumulated during the frost. The cause of the destruction sometimes appears to be *mechanical*, and the sap-vessels to be ruptured by the expansion of the juices in freezing. Probably this is the case with the potatoe.* But the damage is most frequently occasioned by the stimulus of heat too suddenly applied. Hence frozen plants should be wet with the coldest water that can be procured; and hence even the exhalations from a ditch or a tub may be sufficient for their preservation.

* The wild plumb after such frosts in spring becomes a vegetable monster. We observe from the same cause a similar effect on the leaves of the peach tree. In these cases it appears that the vital energy is not greatly weakened, but that the sap-vessels are ruptured, and the juices extravasated.

THE following extract from the Edinburgh Encyclopedia, may be interesting to some of my readers; and
explain a remark in the foregoing section, on the *frost
conductor*.

" Plants as well as animals require a certain degree
of heat, to maintain their existence. It is *pretty* well
determined that plants possess the power of gen-
erating heat. The heat of plants is well shewn in
winter, in meadows, where we *always* find that the
snow dissolves more readily than on the adjacent bare
ground."

[It would be improper to let this exemplification pass
without comment. The statement is incorrect. The
light snows of autumn which fall on bare unfrozen
ground, instantly dissolve, while those which rest on
meadows, accumulate. Why snow melts in the former case can need no explanation. In meadows the
grass, which, either dry or green, is a very imperfect
conductor of heat, prevents its contact with the warm
earth.

A slight covering of vegetable mould, for the same
reason, will prevent, even in severe weather, the level
soil from being frozen; while the atmosphere absorbs
from the naked earth all the heat to a considerable
depth. If, in this situation, a light snow occurs, the
meadow may remain bare; but it will require much cre-
dulity to believe, that the heat which dissolved it, was
generated in the blades of withered grass.]

" If, says WILLDENOW, in a strong frost we put vessels with water, close to a tree, we shall find that the
water is converted into ice, but the tree retains its sap
unfrozen and remains quite unhurt."

[The principle intended to be established in this
quotation, I have no design to controvert, but such un-
skilful attempts at illustration excite our surprise. If
the duration of cold is short, the latent heat of the
water may be absorbed, because the air comes in contact with the sap, and the *interposing* substances are

imperfect conductors of heat. It is a fact well known to every axe-man in our country, that the sap of the beech and of the basswood freezes every winter, and that the hardness which the timber acquires in consequence, adds greatly to his labour. The learned Professor has weakened his argument by urging it too far. Yet the sugar-maple is rarely frozen; but how much of this exception should be ascribed to its vital energy, or how much to its non-conducting properties, I presume not to determine.

The observations of HUBERT are more to the point. The experiments were made on the *Arum cordifolium* (a species of Indian turnip) in *Madagascar,* and in the *Isle of France.*]

"On applying a thermometer to five spadices which had unfolded in the preceding night, a rise of 25 deg. from the temperature of the atmosphere took place. On the following morning the difference between the temperature of the spadices, and the surrounding atmosphere was only 21 deg. and in the evening of the same day it had sunk to 7 degrees."

"Plants also possess a power of resisting high degrees of heat. SONNERAT discovered in the island of *Luconia,* a rivulet, the water of which is so hot, that a thermometer immersed in it, rose to 174 deg. of Fahrenheit. Swallows, when flying seven feet over it, dropped down motionless. Notwithstanding this heat, he observed on its banks two species of *Aspathalus,* and *Vilex agnus castus* which swept the water. Messrs. FORSTERS found the earth near a volcano in the island of *Tanna,* as hot as 210 deg. of Fahrenheit, and at the same time it was covered with flowers."

Such facts give us new views of vegetable life. S. H. LONG in a letter to Dr. S. L. MITCHELL, describing the hot* springs near the Washitaw, presents others

*" Dr. HUNTER who" had previously " visited these springs found a green plant, which seemed to be a species of *conferva,* growing in the hot water; but what is more remarkable, a small testa-

equally interesting. In a spring, the temperature of
which is 151 deg. of Fahrenheit, he noticed *bushes*
growing in the water's edge ; and after stating that in
summer the water is hot enough to draw tea or coffee,
cook eggs or even meat, he remarks that "in the hottest spring I observed *bushes* growing, also abundance
of beautiful *moss* of a deep green colour, and of a vegetating appearance ; and what is still more wonder-
ful, a water insect, larger than the wood louse, but resembling it in shape, lives and sports in the heated ele-
ment."

(a) The splendid discoveries in mathematics by NA-
PIER, NEWTON and others, introduced *the scale and
compass* into every department of science ; and in consequence, from *data* so incomplete as scarcely to admit
of any advancement towards correctness, we find laborious calculations. The following instances of this
state of mind may be noticed, though there is a rever-
ence due to genius, even when its efforts are misdirect-
ed.

NEWTON considered *fluids* to be composed of
spheres that roll over one another ; and calculated the
heat of the *great comet of* 1680, to be 2000 times hot-
ter than red hot iron. GREW ascribed the flavour of
stone fruit to the shape. Sweet plumbs and peaches
were spherical ; but sour juices moved round the prolate spheriod. BOERHAAVE's theory of *digestion* was
entirely mechanical. BORELLI calculated the *force of
the heart* in propelling the arterial tide, to be equal to
the pressure of 180,000 pounds weight. FRANKLIN believed that the *particles of air* were tetrahedrons. The
proximate cause of poisons is referred by medical writers of the last century to the acute angles of those
substances. Acids and alkalis like two wedges formed
a blunt prism by combining ; and oil of vitriol, sheath-
ing its asperities in lime, composed gypsum. Even the

ceous animal adhered to it, and lived in a temperature approaching the boiling heat."

fertility and barrenness of soils were ascribed to the shape of the particles.

Is the reader impatient to know the connexion between these remarks and the place of reference? It shall be explained. About the year 1760, the French Academy asked why the naked hand may be held uninjured to the bottom of a vessel, while the water is boiling? and why, when it ceases to boil, the hand will be burnt? The theory of fluids noticed at page 274, sufficiently explains this phenomenon; but an answer appeared in respectable journals of the day, which curiously illustrates the *mathematical mania* then prevalent. It was premised that the particles of heat had sharp points. When the water boiled, these were directed upwards; but when that process ceased, the points turned round, and falling downward through the bottom of the vessel, *stung* the hand.

NOTE TO PAGE 96.

After viewing so many works of this unknown race, and having our curiosity so often excited, it is natural to desire some resting place for the mind: to adopt some opinion which obtains the support of probability, though it have not the firmness of historic truth.

We hope no apology for feeling interested in the history of this branch of the human family will be required. We hope it will not be said that such essays are futile, and only idle excursions of *fancy*. Every endeavour to arrange the facts relative to these monuments *in one line*, by promoting discussion, will sharpen the eyes of observation, and lead to further discoveries.

On this subject conjecture has already been busy. It is not our intention, however, to examine all the different opinions; because to do this would require more ample materials than the sketch by Dr. DRAKE, and

the *letter* by C. ATWATER, which constitute all the
works directly relating to these monuments, to which
we have access. To exhibit our own view; to examine
some remarks of Dr. ROBERTSON'S; and to notice the
different hypotheses advocated by these writers, will
fulfil our design.

It is no new opinion that America received her population, before the discovery of COLUMBUS, from three
different points of the old continent. The resemblance in stature, features, manners, and language, between the *Esquimaux* and the *Greenlanders*, proves
conclusively that they are branches of the same race;
and the habits and complexion of the *Tartars* and of
some North-American Indians, have induced the belief,
that the ancestors of the latter crossed at Behring's
Straits. Perhaps their geographical position may favour this deduction.

Though some tribes on the southern parts of the continent were found in the same rude state of society;
yet others lived in the midst of cities and cultivated
fields, practising the arts of civilized life. All these
were also distinguished by different languages; and in
some remarkable particulars by a difference of manners. It is therefore conjectured that these nations
ought to claim their origin, either from the primitive
settlers on the south shore of the Mediterranean, or
from their colonies in the west of Europe and Africa.

Several circumstances render this opinion probable.
The *trade winds* sweep westward across the Atlantic
through a space of 60 degrees of latitude, carrying every thing within their current directly to the American
coast; and though it commences at a considerable distance from the African shore, the storms on the neighbouring seas would frequently drive the navigator into
that current; neither ought it to be overlooked that the
danger would be greater before the invention of *the
compass*.

Instances of this kind in modern times have been recorded. BELKNAP who suggested or adopted this opinion, has noticed some which we cannot distinctly recollect; but in the Edinburgh Encyclopedia, article CANNIBAL we find the following:

In 1797 the slaves of a ship from the coast of Africa having risen on the crew, twelve of the latter leapt into a boat, and made their escape. On the 38th day, three still survived, and drifted ashore at Barbadoes.

In 1799, six men in a boat from St. Helena, lost their course; and nearly a month after, five of them, surviving, reached the coast of South America.

These are sufficient to shew the high probability, that soon after the commencement of navigation *without* the straits of Gibraltar, vessels with crews and passengers, would be stranded on the coast of America.

From such, it is presumed, the Mexicans and Peruvians derived their origin. By arriving in wrecks, some of the arts and manners of their native land would be retained; and the suggestion, at least is plausible, that the former, uninterrupted and undiminished by warfare, were soon enabled to extend their settlements rapidly through the fertile regions to the north and north east.

If we consider in what an early age navigation was practised, and consequently how soon after that era, America would receive inhabitants within *the Torrid Zone*, it will appear probable that the Mexicans were a great nation, before either the Tartars or Esquimaux arrived on the northern part of this Continent. A long lapse of ages would be required, before

" The poor disinherited outcasts of man"

would be driven through the wilds of Siberia and the desert regions of Kamschatka. Arriving on the shores of the Pacific Ocean, some skill in navigation would be necessary to pass a strait thirty-nine miles in width ; and savages who are compelled to contend with famine would be tardy in nautical improvement. The American coast is only the border of new deserts which extend to great distances. In taking this view, we ought to consider the slow increase of population among half famished savages ; and the small progress of the Esquimaux, will enforce the remark.

According to this conjecture, it appears that the Mexican colonists had advanced into the 43d degree of north latitude, when they met the wandering bands of the Tartar race. Unpractised in war, they found in these invaders a formidable enemy ; and the locality of their employments as husbandmen, would constantly expose them to attack. The history of our own settlements shows that a martial people, supplied with all the munitions of war, have suffered immensely in contests with the same race ; and may explain why such extensive fortifications appear from the south shores of Ontario to the Pacific Ocean. The manner in which the Mexican Colonists became extinct, is easily conceived.

The objections to this hypothesis which might arise on a perusal of the late Dr. Robertson's history of America, ought to claim our attention. On the subject of peopling this continent, he remarks, "With respect to all these systems, it is in vain either to reason or enquire, because it is impossible to come to any decision." Now we think this is deciding with less skill than promptness. We have not discovered that historical evidence ought to differ very essentially from legal evidence. We believe that a well connected series of facts, all tending to one point, even without touching it, is more satisfactory to the mind than the assertions of a witness, who is biassed by interest or led astray by imposition ; and whose testimony has no concurring evidence. We have no design to impair the credit of history ; but we cannot forget the very slender authorities that support some of its most interesting passages. We find, after collecting accounts of important transactions in our own times from eye witnesses,

much disagreement. We reflect how vague traditional
reports had become in a lapse of ages before the historian had " turned them to shape." Indeed, the cases
in which conflicting evidence appears, are numerous ;
and if in the course of this esssy we should encounter
similar difficulties, we shall only endeavour, like histo-
rians, to adopt the most plausible opinion.

" We lay it down as a certain principle, says Dr.
ROBERTSON, that America was not peopled by any nation
of the ancient continent which had made considerable
progress in civilization. Even the most cultivated nations of America, were strangers to many of those simple inventions which were almost coeval with society
in other parts of the world. From this it is manifest,
that the tribes which originally migrated to America,
came off from nations which must have been no less
barbarous than their posterity, at the time when they
were first discovered by Europeans. If ever the use of
iron had been known to the savages of America, or to
their projenitors ; if ever they had employed a plough,
a loom, or a forge, the utility of these inventions would
have preserved them ; and it is impossible that they
should have been abandoned or forgotten. We may
conclude then, that the Americans sprang from some
people, who were themselves in such an early and unimproved stage of society, as to be unacquainted with
all those necessary arts, which continued to be
unknown among their posterity when first visited by
the Spaniards."

These remarks would apply with much propriety and
force to a stationary people, or to large numbers who
quietly migrated in a body ; but according to our view
of the manner in which America received its first inhabitants, the whole of this reasoning becomes nugatory.
Few indeed are the citizens of any country who know
how to take iron from the mine and manufacture it into
common utensils ; and still rarer is the individual, who
after suffering shipwreck on a foreign coast,—while lan-
guishing an exile, and roaming in the search of daily

food,—would have courage to explore the desert, to disembosom the hidden ore, and to determine on permanent improvements. If few arts were transplanted in America it ought not to excite our surprise. The class of people most likely to be stranded would be sailors and fishermen ; neither ought we to judge of the arts of their countrymen, from such feeble attempts as they might make to imitate what they never had practised ; and if the skill had been acquired, the materials must have been wanting. Even if the cultivator had been thrown on the shore, his knowledge would have been unavailing. No plant, the former object of his culture ; no beast to relieve his labour by participation ; no implement to subdue the soil,—the agriculture of his country could only be *remembered*, not practised.

Let it not be said, that if mariners from the Mediterranean had been stranded on the shores of America, *letters* would have been introduced. Learning was not generally diffused among the sailors of ancient times. Dressed skins and the leaves of the Papyrus were so valuable in Greece, that bleached bones from the fields have been used as a substitute ; nor has Nature disclosed materials for books to the wanderer in the desert. The aversion of savages to literature is well known, and difficult to overcome ; and the retention of the unwieldy alphabet of China, notwithstanding the opportunities of the inhabitants to acquire a better, will illustrate these observations. Indeed the imperious demands for food, for clothing, and for safety, would supersede other considerations, even with the scholar, and engross all the faculties of his mind.

But these remarks acquire additional force when we reflect on the wretched condition of some who have floated across the Atlantic. Every article of food has been devoured. Every feeling of humanity has been stifled by continual suffering. Neither is this recital the offspring of fancy :—in both instances which we have taken from the Encyclopedia, the survivors were Cannibals.

A remarkable ferocity, induced by this mode of living, has prevailed wherever it has been adopted. Even those who were exemplary, became ungovernable ; nor can we be persuaded that any people would ever resort to such food, in the first instance, except in cases of extremity. The traces of this custom amongst the South Sea Islanders, some of whom have been blown off to sea in their canoes, favour this opinion. Indeed by referring to such disastrous voyages, new light is thrown on the prevalence of this horrid repast among the Mexicans ; we are enabled to account for the total absence of the corn, and the esculent herbs of the eastern continent ; and we obtain a strong argument in favour of their Egyptian or Syrian extraction.

We have suggested that the ancestors of the Mexicans crossed the Atlantic. There is the highest probability that those Cast-aways were of different nations ; and though they reached the American coast in succession ; and though their offspring may have assimilated into one people, yet something of the manners of those nations would be retained ; and we think such traces are clearly discoverable in America.

We refer the origin of mounds to the Egyptians. The first efforts of building pyramids must have been rude ; such would not long withstand the plough or the spade ; and if America had been cultivated by different races of men, most of those which form the subject of this paper would long since have disappeared. Indeed, very few within the United States will be left for the inspection of future ages.

The pyramids that now astonish the traveller were built in the latter ages of Egyptian greatness ; yet no simular of this figure has been found in any nation so perfect as in Mexico. It is remarkable that the quadrangular base ; the surface composed of stones ; and the platform at the top are preserved in both the Mexican and Egyptian pyramids.

Receding from these countries, the colonists appear to have substituted the Cone for the Pyramid, and to

have been satisfied with works of inferior magnitude.
As far as the conquests* and colonies of SESOSTRIS
extended,—and the shores of Greece which received
Cecrops and Inachus,—this form has prevailed as well as
in the regions to the north and north eastward of Mexico ; and it is probable that the mounds in the British
Islands ought to be ascribed to some branch of the same
race. The Phenœcians were early acquainted with
those shores.

The custom of raising *tumuli* round the urns of
their heroes, was only practised by the Greeks in the
ruder ages. That this was *practised*, however, we have
the evidence of HOMER. Thus the shade of Elpenor is represented speaking to Ulysses :—

> " ————————— With my arms
> (What arms so'en I left) burn me, and raise
> A kind memorial of me on the coast,
> *Heapt high with earth* ; that an unhappy man
> May yet enjoy an unforgotten name.
> Thus do at my request ; and *on my hill
> Funereal*, plant the oar with which I rowed."—COWPER.

Again, in a succeeding book of the Odyssey, Ulysses says,

> " The dead consumed, and with the dead his arms,
> *We heapt his tomb* ; and the sepulchral post
> Erecting, fixed his shapely oar aloft."

The shade of Achilles is also represented speaking
to Agamemnon :—

> " Thou shouldst have perished full of honor, full
> Of royalty, at Troy ; *so all the Greeks
> Had raised thy tomb.*"—IB.

Other remarkable customs have obtained on both
sides of the Atlantic. We are aware that " two tribes

" * The Scythians as far as the Tanais, Armenia and Cappadocia were conquered. He left a colony in the ancient kingdom of Colchos, situate to the east of the Black sea, where the Egyptian customs and manners have been ever since retained.'
ROLLIN.

placed in two remote regions of the globe, living in climates of the same temperature, existing in the same state, and resembling each other in the degree of their improvement, must feel the same wants, and exert the same endeavours to supply them."* But in proportion to the number of opinions respecting supernatural powers, and the rites of propitiation observed amongst the nations of the earth, will be the probability that those who have had no communication will not agree; and the chance for this discordance will be increased in rites of " arbitrary institution," and more especially in such as are not founded on our sympathies, but abhorrent to our nature.

To support the opinion that a Syrian custom was received and adopted in Mexico, it is not necessary to believe it introduced by the founders of that empire. The frequent relapses of the Israelites into idolatry, prove with what facility an ignorant people at any period may receive the most debasing superstitions. In the latter ages of the Jewish monarchy, even *human sacrifices* became frequent. Neither are we left in doubt whence these horrid rites were derived. The sacred historian expressly declares that the Jews " went after the heathen who were round about them; and caused their sons and their daughters to pass through the fire." 2 Kings, xvii. 15. 17. The same abominations were introduced at Carthage. The *probability* that some of the natives of that city were thrown on the coast of America, we consider to be fully established; and the description of those murderous sacrifices will support this opinion.

" The aspect of superstition in Mexico, says Dr. Robertson, was gloomy and atrocious. Its divinities were clothed with terror, and delighted in vengeance.—Of all offerings, human sacrifices were deemed the most acceptable.—Torquemada extravagantly asserts, that twenty thousand children, exclusive of other victims,

* Robertson's History of America.

were slaughtered annually.—But B. de las Casas declares that the Mexicans never sacrificed more than
fifty or a hundred persons in a year. B. Daz del Cas-
tillo, however, relates that an enquiry having been made,
it was found that about two thousand five hundred were
sacrificed every year in Mexico."

We will now compare this with Rollin's account of
the Carthaginians. " The second Deity particularly
adored by them, and in whose honor human sacrifices
were offered, was *Saturn*, known in Scripture by the
name of Moloch; and this worship passed from Tyre
to Carthage.—Mothers made it a merit, and a part of
their religion, to view this barbarous spectacle with dry
eyes, and without so much as a groan; and if a tear or a
sigh stole from them, the sacrifice was deemed less acceptable to the deity, and all the effects of it were lost. The
Carthaginians retained this barbarous custom till the
ruin of their city, (and it appears from Tertullian that
it prevailed in Africa long after.) In times of pesti-
lence they used to sacrifice a great number of children
to their gods.—At the time that Agathocles was just
going to besiege Carthage, its inhabitants seeing the
extremity to which they were reduced, imputed all
their misfortunes to the just anger of Saturn, because
that instead of offering up children nobly born who
were usually sacrificed to him, he had been fraudulent-
ly put off with the children of slaves and foreigners.
To atone for this crime, two hundred children of the
best families were sacrificed to Saturn; besides which
upwards of two hundred citizens from a sense of
guilt of this pretended crime, sacrificed themselves."

The resemblance in the manner of performing these
sacrifices in two countries separated by a wide ocean,
is very remarkable. " The Great Temple of Mexico,
says Dr. Robertson; was a *solid mass of earth* of a
square form. It terminated in a quadrangle of about
thirty feet, where were placed a shrine of the Deity,
and two altars on which the victims were sacrificed."—

"They have built *the high places* of Tophet, says the Prophet, which is in the valley of the son of Hinnom, to burn their sons and their daughters in the fire." Rites so detestable, and altars so similarly constructed, were surely derived from the same people.

It will agree with our views of this subject to find other superstitions of the eastern nations in other parts of America. We have therefore examined the history of the Peruvians. The same historian whom we have so frequently quoted, observes, that " The Sun as the great source of light, of joy and fertility in the creation attracted this principal homage. The Moon and Stars as co-operating with him were entitled to secondary honors.—One part of the land, capable of cultivation, was consecrated to the Sun ; and whatever it produced was applied towards the erection of temples, and furnished what was necessary towards celebrating the public rites of religion. The temple of Pachacamac together with a palace of the Inca, and a fortress were so connected together, as to form one great structure above half a league in circuit."

It ought not to be expected that the Peruvians without a knowledge of iron could produce a temple equal to those of Balbec or Palmyra. It is remarkable, however, that the worship of the Sun should be only known in *one district of Asia* and amongst *three nations* of the Western Continent. After describing the religion of the NATCHEZ, Dr. Robertson remarks ;—" The ancient *Persians*, a people far superior in every respect to that rude tribe whose rites I am describing, founded their religious system on similar principles ; and established a form of public worship, less gross and exceptionable than that of any people destitute of guidance from revelation. *This surprising coincidence in sentiment, between two nations in such different states of improvement, is one of the many singular and unaccountable circumstances which occur in the history of human affairs.*"

We have already shewn that this historian, by deductions manifestly erroneous, had debarred himself from
the explication of this extraordinary fact. To us, it
proves that those rites were derived from the Mediterranean.

"In *Bagota,* the sun and moon were also the chief
object of veneration. Their system of religion was
more regular and complete, though less pure than that
of *the Natchez.* They had temples, altars, priests,
sacrifices, and that long train of ceremonies, which
superstition introduces wherever she has fully established her dominion over the minds of men. But the rites
of their worship were cruel and bloody—they offered
human sacrifices."*

It is worthy of notice that the same strange mixture
of idolatry prevailed amongst the Israelites in the reign
of Hoshea:—"They worshipped all the host of Heaven, and caused their sons and daughters to pass
through the fire. 2 Kings, xvii. Manasseh, King of
Judah, adopted the same practices. The people, who
were sent by the Assyrians to inhabit the land after the
captivity of Israel, added the Jewish worship to their
former idolatries; and the sacred historian remarks
" that the Sepharvites burnt their children in fire to the
gods of Sepharvain," yet "feared the Lord." 2 Kings
xvii. 31.

The worship of the celestial luminaries was very
prevalent in Judea a short time before the captivity.
On the accession of Josiah to the throne, " he put down
the idolatrous priests—that burnt incense to the *sun,*
and to the *moon,* and to the *planets,* and to *all the host
of Heaven.* And he took away the horses that the
Kings of Judah had given to the *sun,* and burnt the
chariots of the *sun* with fire" 2 Kings xxiii. 6. 11.
The declarations of Jeremiah also show the extent of
this idolatry. " At that time, saith the Lord, they shall
bring out the bones of the Kings of Judah, and the

---

* Robertson's Hist. Amer.

bones of the princes, and the bones of the priests, and the bones of the prophets, aud the bones of the inhabitants of Jerusalem, out of their graves : and they shall spread them before the *sun,* and the *moon,* and *all the host of Heaven,* whom they have loved, and whom they have served, and after whom they have walked, and whom they have sought, and whom they have worshipped." Jer. viii.

With the prevalence of this religion will be the probability that some of its votaries, in the manner already suggested, had been thrown on the coast of America ; and the similar appearances of this idolatry on both continents justifies the opinion.

The structure of the Mexican aqueducts leads the imagination at once to the shores of the Mediterranean.

" The ostentation with which the grandeur of Montezuma was displayed, whenever he permitted his subjects to behold him, seems to resemble the magnificence of the ancient monarchies of Asia." Dr. Robertson, from whom this remark is taken, had determined neither " to reason nor enquire." We consider it an offering at the shrine of truth, and receive it as an evidence favourable to our view.

In Mexico the boors or peasants were attached to the soil. Nothing like this can be found among the free savages of the north ; and furnishes a conclusive argument against the arrival of this order by the way of Behring's straits.

It will be proper to obviate an objection which might arise from the common accounts of the unvarying colour among the aboriginal Americans ; because the offspring of different nations would be expected to retain some corresponding traces of complexion. For this attempt, however, some apology will be necessary. We regret that neither time nor means has favoured our researches on this subject to the extent that it merits ; although our enquiries have satisfied *us* of the fallacy of that opinion.

Of the uniform copper colour of the Indians, Dr. WILLIAMS remarks in his history of Vermont:—" It has been customary to write in this language, but we are far from being certain that it is either accurate or proper. It has been taken for granted, but it has never been examined, whether the Indian colour is the same in every part of America. ' On the north west part of our continent the complexion of the Indians is *lighter* than that of the southern Indians, and some of the women have rosy cheeks.'* Of the Indians of Paragua we have this account : ' They are generally of an *olive complexion*, some *darker*, some *lighter*, and some as *white as the Spaniards*."* " The inhabitants of *Boroa*, say the Edinburgh Encyclopedists, a tribe in the heart of Araucania are *white* ; and in their features and complexion little inferior to the northern Europeans."-BAR-

117 TRAM asserts that " the Cherokees are by far the largest race of men I have seen ; their complexion lighter and somewhat of the *olive cast*, especially the adults ; and some of their young women are *nearly as fair and blooming as European women*."—Le Raye says "The Mandans and Gross-Ventres are of the lightest complexion and are the largest Indians on the Missouri. Their hair inclines to a chestnut colour, and in some instances has a slight curl." Of the Flat Heads, he says, "their skin is an *olive colour*."—" There are some of the *aboriginal Cherokees* who have never used any particular care to guard their faces from the action of the

118 sun, who have *good complexions*." R. J MEIGS, sen'r.

From M'KENZIE's Travels, we collected the following notices :

" As far as we could discover through the coat of dirt and grease, [the Dog Ribbed and Slave Indians] are of a fairer complexion, than the generality of Indians who are natives of a warmer climate." The complexion of the Rocky Mountain Indians was *"a swarthy yellow."* A woman from the coast had " an oblong face and grey eyes." The NEGUIA DINAIS " *had fairer*

* MORSE.

complexions, or rather were more cleanly than any of the natives we had seen. *Their eyes though keen and sharp are not* of that dark colour so generally observed in the various tribes of Indians; they were on the contrary of *a grey hue with a tinge of red."* The complexion of the Indians on the river which discharges into M'KENZIE's Outlet " is *between the olive and the copper,* having *small grey eyes with a tinge of red. The hair is a dark brown inclining to black."* At Fort Harrison we saw Indians of a *dark olive colour;* and M. Birkbeck says, " Their complexion is various; some dark, others not so swarthy as myself; but I saw none of the copper colour I had imagined to be their universal distinctive character."

In perusing Dr. Robertson's History of America, we are pleased with the beauties of his style; we admire the ingenuity of his deductions; and we rejoice at the evidences of his candour; but our regret is not unfrequently excited at discoveries, that he had not raised his head above the mists of that "wretched Philosophy" which was so prevalent in Europe during the last century, and which has been so ably exposed by the late President JEFFERSON. In that history, the aborigines are described as beardless by nature. Few of our readers, indeed, will require any proof in opposition to this assertion; and consequently their peculiarity as a race, will not be brought against our hypothesis; yet to such cloistered sages as are not released from that prejudice, we submit the following extracts from M'KENZIE:—" Some of the Chippewyans prefer a *bushy beard* to a smooth skin." In speaking of the Dog Ribbed and Slave Indians, he says, "The *beards* of some of the old men *were long."* On the river discharging into M'Kenzie's Outlet, " I gave the Chief a pair of scissors, whose use I explained to him by clipping his *beard,* which was *of great length,* and to which he immediately applied them." M. BIRKBECK, in speaking of a Shawanee Indian, also says, " This man exhibits a respectable beard, enough for a Germanized British officer of dragoons."

The appearance, yet scarcity of iron is strong evidence that it was procured from wrecks on the coast.

The evidence which we have collected respecting the languages on the opposite shores of the Atlantic, is but little, though favourable to our hypothesis. " The Chilian is in no respect connected with the other American languages, and differs essentially in both its words and construction. With the exception of *x*, the Chilian alphabet is the same as the Latin ; and like the Latin also, its harmony is injured by the too frequent recurrence of the letter *u*."—EDIN. ENCYC.

In the same work, article, *Canaries,* we find the following : "The language of Teneriffe, according to Mr. Glas has some resemblance to the Peruvian, and some other American languages."

Having thus shewn the reasons for our opinion, that America within the Torid Zone, received its aboriginal inhabitants across the Atlantic, we will proceed to examine the evidence relative to Mexican Colonies within the United States.

The traditional account of the Mexicans, relative to their origin, tends to prove the correctness of our view. " Small independent tribes moved in successive migrations from unknown regions, towards the north and north west ; and settling in different provinces of Mexico, began to practice the arts of social life."* The formation of such tribes, we would naturally expect from the descendants of Cast-aways. We are also informed that after a lapse of some centuries, a more civilized people advanced southward from the border of the Californian Gulf. This tradition has a remarkable accordance with the retreat of the ancient inhabitants before the Tartar race ; and the works which still remain in that country among the rud'est savages, prove the evacuation or extinction of a civilized people.

* ROBERTSON.

Dr. DRAKE in his " *Picture of Cincinnati,*" has the following remarks on these remains of antiquity : " The Lakes and the Gulf of Mexico appear to be the northern and southern boundaries of the region containing these ancient works. M'Kenzie does not mention them in his voyages and travels to the north west through the Lakes,-[nor across the Rocky Mountains to the Pacific Ocean] ; but Bartram saw them in various places in Georgia and Florida. Between the Ohio and the Gulf they appear to be much fewer than between that river and the Lakes. As to their north latitude, 43 degrees may perhaps be the limit. On the east they are bounded by the Alleganies ; on the west they extend to the Pacific Ocean ; but *are found of the greatest magnitude and grandeur in some of the southern provinces of Mexico. From that country, indeed, they seem to decrease in size, beauty and regularity, in a ratio corresponding directly to the distance.*"

This statement, to our apprehension, goes far towards proving that the ancient inhabitants of the Ohio country were of the same race as those who built the mounds in Mexico ; and perhaps this inference is not disputed. But the late Professor BARTON held the opinion that the descendants of that people degenerated into the present race of savages. To a notion so repugnant to all that we know of human kind, we have long felt the utmost reluctance to accede. It is therefore with much satisfaction that we copy the following paragraph from an author, who has shed a lustre on American literature : and its value is increased by the circumstance that it was written without any reference to those antiquities.

" Where and when has this transmutation of civili zed into savage life been realized ? Where are the chronicles from which the history of it is extracted? Is there extant a volume, either sacred or prophane, in which we find the event substantially recorded ? We believe we may defy contradiction in replying that there is not. We have, ourselves, often conversed with the most enlightened and observant travellers, and not unfrequently looked into history, ancient and modern, universal and local, civil and military—the annals of the early as well as the middle and declining periods of nations : yet never through any channel, has such a fact as the foregoing been presented to our notice. We have never observed, read, or heard of a single instance where a people once civilized, have either become themselves absolutely savage, or planted remote countries with savage colonies. Nor does it comport with our ideas of the principles of human nature, and of the springs of human actions, to admit that such an event has ever taken place.

" Through the medium of history have we seen nations gradually emerging from the degradation and wretchedness of savage, to the dignity and comforts of civilized life ; but we fearlessly challenge the whole records of nature to show us the picture completely reversed."

The remarks of Dr. ROBERTSON, are equally pointed and conclusive. "Although the elegant and refined arts may decline, or perish, amidst the violent shocks of those revolutions and disasters to which nations are exposed, *the necessary arts of life, when once they have been introduced among any people, are never lost.* None of the vicissitudes in human affairs affect these, and they continue to be practised as long as the race of man exists."

C. ATWATER also judiciously remarks, that " these ancient works are not found east of the Allegany Mountains ; but the Indians were not only found on that side of those mountains, but were as much more numerous along the very shore of the Atlantic Ocean, in proportion to their settlements back from the sea, as our present population is now. If those inhabiting the sea coast were the same kind of people, why did they not raise forts and mounds similar to ours ?"

In " *the Picture of Cincinnati,*" there is much to

admire and approve; and our respect for the author is heightened by his exemplary modesty. We believe, however, that in advocating the opinion of the late Dr. Barton, he has been betrayed into error.

In the concluding paragraph on these antiquities, we find the following remark :—" Several facts have appeared in its support. Of these, the only one which I shall mention, is the existence, in the large mounds, of fragments of earthen ware, which have in their composition a perfect identity with that fabricated since the discovery of America, even up to the present time, by many of the tribes low on the Mississippi."

But we feel confident that the weight of this evidence will be trifling on a strict and candid examination. It will scarcely be asserted that barbarians learn nothing of the people whom they subdue. That they should not perceive the advantage of the fine arts, is not surprising; but the convenience of vessels for culinary purposes must be obvious to the greatest savage. At the same time that the conquerors of the ancient race became possessed of such vessels, they would also obtain possession of the manufacturers; and from the general custom of taking prisoners among the North-American tribes, we have no good reason to believe that this art would remain unknown. In the strong and impressive language of Dr. ROBERTSON, we therefore repeat, " the necessary arts of life are never lost."

Probably to show the gradual declension of the ancient inhabitants, Dr. DRAKE has attempted " to distinguish the remains which are termed *ancient* from those which are *evidently modern*," and after an enumeration of many relics he adds: "The remaining works of a modern date, are stone and sometimes earthen tumuli; which are distinguishable from the ancient *by their diminutive size ;* and *from being disconnected with any extensive fortifications,* or other remains."

The ingenious Author, we are persuaded, will admit on reconsidering the subject, that the last sentence contains no just characteristic for a separate classification. He well knows that no animal or vegetable would be referred to another species because it happened not to attain the common size. There could be no necessity that the ancients should finish every work which they began on a large scale; and indeed there is reason to believe from the appearance* of these remains, that many of their colonies were destroyed when their fortifications were in a progressive state.

The hypothesis of C. ATWATER, as detailed in his letter to the President next demands our attention. It was written for publication, and received that honour through the hands of Dr. MITCHELL.

"My opinion is, that the people who built our forts, migrated from hence to the Mexican Gulph, crossed it, and were the first settlers of the West Indian Isles, and the whole of South America—that our Indians came here long before them, crossed the Alleganies, and settled all along the Atlantic coast in the present United States; that when at a far later period those who erected our old forts come here [hither] they were pressed upon every side by the first settlers—that finding the navigable waters all leading south, few or no inhabitants to oppose their going in that direction—finding also the climate much milder, the soil generally better, and of course the greater ease in supporting themselves, they followed the water courses downward and settled themselves in Mexico and Peru long before Columbus found their posterity in these countries."

The first idea that presents, on considering this supposition, is the improbability.

It is improbable that Tartars from Behring's Straits first located themselves on the maritime coast of the United States. From the remoteness of the two positions, it is entirely unsupported by the doctrine of

---

* The Fortification which is situate on the hill south of Auburn, for instance, was not completed; for between the finished parts of this ditch and bank, there are spaces of several rods, which are too wide for gate-ways.

chances ; and the objection is strengthened when we reflect, that not only the Chippewan Mountains were interposed, but also the whole range of Alleganies. Their
predilection for a south-east course is unaccounted for,
and must have been remarkable if neither mountains
nor rivers could turn thom aside.

It is improbable that a people retaining any vestige of
civilization, would arrive in the Ohio country by the
way of Kamschatka. If the tribe had started with any
knowledge of agriculture, it would have become extinct in
the course of such perpetual wanderings ; for without
any fixed object in view, we cannot be persuaded that
this journey would be accomplished in one age.

It is improbable that Mexico was originally peopled
from the Ohio. The chance for wanderers from Behring's straits to reach the former country, is greater
than to locate themselves on the eastern branches of the
Mississippi. The assertion of Dr. DRAKE, that the
mounds "*decrease in size, beauty and regularity in a
ratio corresponding directly to the distance from Mexico*," proves, we think, that that was the mother country
of this race. Other considerations *compel us* to with-
hold our assent. The head of a Peccary* has been
found in a salt petre cave in Kentucky ; and as this
quadruped is peculiar to Mexico, its appearance in that
cavern, according to the hypothesis under review, is
anomalous and inexplicable, for the current of emigration had an opposite course ; but the fact is easily explained, if a Mexican colony were once inhabitants of
the Ohio country ; and, indeed, we consider this discovery as a strong proof of the correctness of our hypothesis.

Other views have also a bearing against that conjecture. It has been stated, that Indian corn is only indigenous to South America. I have not learned the facts
on which this opinion is founded ; but as it has been
advanced without any reference to this discussion ; and

*The Mexican Hog—*Picture of Cincinnati,* p. 67.

as this plant has never been found growing indigenously in the United States, it merits consideration.   Assuming it therefore as a fact, the deduction will be
clear, that this grain could only have been brought hither by a people migrating nothward ; and the change must
have been gradual, like the advancing of a colony.   A
long lapse of years would be necessary to produce
that accommodation to climate which has been effected
in this plant.   In South Carolina, 190 days are required for its growth and perfection ; in New York, its
vegetation is completed in ninety-six days.   How the
Tartar race came to cultivate it, involves no difficulty.   Their women performed all the labours of the
field, and their female prisoners would be acquainted
with its value and its culture.   In this manner we presume, it spread to the eastward beyond the limits of the
Mexican colonies ; and has continued a prime object of
attention, long after their empire became extinct.

The fortifications at Circleville, and at other places,
evince a population, not only too numerous to be supplied with food from the forest, but too laborious to be
engaged in such uncertain pursuits ; and on what did
they subsist ? becomes the question. Nothing of this
part of their history is known. None of our indigenous vegetables seem well adapted to supply their
wants ; and as the regions which they inhabited, were
all favourable to the production of Indian corn, it is no
improbable conjecture that this grain was their staff of
life.

It has been suggested that the mounds near the Don were
built by the Scythians ; and that the same race extending their settlements by the way of Behrings straits,
built the mounds in Mexico. But we have not learned
that mounds have been discovered in the north eastern
parts of Asia, nor in any part of America northward of
California, though we have read the reports of some
travellers through these countries. We must therefore
be allowed to doubt. In this state of mind we consider it utterly improbable, that any people would leave

the banks of the Don, traverse the whole extent of
Siberia and Kamschatka, cross Behring's straits, explore
the western coast of America, continually pursued by
famine, and arrive in California, in sufficient numbers
to retain their original manners, and to undertake the
construction of mounds.   What could ensure the performance of such an expedition ? Neither the oppressor,
nor the avenger, would continue the pursuit to such
distances.   A knowledge of that remote clime could
not have reached them ; grievous privations would
meet them at the outset ; and new modes of living
must be adopted.   The supply of bread would fail in
the wilderness—the milk of their herds and the covering of their flocks must be relinquished—the mother
and the child constrained to traverse the desert on
foot,--and in every district, the task of procuring subsist-
ence would occasion long delays.   The peopling of desert countries, in all ages must have been forced,

——————— as in a rolling flood,
Wave urges wave.

*⁎*Dr. ROBERTSON's argument respecting the savage-
ness of those people whose progeny populated America before the arrival of Europeans, is a curious instance
of the fallacy that *may* attend logical deductions.   " If
ever the use of iron had been known to the savages of
America, or to their progenitors, says the historian, it is
impossible that it should have been abandoned or forgotten."   He believed, however, that these savages were the descendants of Noah.   He must have believed, also, that Noah used iron in constructing the
Ark, for he remarks " the inability of the Peruvians
to work in wood ;" but the inconsistency which these
premises involve, is evident.

⁙

Since the foregoing essay was written, we have obtained, for the first time, the perusal of *Clarke's Travels in Russia*.   The subjoined paragraphs are copied
from that work.

" Throughout the whole of this country [South of

Russia] are seen dispersed over immense plains, *mounds of earth* covered with a fine turf, the sepulchres of the ancient world, common to almost every habitable country. If there exists any thing of former times, which may afford *monuments of antedeluvian manners*, it is this mode of burial. They seem to mark the progress of population *in the first ages after the dispersion ;* rising wherever the posterity of, Noah came,—whether in the form of a *mound* in Scandinavia and Russia ; a *barrow* in England ; a *cairn* in Wales, Scotland and Ireland ; or those heaps which the modern Greeks and Turks call *tepe ;* or lastly, in the more artificial shape of a *pyramid* in Egypt,—they *had all universally the same origin.* They present the simplest and sublimest monument which any generation could raise over the bodies of their progenitors ; calculated for almost endless duration, and speaking a language more impressive than the most studied epitaph upon Parian marble."

" In low flat countries, where there were no mountains nor hills, *they raised artificial ascents* for their altars. But sacrifices were offered upon the sepulchres of their dead, as upon altars."

" From periods the most remote,—from those distant ages, when the Milesian settlements were first established upon the coast of the Euxine, a trade with the inhabitants of the country, which extended even to the Palus Mœotis and the mouth of the Tanais, had been carried on ; and, *it is perhaps, to those early colonies of Greece that we may attribute most of the surprising sepulchral monuments, found on either side of the Cimmerian Bosphorus.*"

" The size, grandeur, aud riches of these [tumuli] on the European and Asiatic sides of the Cimmerian Straits, excite astonishing ideas of the wealth and power of the people by whom they were constructed ; and in the view of labour so prodigious, as well as of expenditure so enormous, for the purpose of inhuming a single body, customs and superstitions are manifest which illustrate the origin of the Pyramids of Egypt, the caverns of Elephanta, and the first temples of the ancient world. In memory of "the mighty dead" long before there were any such edifices as temples, the *simple sepulchral heap was raised,* and it became the altar upon which sacrifices were offered. Hence the most ancient heathen structures for offerings to the gods were always built upon tombs, or in their immediate vicinity. The discussion which has been founded on the question, whether the Egyptian Pyramids were tombs or temples, seems altogether nugatory,--being one, they were necessarily the other."

"*It seems to have been the custom of the age in which these heaps were raised, to bring stones or parcels of earth, from all parts of the country to the tomb of a deceased sovereign or near relative.*"

Persons disposed to visit ancient fortifications, may find remains at the following places:—

1. About two miles southeasterly from *Aurora.* A triangular area of one or two acres, is protected on two sides by precipitous banks; and on the other by *two ditches.* Bones of animals and fragments of ancient earthen ware are found in beds of ashes.

2. On the hill south of *Auburn.* Also, a circular ditch, enclosing about two acres, 1 1-4 miles N. N. E. of Auburn. The only opening or gate-way appears in the side adjacent to a spring, and is formed by extending one end of the ditch beyond the other. This simple contrivance, rendered such mounds as those of Circleville unnecessary. No vestige of iron has been discovered, though fragments of earthen ware are numerous.

3. On the west side of the Seneca river, N. W. from *Montezuma.* On the east shore near this village, a small mound appears.

4. We also learn that considerable fortifications are visible near Black river, between Brownsville and Le Ray.

NOTE TO PAGE 128.

Ceilings in the Ohio country frequently separate from the laths, and fall. To prevent this failure is an object of importance, though it has been much neglected. Perhaps it has not been well understood.

Clay with water forms a paste, and the mass hardens as the moisture is absorbed by the atmosphere. This process will continue until the equilibrium be restored : in other words, till the clay and air possess equal degrees of humidity. But, unlike lime which absorbs carbonic acid and then hardens into stone, clay undergoes no material change ; and except when its cohesion is increased by high degrees of heat, remains always susceptible of being reduced to the same ductile state by the simple addition of water. When, therefore, the roof, the weather boarding, or the floor above the ceiling admits moisture between the laths and the mortar, the latter will fall by its own weight.

Plasterers, who consult their own convenience more than the welfare of their employers, prefer a portion of clay in the mortar, because in the application, it is more adhesive than pure lime and sand ; but those who build for posterity will firmly reject such practices.

Pit sand commonly contains a portion of clay. Even this ought to be separated ; and by taking a hint from the process of nature in creeks and rivers, it may be easily effected. A box of boards sufficiently large, should be placed under a spout of water, and then partly filled with the material to be cleansed. Continual agitation by means of a broad hoe or shovel, will load the stream with fine earth, and in a few minutes the pure sand will settle to the bottom.

Too much quick-lime is generally used in mortar ; and on this point science and experiment agree. This ingredient is only soluble in 500 times its weight of water ; all that is dissolved soon hardens into stone, and all that is not dissolved acquires the state of chalk.

119

This substance interposed will consequently weaken the cement. Mortar composed of only one eighth or one tenth of lime has proved to be the best that we have examined, though the workmen complain that it crumbles.

Agreeably to this statement, it is evident that fine sand will be better than coarse ; because the larger interstices of the latter will not be filled with so small a quantity of lime. But as coarse sand has been commonly found more pure, it has usually been employed on the outside of buildings ; and a reference to such facts may occasion some doubts, but I have seen no mortar so hard as some composed of the finest clean quick-sand.

━━

NOTE TO PAGE 140.

" The green parroquet with a yellow crown, a species of parrot, is very common. It has a harsh unpleasant note, and although easily tamed, it cannot be taught to imitate the human voice. The habits of these birds in some respects, are singular. They are always seen in flocks, which retire at night into hollow trees, where they *suspend themselves by their bills*. These birds also retreat to hollow trees in winter. There have been found, after a severe winter, prodigious numbers in a large tree, filling the whole cavity, where they had perished by the severity of the cold."—*Topographical* 120 *description of the State of Ohio, &c.*

SUPPLEMENT.

—

THE interesting communication which follows, was received from one of our most distinguished citizens. To the merchant it must be valuable ; but no friend to his country can be indifferent to the advancement of commerce, population and industry,

Extract of a Letter from Detroit, 8th *July,* 1818.

"In conformity to my promise, enclosed is an official statement from the Collector's Office in this place, in relation to your queries.

"At Buffalo I was fortunate in finding Capt. BUTLER, on his way to open Grand river, where a company is formed for that purpose. Capt. BUTLER has made himself celebrated by opening eight bars from Middletown to Hartford, on Connecticut river, so as to admit the free passage of nine feet instead of five feet water. His plan is novel, simple, cheap and effectual. It is merely to drive in piles over a sand bar, from the opposite sides ; to leave a sufficient opening, and then fill in brush. The first freshet settles the sand among it, so as to form a complete beach, and by the pressure of the water through the passages, a permanent channel is forced open.

"At Buffalo, the obstacles are easily removed, and a good harbour and basin may be formed for about 25 or 30,000 dollars. About 600 feet from the shore, we found sand, and 10 1-2 feet water; at 1463 feet, 18 1-2 feet water; the last 900 feet clay, and good anchorage. Within the creek, abundance of water, and room enough for the British navy.

"At Dunkirk, 45 miles west of Buffalo, we found a spacious bay, with two channels leading into it; the one on the west, 12 feet water; on the east, 10 feet. In front of the bay, Nature has formed a barrier of flat rocks about 50 feet wide, but unfortunately it is about four feet below the surface of the lake. It is in the hands of wealthy men in Albany, who have erected an expensive pier within the bay, and have laid out a town. They contemplate piling stones on the rock in front. Should this be successful, an excellent harbour will be formed.

> From Buffalo to Dunkirk, is   45 miles.
> Dunkirk to Erie,   45
> Erie to Grand river,   75
> Grand river to Cleveland 30---195

"At Grand river, the bar will be effectually removed, and a good harbour formed, (the first on lake Erie) during this month, as BUTLER is there with a large force, and pressing it with vigour.

" At Cleveland, 30 miles above Grand river, a bar across the entrance (as usual,) is the only obstacle to a good harbour; as there are from 18 to 25 feet water, five miles up, we started them to go on immediately.

"A light house is now erecting at Buffalo, and another at Erie. In conclusion, as the steam boat is on the point of starting on this lake—the light houses erecting—harbours forming—and the lake more free of shoals and rocks than any other navigation of a given extent, —a great change is on the point of taking place."

COMMERCE AND NAVIGATION OF THE UPPER LAKES.

List of Vessels navigating Lakes Erie, Huron, Michigan, Superior, Masters' Names, &c.

Vessels.	Masters.	Belonging to	Tons.	95ths.
American Eagle	William Gaylord	Cleveland	48	67
Aurora	Charles Fitch	Sandusky	31	69
Black Snake	J. Wilkeson	Cleveland	21	03
Boxer	S. Wilkeson	Detroit	16	60
Dove	H. G. Cooley	do.	13	55
Com. Decatur	S. Barney	do.	49	14
Diligence		Presqu Isle	32	38
Diana	—— Ferris	Cleveland	8	00
Experiment	S. Johnson	Buffalo	29	69
Erie	R. Gillet	do.	77	41
Eagle	Joseph Hammond	Detroit	28	03
Eliza	W. Brown	Sandusky	23	82
Franklin	J. F. Wight	Presq Isle	73	00
Firefly	D. D. Norton	Detroit	24	09
Friendship	J. R. Kelley	Cleveland	59	10
Geo. Washington	J. Burnham	Presqu Isle	99	73
Sloop, Gov. Cass		Detroit	30	58
Schr. Gen. Scott	G. Tucker	Sandusky	20	23

Vessels.	Masters.	Belonging to	Tons.	95ths.
do. Jackson	C. Blake	Detroit	60	00
do. Brown		Sandusky	31	22
do. Wayne	J. Rough	Buffalo	85	38
Sloop Hannah	O. Coit	do.	48	73
Schr. Hercules	E. Church	Detroit	59	18
Hornet		Cleveland	11	64
Industry		Sandusky		
Independence	J. Brooks	do.	21	00
Leopard	J. Baldwin	do.	18	00
Michigan	W. Norton	Buffalo	132	36
Monroe	M. Connor	Detroit	28	70
Maria	G. Leet	do.	24	28
Miami		do.	10	46
Merchant		Cleveland	21	51
Nautilus		Sandusky	23	00
Neptune	Johnson	Cleveland	61	64
Olive Branch	J. Robson	Detroit	14	19
Com. Perry	H. Johnson	Presqu Isle	42	50
Salem Packet	R. Ward	Buffalo	27	00
Buffalo Packet	G. Cady	do.	12	00
Paulina	J. K. Whaley	do.	27	25

Vessels.	Masters.	Belonging to	Tons.	95ths.
Pilot	Th. Rumage	Cleveland	27	05
Sloop Perseverance	T. Johnson	Presqu Isle.	28	65
Schr. Ranger	R. A. Naper	Detroit	16	79
Superior	R. Eaton	Cleveland	35	08
Sloop Lucy Jane	J. Richards	Presqu Isle	70	73
Schr. Traveller	C. Brown	do.	15	00
Union	J. Beard	Cleveland	22	23
Sloop Venus	Foster	Buffalo	104	30
Schr. Widow's Son	J. F. Rupley	Sandusky	14	00
Wasp	G. Shaw	Detroit	40	79
Wolf	H. Ramsdel	Sandusky	18	00
		do.	28	78
			1867	08
Add for vessels under 10 tons burthen, and for vessels omitted or not known			200	87
Total American Tonnage on the Lakes*			2068	00

* It has been stated that 15 sail of these vessels were stranded in a storm, which happened in the beginning of last winter.

" The vessels belonging to the districts of Buffalo, Presqu Isle and Detroit, are employed principally in the transportation of goods from Buffalo to Detroit, Mackinaw, and other places above this place. Those vessels owned in Sandusky and Cleveland are employed in transporting the produce of the State of Ohio to Detroit ; and, also, for the supply of the several military posts on the Upper Lakes. In return voyages, they are generally laden with fish, peltries, cider and apples. Foreign importations are seldom brought in vessels of considerable size ; as, from the facility of communication, it is more convenient to bring them in small boats, canoes, &c.— and they consist principally of goods suitable to the Indian trade, as blue and scarlet cloths, handkerchiefs, shawls, blankets and trinkets.

" The exports to foreign ports, consist principally of beef, in droves and salted, butter, pork, cabinet wares, and salt.—During the year beginning the 1st of April, 1817, and ending 31st of March, 1818, were exported to Canada 344 *horned cattle*, value $4420.— 219 barrels of *flour*, value $2541.—10 barrels of *pork*, value $250.— 110 barrels of *salt*, value $806.—30 firkins of *butter*, value $481.— 19 cwt. of *tallow*, value $475.— 20 cwt. of *lard* value $458.—1049 bushels of *corn*, value $2537.—13468 *furs*, value $134, with some articles of less value. Total, $11370.

" The imports of foreign goods during the same period, consisting of articles suitable to the Indian trade, iron and spirits, amounted to $12255.

" During the same period, there were exported to other American ports, 870 barrels of *fish*, value $8700.— 536 barrels of *cider*, value $2680.—230 barrels of *apples*, value $575.—1378 packs of *furs*, value $110240. Total, $122195.

" During the same period, there were imported from other American ports, 837 barrels of *whiskey*, value $28458.—1072 barrels of *flour*, value $8576.—428 firkins of *butter,* value $3867.—373 firkins of *lard,* value $2984.—683 barrels of *pork,* value $17075.—273 barrels of *beef,* value $5460. Total, 66420.

" It will be observed that the importation of foreign goods by our merchants, from New-York and Boston, is omitted, as no reasonable data can be found, on which to estimate their value ; but certain it is, that they far exceed the value of exports to those places, leaving a great balance against this place—which balance is made up by the disbursements to the troops stationed at this and other posts within this territory, and by disbursements in the Indian department. And it will naturally occur, that the great importation of American produce, is also, chiefly intended for those departments. The sale of the public lands, and the consequent increase ef population, will of course enhance the demand for provisions, until such time as the country can depend upon its own resources, which will probably be many years. Meanwhile the orchards and fisheries of this country, will greatly contribute towards repairing the balance which would otherwise appear against the Territory."

Commerce and Navigation of Cayuga Lake.

THE statement which follows was obligingly furnished by S. WILLIAMS, Merchant, of Union Springs.

" In the last six years there have been launched on Cayuga lake, seven schooners, carrying from fifty to eighty five tons. Five of the largest have descended Seneca river to lake Ontario. There are now on the lake about thirty vessels and boats, carrying from 18 to 50 tons.

" Boats are generally employed in transporting Flour , Pork, Pot-ashes, &c. to Schenectady, and Oswego Falls. Their return loads are merchandize from Schenectady, or salt from Onondaga.

"Schooners are employed in freighting Plaster from the quarries, to the head of the lake; from whence they bring large quantities of pine lumber. In one season there has been received at Ithaca, and at Port L'Orient, at the head of the lake, 9000 tons of plaster, and 4500 barrels of salt; the greater part of which was transported by land to Owego, and from thence in arks down the Susquehanna to Pennsylvania.

"The extensive quarries of plaster along the shore of this lake in Aurelius, the salt springs along its outlet the forests of valuable pine about its inlets, the fertility of the soil in its vicinity, the salubrity of its situation, and above all, its proximity to the Susquehanna river, have already made its waters the medium of a profitable trade; and the increased facility of communication with the North River, when the grand canal shall be completed, will undoubtedly make it a still more important link in the chain of trade between this state and Pennsylvania."

―――

Extract of a Petition, circulated for signatures in Chatauque County, 1819.

"The county of Chautaque presents the most easterly, shortest, and best communication from the waters of Lake Erie to the boatable waters running into the Allegany. The distance from Dunkirk, through the village of Fredonia, to the head of the Casdagua Lake, is less than eight miles.

"The waters issuing from the Casdagua, after running about forty miles, and forming a junction with the outlets of Bear and Chautauqe lakes, joins the Conewango, and unites with the Allegany eighty miles below Olean. The Casdagua is a smooth, gentle stream, no where interrupted by rapids, or broken by falls; its navigation however is obstructed in some places by timbers falling across the stream, which might easily be removed. These obstructions are less frequent below the outlet of Bear lake, about five miles below Casdagua. Below the junction of these streams, it has the appearance of a canal, until it unites with the Allegany, and is of sufficient depth and width for boats carrying from ten to twenty tons burthen, and fifty dollars per mile judiciously expended in its improvement, would render the navigation, at all seasons of the year, easy and safe.

" It is a well known fact, that the principal part of the goods carried to the Western States bordering on the Ohio, are brought from Philadelphia to Pittsburgh, at a sum not less than $160 per ton, whereas they might be carried from New-York by the way of Hudson, Mohawk, Lakes Ontario, Erie and Casdagua, down the Allegany to Pittsburgh, for a sum less than $100; and in case of the completion of the Grand Canal, for $30, saving to the owner $130 per ton, and from Pittsburgh to St. Louis, (the capital of Missouri,) for an additional sum of $20; in all $50 from the city of New York to St. Louis, being $70 less than now charged by steam boats from New Orleans to that place."

———

Extract of a letter from B. F. Stickney *to the corresponding secretary of the Western Emigrant Society, dated,* " Indian Agency, *(near Fort Wayne) January,* 20, 1818."

" The country from near the southern extremity of Lake Michigan, to near the river Ohio ; and from Lake Erie, to near the river Mississippi, is very level, alluvial, and the products of the soil, in general, extremely luxuriant. It is well known to you, that *near the Ohio, the land is hilly.* The country on the southern extremity of Lake Michigan, and the western side, is hilly ;* and on the Mississippi, from about one hundred miles above Prarie Du Chien, to Lake Pippin is also hilly, or

---

* Some account of the *formation* of these hills, must be very interesting to Geologists All the hills that we saw in the Ohio country, chiefly consist of the remnants of horrizontal strata. What are these ?

perhaps we may say mountainous.   Those mountains
are undoubtedly of volcanic origin, abounding with me-
talic iron, that has been thrown out of the volcano as
lava, or in the manner of cinders.   It is rare to find
any rocks or stones upon the surface of all this great
extent of country.   To the west and north of this,
the country is principally prairie, except on the water
courses.   To the south and east, it is clothed generally
with a very heavy growth of timber.

"Within a period of about six years, the extremes of
heat and cold have been 99 1-2 deg. above 0, and 16
deg. below, of Farenheit.   As I have not kept a diary
of the weather, my statement in relation to the rains,
winds, fogs, and cloudy weather, must be founded upon
conjecture.   *The quantity of rain is great.*   I should
think to exceed one hundred inches per annum.   The
winds are mostly from the *western* and *northern* quarters, rarely blow violently ; but when they do it is of
short duration.   *Fogs* rather rare ; and *more cloudy
weather than is usual in the Atlantic States.*

"The   Wabash   pursues a diametrically opposite
course to its junction with the Ohio.   *In the highest
water* of those rivers, their waters are united at the
dividing ridge, and *you may pass with craft from one
river to the other.*   There is a wet prairie, or swamp
covered with grass, that extends from the head water
of the Wabash to the St. Mary's, and discharges its
water into both rivers, which is about seven miles from
one to the other.   At low water this swamp is about
eight or ten feet higher than the water in the rivers.
It is composed of soft mud that may be penetrated with
a pole twenty feet ; of course it will be but a small expense of labour, to connect the waters of those two
rivers together, by a *canal,* that would be passable at
the lowest water.

" The *St. Mary's* takes its rise about seventy miles
south east of the *Auglaize* from the same tract of country,
where the Big Miami of the Ohio, and some of the
branches of the Wabash, take their rise ; indeed, *one of*

its principal branches, and one of the branches of the
St. Mary's issue from the same small lake, in a large
wet prairie. It discharges at this place, and in all its
meanderings, is about 170 miles ; and is navigable with
boats at the times of high water, in its whole extent.
With a portage of twelve miles from its head, you enter the navigable waters of Lorime's creek, discharging
into the Big Miami of Ohio.

" The *Illinois* river is navigable in its whole extent,
for boats of considerable size.; and, with a little improvement, might be rendered so for sloops of war. Its
head is within forty miles of Lake Michigan, as you
travel by land, and sixty by water. And its course
about south-west by south, about 400 miles, discharging
into the Mississippi.* The *Auplain* river is the most
important, branch of the Illinois, in relation to its navigation. It takes its rise within about twenty miles of
Lake Michigan, running from north-west to south-east
almost parallel to the western shore of the Lake, until
it approaches within twelve miles of it, where *it divides its waters, throwing part into the Lake,* making
what is called Chicago river, *and the remainder into
the Illinois* ; continuing the course and name
of Auplain until it unites with the Kankakee. *By
this extraordinary work of nature,* in the disposition of
her water courses, *a navigation is afforded for boats* in
the spring of the year, and other times when the water
is high, *from Lake Michigan to the Illinois river.* And,
when the water is at its lowest, a portage of only nine
miles is required. *The elevation of Auplain river is only four and a half feet higher than the Lake.* Being soft
mud or clay, the expense of labour will be very small,
to draw water from Lake Michigan into Illinois river.
It would be a very small expense, compared with its
importance to the nation *to furnish a depth of water,
sufficient for sloops of war to pass and repass from the
Mississippi to the Lakes.*"

* It will be perceived that the Auplain is synonymous with
Des Planes.

ERRATA.

☞ I intended not to trouble the reader with any apology, either on account of ill health, or of a series of disappointments which have deferred this publication. But the following errors require an excuse. The printing office is fourteen miles from my residence ; and of several *forms* it was not practicable to inspect a second *proof.*

Page 6, line 11, for *from* read *than.* P. 7, l. 12, after *lake* read *Ontario.* Do. l. 13 after *rocks* read *of this species,* P. 26, Note, l. 5. read *courses.* P. 57, l. 35, read *depended* P. 62, l. 31, read *Falls.* P. 63, l. 14, for *or* read *nor.* Do. l. 23, read *encouragement.* P. 88, line 5, read *unpromising.* P. 91, l, 26, dele *of,* P. 110, Note, dele *is.* P. 111, Note l. 4, for *to* read *at.* P. 121, l. 33, for *north* read *north-west.* P. 135 Note, read *sulphuretted.* P 142, l. 13, for *turn* read *l-wn.* P. 160, l. 15, read *outset.* Do. l. 30, after *writing* read *with.* P. 179, l 26, after *summer* read *saw* P. 193, l. 2, after *and* read *the last is.* P. 194, l. 21, read *met.* P. 202, l. 22, read *vernal.* P. 215, l. 6, for *is* read *in.* P. 218, Note, l. 6, read *nourishing* P. 247, l. 7, after *lake* read *and in a strong;* &c. dele *and .* P. 249, last line for 30 read 100. P. 250, Note, read *Chemical* P. 252. l. 29, for *where* read *whence.* P. 253, l. 22, dele *with.* P. 255, l. 20, read *divergence.* P. 256, l. 30, for *where* read *whence.* P. 273, l. 13, in a few copies for *hole* read *hill.* P 305, in some copies read Brownsville·

Note to P. 241.—Chill-e-cotbe is the correct pronunciation.

Note to P. 297.—A few sepulchral mounds appear on the east of the Allegany Mountains.

☞ We learn that the village at " The Four Corners" P. 29, is now called WESTFIELD.

☞ In speaking of fish having been *converted into stone,* we only alluded to infiltrations which have preserved the shape of the animal·

THE END.

P. 6. bot. l. the word *Though* begins a new paragraph. P. 19, after line 15 read 27 *miles.* P. 34 1st note, read *this bank.* P. 35, after l. 31, r. 25 *miles.* P. 49, l. 22 for *are* r. *is.* P. 54, for *at* r. *of.* P. 57 for 1st r. 10*th.* P. 60 after l. 13 r. *the.* P. 97 after *removed* in 5th l. r. *The.* P. 105 after l. 2 r. 24 *miles.* P. 108, after l. 11, r. 30 *miles.* P. 112 after l. 2. r. *about* 35 *miles.* P. 127, l. 12 r. *from.* P. 140, l. 10, r. *produce.* P. 142, l. 7. r. *branch.* P. 150, note, r. *are.* P. 156, l. 11, after *timber* r. *for.* P. 179. l. 12 for *oak* r. *ash.* P. 203 l. 14, r. *eastern.* P. 229, l. 12, r. *mill is.* P. 248, 1st. note, l. 3. r. *phenomena.* P. 263 l. 18, r. *bench.* P. 278, last l. r. *in contact with the surface ; but it cannot come in contact with the sap.* P. 313, l. 4. r. *Sch. Rachel.* P. 320, r. *Chill-e-coth-e.*

Notes on Thomas's Geological Observations

by

JOHN W. WELLS and GEORGE W. WHITE

Books and other references mentioned in the Introduction or in the Notes are listed in alphabetical order by authors in the Bibliography following the Notes. Also listed in the bibliography are those authors referred to by Thomas.

Thomas's own often long and elaborate notes at the end of his text were not referenced in the original text. In this edition the symbol "T," with a figure for the page, has been added in the margin of the text to indicate that Thomas did provide a note at this place and the page on which it is found.

p. 2   1. **THE GREAT LIMESTONE LEDGE**—The escarpment of the Devonian Onondaga Limestone separating the Allegheny Plateau from the Ontario Lowland. Further notes on Thomas's ideas of the rocks of western New York are found in Wells, *Early investigations of the Devonian system in New York,* (1963, p. 31-33)

p. 3   2. **Plaster, of the cockscomb kind**—Twinned crystals of selenite.

p. 4   3. **Plaster quarries**—In the Union Springs area the gypsum occurs in the Forge Hollow member of the Upper Silurian Bertie Limestone formation, and was extensively quarried for "land plaster" until the end of the 19th Century.

p. 4   4. **Cayuga Bridge**—This wonder of backwoods engineering in its day, was a wooden structure across the northern end of Cayuga Lake, over a mile long, opened in 1800 and finally abandoned in 1857 (Wells, *The Cayuga Bridge,* 1958).

p. 6   5. **these ridges**—Drumlins; good description of these on p. 253. For an appreciation of Thomas's astute observations on the glacial phenomena of western New York, which he attributed to the Deluge or a deluge, see Von Engeln (1936).

p. 10   6. **Phelpstown plaster**—see Thomas's note, p. 265. The gypsum then worked along the outlet of Canadaigua Lake in the town of Phelps occurred in the Camillus Formation below the horizon of the Union Springs plaster.

p. 11   7. **Carver's description**—Jonathan Carver, *Travels through the Interior Parts of North America . . .*; Carver's *white* stone is the Ordovician St. Peter Sandstone. The reference is to p. 100-101 of the London 1778 (also 1781) edition. Thomas was probably quoting from one of the later American editions; which one might be identified by the italicized words, as in no London edition are there any words in italics.

p. 11   8. **aluminous schist, or clay slate**—On Cayuga Lake—Hamilton Group (Middle Devonian); on Honeoye Lake—Cashaqua Formation (Upper Devonian).

p. 14   9. **half a mile west of Churchill's**—Thomas did not recognize this block of limestone as an erratic. It is composed of Late Silurian dolomitic limestone glacially transported at least a mile southward from its bedrock site and weathered to an hourglass form. It was figured and described by James Hall in *Geology of New York,* Part 4, p. 341, fig. 165, 1843, and is still to be seen in a field to the north of N. Y. Rte. 5, about two miles west of Stafford, Genesee County.

p. 15   10. **Clay slate . . . split into prisms**—The regularity of the jointing in the Devonian shales is notable.

p. 15   11. **Twenty-two miles east of Buffalo, limestone**—Onondaga Limestone (Middle Devonian).

p. 16   12. **surface . . . becomes remarkably smooth and even**—The backslope of the Onondaga Limestone scarpment.

p. 18   13. **Handsome limestone**—The Middle Devonian Tichenor Limestone (Hamilton Group), a single bed about 18 inches thick on the Erie shore. The "similar strata . . . on the eastern shore of Cayuga Lake" are also in the Hamilton Group, but in the vicinity of Levanna and Aurora, to which Thomas is referring, are stratigraphically lower than the Tichenor. It is worth noting, however, that Thomas recognized the identity of the fossils of the Hamilton.

p. 19   14. **Springs of petroleum**—Years later (1830) Thomas demonstrated, on the basis of his recognition of the southerly dip of the rocks in central and western New York, that the coal beds were stratigraphically much higher than these rocks and that there was little, if any coal in New York.

p. 20   15. **periodical rising and falling**—We now know that there is a regular periodical influence, but in 1816 there had not been a sufficiently long period of observation to establish this; however, Carver (1778, p. 146-147) had reported that the French had observed at Mackinac a three foot rise and fall over a period of 15 years.

p. 20   16. **Ferruginous sand**—beach concentrations of heavy minerals from the glacial drift. "It is used for writing," *i.e., pounce,* black sand used as a dusting powder for drying ink before the invention of blotting paper.

p. 22   17. **Singular kind of fossil**—Good description of the septarian concretions common in the Devonian shales, and one of the earliest references to the southerly dip of the New York Devonian strata.

p. 25   18. **this place [Walnut Creek]**—now Silver Creek, at confluence of Walnut and Silver Creeks.

p. 27   19. **mica slate**—The Late Devonian shales, siltstones and sandstones in western New York and northwest Pennsylvania are generally strongly micaceous and Thomas's reference to them as mica slate at this date is not surprising. "Mica is sometimes so much intermixt with common sand-stones that they can scarcely be distinguished from mica slate" (Bakewell, 1813, p. 71).

p. 28   20. **this ridge**—Thomas is now on the Ridge Road (U.S. 20), the beach of Glacial Lake Warren. The "hill on the left" is the so-called "Portage" Escarpment, rising south of the lake plain, sustained by rocks younger than those of the Portage (Chemung) Escarpment in central New York.

p. 29   21. **fountain**—This natural gas spring was later used as a source of fuel in a lighthouse at "Urbana" (now Barcelona; the "Four Corners"—Westfield).

p. 31   22. **Gibsonville**—Now Northeast. Until 1819 known as Burgettstown; changed to Gibsonville, 1819, and to Northeast in 1834.

p. 35   23. **the ridges**—these are the several separate ridges of the Ashtabula (Lake Escarpment), Hiram and Lavery end moraines along the base and on the slope of the Portage Escarpment, which rises prominently a few miles inland from the southern shore of Lake Erie. These moraines are composed of clay-rich till, poor in stones (Shepps and others, p. 38-46 and map). At the "summit of this great ridge" Thomas had reached the top of the Portage Escarpment.

p. 36   24. **Le Boeuf . . . creek**—now called French Creek.

p. 39   25. **blocks of granite**—Meadville is well within the glaciated region and erratics are common.

p. 40   26. **Near this ferry**—Thomas's route from Meadville must have been along a road about the location of the present U.S. 322, to a point about 4 miles NW of Cochranton. Leaving the valley of French Creek the travellers encountered the Lower Pennsylvanian coal measures from this point on, and Thomas was quick to note the change.

p. 42   27. **road . . . through . . . Mercer,**—Now the route of present U.S. 19, is really not "more circuitous." It is more on the uplands and is less hilly than the route followed by Thomas from French Creek south, apparently along the location of the present Pennsylvania Route 173. However, in 1816 the Mercer road was probably little used and was a track winding amongst trees and stumps.

p. 45   28. **Slippery Rock Creek**—Thomas may have crossed Slippery Rock Creek at Crolls Mill, about 2½ miles south of present Slippery Rock village, having followed the route of Pennsylvania Highway 173 to Slippery Rock village and thence south along the route of present Pennsylvania Highway 528. He passed out of the glaciated region 3½ miles south of Slippery Rock Creek (Shepps and others, map).

p. 46   29. **These hills**—While Thomas understood that the topography is the result of stream erosion, and not "convulsions and dislocations," he did not recognize how effective stream erosion is in consolidated rocks (but see pp. 65-66 and 76).

p. 48   30. **parts of sand rock**—One must admire Thomas's sound observations on the differing morphologies of river and beach sands.

p. 53   31. **coal**—Thomas's thoughts on the origin of coal, at that time still disputed, are important. His realization that the anthracite coal of the "heads of the Schuylkill" is either older or affected by "convulsions . . . which have not reached this country" is possibly the earliest American statement of the difference between bituminous coal and anthracite in composition and origin.

p. 55   32. **questionable, whether such conformity**—Here Thomas is questioning the "onion skin" theory of Werner and his followers, which asserted that sedimentary formations had a world-wide extent.

p. 59   33. **smoke**—air pollution is not a phenomenon restricted to the present day; indeed, Pittsburgh is freer of smoke in 1970 than in 1815!

p. 63   34. **height of the coal stratum**—Thomas's estimate of 470 feet is high—the Pittsburgh coal bed is nearer 350 feet above the river.

p. 66   35. **a deluge**—In spite of his previous suggestion (p. 46), Thomas felt the need of a deluge to excavate valleys.

p. 70   36. **the Navigator**—An elaborate and highly popular guide by Zadock Cramer to Ohio River navigation and the adjacent lands; many editions, 1806-1824.

p. 70   37. **ASHE**—Although Thomas was a quiet and broadminded man, here he, as many others have been, is severe in his condemnation of the notorious Thomas Ashe, who wrote *Travels in America . . .* (1808); although on p. 110 (footnote) he gives Ashe due credit for *one* truthful statement.

p. 79   38. **Charleston**—now called Wellsburg; 15 miles north of Wheeling, West Virginia.

p. 79   39. **Dr. Drake**—Daniel Drake, in *Natural and Statistical View, or Picture of Cincinnati and the Miami Country,* (1815, p. 14) says "534 yards."

p. 81   40. **D. STEER'S**—probably a misprint for J. Steer (see p. 85). Joseph Steer was a Quaker who had a flouring mill and woolen mill, the latter constructed for him by the father of William Dean Howells, on Short Creek, at or near the present village of Pine Valley in southern Jefferson County.

p. 82   41. **Mount Pleasant**—still the site of an important Quaker meeting house.

p. 83   42. **Coal**—The great Pittsburgh coal bed, the lowest unit of the Monongahela Series of Pennsylvanian age, crops out about 100 feet above stream level in the valley of Long Run. It is one of the important coal mining areas of Ohio (Lamborn, 1930, p. 208 and map III). The "iron ore" was probably "clay ironstone" (impure siderite) nodules which occur in the Pennsylvanian shales. In the Mt. Pleasant region these were never of economic value.

p. 84   43. . . . **large bodies of earth** . . .—Slump and earth flows are indeed common on the hillsides of this region. The clay shales of the Monongahela and Dunkard (Permian) rocks are particularly prone to move down slopes, just as Thomas describes. This characteristic must be taken into account in road location, in strip mining, and in location of buildings. With his engineering interests Thomas would be particularly impressed by the landslides of this region.

p. 85   44. **the east hill**—The total relief 2 miles east of Dillonvale is about 500 feet, but the hill Thomas measured rises about 400 feet above the valley. The coal (Pittsburgh), as Thomas surmises in his footnote, is indeed present on both sides of the valley.

p. 85   45. **spring house**—Thomas is one of the earliest environmental geologists in the "western country." Springs are common where impervious strata crop out along the hillsides in the Allegheny Plateau. Mr. Steer's house, on the floodplain of Short Creek, would have been below the usual spring lines and thus he could conduct the water (at a temperature of about 54°) in pipes to his house.

p. 86   46. **Morristown**—The route from Mr. Pleasant to Morristown was over the extensive upland of southern Harrison County, probably by way of the present villages of New Athens and Flushing. Morristown is at the margin of the Flushing escarpment (Stout and Lamb, 1938) and overlooks the considerable lowland of Stillwater Creek to the west. His "valley of a small creek to the northwest" is that of Coal Run, a tributary to Stillwater Creek.

p. 87   47. **coal is less plenty**—From Morristown to Cambridge, Thomas was traveling mainly over Conemaugh strata, which contain few and thin coal beds.

p. 87   48. **Few's**—probably at the present site of Norwich in eastern Muskingum County.

p. 88   49. **less inviting**—A delicate observation by Thomas—the soils derived from the Conemaugh rocks west of Morristown are indeed less productive than those from the more calcareous Monongahela rocks from Mt. Pleasant to Morristown. The contrast is obvious today.

p. 88   50. **coal from . . . bed of the river**—The sandstone referred to is probably the Homewood Sandstone, upper Allegheny Series, lying below the Brookville Coal and Putnam Hill Limestone. At Zanesville three limestones are exposed, the Lower Mercer at river level, the Upper Mercer, and the Putnam Hill about 75 feet above the Lower Mercer (Stout, 1918, p. 131 and Plates VI-A and VIII-A). Several coal beds are exposed from river level to the hilltops.

p. 89   51. **Jonathan's creek**—The limestone in this creek bed is the Upper Mississippian (Chesterian) Maxville Limestone. This limestone, as much as 60 feet thick, has been extensively used for cement and lime manufacturing (Stout 1918, p. 35).

p. 91   52. **New-Lancaster**—Thomas's route was along a road now U.S. 22, the ancient "Maysville Pike." He reentered glaciated territory about 10 miles south west of Zanesville, and as he noted, p. 91, left the region of coal-bearing rocks 12 miles east of Lancaster.

p. 91   53. **The standing rock**—Now called Mt. Pleasant, an impressive mass of *Black Hand Sandstone* of lower Mississippian age, which rises in a 200 foot high vertical wall in the park in the north part of Lancaster.

p. 94   54. **circular fortification**—Thomas's description of the work of the mound builders at Circleville is a very early account and illustration. These mounds early excited the interest of all intelligent travellers.

p. 99   55. **Granite**—Although Thomas had again crossed into glaciated country about 10 miles southwest of Zanesville and about 55 miles ENE of Circleville, he did not find crystalline erratics very noticeable until he got closer to Circleville.

p. 99   56. **Clarke**—Edward Daniel Clarke, first professor of mineralogy at Cambridge University and author of a voluminous work on his travels (1810).

p. 100   57. **Old Chillicothe**—This is not the present city of Chillicothe, but was a hamlet called "Oldtown" on early maps, about the location of the present Frankfort, 12 miles northwest of the city of Chillicothe (McFarland, 1903). Thomas's route appears to have been somewhat south of the present Ohio Route 138 from Circleville to Greenfield.

p. 103   58. **fine limestone for building**—Late Silurian dolomitic limestone.

p. 103   59. **Coal . . . in the hills**—Thomas received an erroneous report from someone who mistook for coal the black Devonian shale which crops out east and southeast of the Greenfield.

p. 105   60. **Horizontal limestone**—Thin-bedded Cincinnatian limestone (Ordovician) with interbedded calcareous shale, notably fossiliferous.

     It is puzzling that Thomas spent so little time in Cincinnati and did not call upon Dr. Drake, whose work he knew very well. It is also curious that Thomas did not visit the Big Bone Lick, about 6 miles east of where he crossed the Ohio River. It may be that he had determined that Dr. Drake was not in the city; possibly his major mission in the Vincennes region required him to travel as quickly as possible.

p. 106   61. **My ingenious friend Jethro Wood**—(1774-1834), perfected his famous cast-iron plow while living in Scipio. Samuel A. Mitchill was instrumental in sending two of these to Alexander I of Russia in 1819; see: Mitchill (1819), and Wheeler (1882, p. 116-124). The plows were duly received, and the emperor sent a valuable diamond ring to Mitchill for Wood, but it is said that Mitchill kept the ring.

p. 111   62. **Rising Sun**—Thomas probably travelled from Covington along the present route of Kentucky Highway 18, but the distance to Meeks' Ferry is less than the 25 miles he gave (p. 108).

p. 114   63. **stones of the gun-flint kind**—Chert in Middle Devonian Jeffersonville Limestone.

p. 115   64. **professor Davy**—Humphry Davy, *Elements of Agricultural Chemistry* (1813).

p. 118   65. **four miles west of Madison**—Thomas climbed from the Ohio River valley to the upland at about the site of Hanover, near the present Hanover College campus.

p. 120   66. **seven hundred feet**—Salt was one of the two indispensable materials for the early settler—ammunition was the other. It is significant that Thomas records drilling for salt to a depth of 700 feet, whereas much later, the first well drilled specifically for oil, at Titusville, Pennsylvania in 1859, was only 69 feet deep and was drilled with considerable difficulty.

p. 121   67. **the Knobs . . . VOLNEY**—C.-F. Chasseboeuf, Comte de Volney, *Tableau du Climat et du Sol des Etats-Unis,* Paris, (1803): Thomas probably was referring to the Philadelphia edition (1804) rather than to the French. Volney's "vast lake" was the body of water sustained by the mountains to the east in which the limestones and other rocks of the Interior were deposited, an hypothesis developed earlier by Lewis Evans and elaborated by S. L. Mitchill.

For *the Knobs*, Volney used the term "côtes" (1803, Vol. I, p. 93); "banks" in the English translation (1804, p. 71). Thomas gives a good description of the Knobstone Escarpment, the eastern margin of the Norman Upland formed by the Lower Mississippian (Knobstone = Borden) rocks, which rises several hundred feet above the Devonian shale and lower Paleozoic limestone lowland to the east. The block diagram (Berger and others, 1966), included in this book, shows the escarpment and the associated physiographic regions of Indiana that Thomas crossed and described. Also see Fenneman, (1938, figs. 117 and 118) for excellent diagrams of these features with rock units named.

p. 122   68. **Chrystallized stones**—The siliceous geodes for which these rocks are famous.

p. 125   69. **The country westward of the Knobs**—the surface of the Norman Upland. The limestone sinks in the Mississippian limestone, overlying the Borden strata, form a karst topography like that "round New-Lexington." These sinks are shown on the physiographic diagram south of Bedford.

p. 129   70. **Second class . . . beds of gypsum**—Thomas developed this original idea of settling of strata resulting from solution of underlying gypsum from his knowledge of the topography over the gypsum deposits in his home region. See p. 244.

p. 129   71. **degrees of solubility**—An early consideration of solution of limestone to form caverns.

p. 129   72. **plaster**—Here Thomas means calcium carbonate.

p. 130   74. **Half-Moon Spring**—The rise pit of Lick Creek, about three miles southeast of Paoli, Orange Co., Indiana. See: Mallot 1944, Fig. 9 shows this spring.

p. 136   75. **whetstones**—Sandstone from the upper Mississippian and lower Pennsylvanian rocks north of French Lick has been used extensively for manufacture of abrasive stones (Logan, 1922, p. 780).

p. 137   76. **New York**—Thomas is not clear on the origin of the mammoth bones in that state. Is he suggesting that they were rafted there from some such gathering ground as Big Bone Lick?

p. 140   77. **hard slate rock**—Hard shales of the Allegheny series (Patton, 1956).

p. 141   78. **C. F. RAFINESQUE**—See Rafinesque, 1817.

p. 142   79. **Sand rock**—Sandstone strata in the uppermost Allegheny Series (Patton, 1956).

p. 149   80. **Jefferson's Notes**—Possibly the Third American Edition (1801) of Thomas Jefferson: *Notes on the State of Virginia* . . .

p. 151   81. **blackness and depth of the soil**—Thomas had been travelling generally over the region of forest soil ("gray-brown podols") but now he had come to the margin of the dark prairie soils developed under grass vegetation.

p. 155   82. **Wood**—It is well known that the earliest settlers shunned the open prairie and settled in or at the margins of wooded areas, generally along the streams.

p. 170   83. **prospect of La Motte Prairie**—This was from Merom (see p. 219 for further description) across the Wabash River in Illinois, and northeast of the present Robinson, Illinois.

p. 175   84. **Prairie Creek**—Thomas was following the valley of the Wabash River, which indeed in times of wet weather would not be passable. The modern route from Vincennes to Terre Haute, U.S. Route 150, is a more or less straight northerly route on the flat upland, which was quite unsettled in 1816.

p. 178   85. **irregular hollows**—just north of Terre Haute Thomas entered the region of Wisconsinan glaciation with much fresher topography and with kettleholes in the morainic areas (Wayne, 1958).

p. 182   86. **durable fountains**—Spring Creek is aptly named and Thomas recognized that its high base flow was maintained by ground water discharge in dry weather.

p. 187   87. **END**—Thomas's diary ends when he reached the north limit of the "New Purchase," which he was examining for possibilities of settlement, some 12 miles north of Terre Haute, north of the Parke-Vigo county line.

p. 198   88. **Cook's last Voyage**—Which edition Thomas is likely to have seen is uncertain, but it may have been the New York, 1795 edition, *Cook's Third and last Voyage to the Pacific Ocean* . . . (*abridged from the quarto edition*).

p. 203   89. **a good lather with soap**—Thomas's report is probably the first on the composition and change in chemical composition of Ohio River water. He understood the reason for the variations.

p. 215   90. **WESTERN GAZETTEER**—Thomas's paper on health conditions in Indiana was published in S. R. Brown's *The Western Gazetteer*, 1817, pp. 351-355.

p. 218   91. **Edin. Encycl.**—*The Edinburgh Encyclopedia . . . conducted by David Brewster.* First American Edition, Philadelphia, 1812-1813: vol. 1, p. 494.

p. 226   92. **Coal**—Terre Haute is now the center of a large mining industry; confirming Thomas's prediction.

p. 226   93. **copper**—The mass of copper was a glacial erratic and Thomas's "conjecture" of its origin from the Lake Superior region was a prescient one.

p. 232   94. **cornstalk**—Fossil *.Calamites* of Pennsylvanian age, preserved by internal filling, just as Thomas assumed.

p. 232   95. **table land**—Excellent description of the Norman Upland, the eastern margin of which is the Knobstone Escarpment.

p. 233   96. **Stalagmites, or dumpling stone**—Siliceous geodes. See p. 122, Note 68.

p. 234   97. **Volney's imaginary Lake**—Thomas's strictures here on the inadequacy of this hypothesis (see p. 121) are evidence of his grasp of topography.

p. 236   98. **The subsoil**—Thomas, the practical hydrologist, recognized the great variation in infiltration of rainfall in different materials and the subsequent later release of ground water to provide "durable" stream flow.

p. 237   99. **VARIATION OF THE MAGNETIC NEEDLE**—Thomas's observations, especially of the movement of the "line of variation," are very early (the earliest?) ones for the western country.

p. 239   100. **Northern Expedition**—A reference to this article on icebergs in *American Magazine and Critical Review,* vol. 4, p. 233, 1819.

p. 240   101. **Fort Harrison [Terre Haute] to Ft. Wayne**—This implies that Thomas returned by way of Fort Wayne, which he reached by traveling up the Wabash valley. He definitely states that in Ohio he passed through Dayton, Xenia, and Madison County, probably London, on his return. If he travelled to Fort Wayne, his return was by a circuitous route.

p. 246   102. **no vestige of the human race**—John Stearns, M.D., Annual Address to the Medical Society of the State of New York, *American Monthly Magazine and Critical Review,* vol. 4, p. 463, 1819.

p. 247   103. **Ridges**—This is the first detailed description of the famous drumlin belt on the lake plain south of Lake Ontario between Syracuse and Rochester. Thomas's speculations on these symmetrical, aligned hills associated with continental glaciation, whose origin is still to be satisfactorily explained, are another evidence of his keen observation. He dismisses water as a cause of their shape and while floating ice may have rafted blocks of rock it could not have placed them within the hills, and ascribes them to *a* deluge, for which he adduces other local evidence, a deluge that *moved up an inclined plane.* He rightly denies that *convulsions of our elements* were responsible, and calls (p. 249) on external tidal forces to move the dense mixture of water, sand, and large pieces of rock—a sort of tidally-induced density current from the north, and even devises an experiment (p. 255) to illustrate this.

p. 249   104. **Great Rock of Montezuma**—This appears to refer to a large erratic in the vicinity of the village of Montezuma northeast of the foot of Cayuga Lake, but no such rock is now to be seen there.

p. 249   105. **Dr. Drake**—The writings of Dr. Daniel Drake were the first to ascribe transport of erratics "in cakes of ice" (Drake, 1815, p. 75).

"Dr. Meade," referred to by Thomas on p. 250, described erratics in New York (Meade, 1817). Thomas's reference on p. 252 to Cuvier is a quotation from the American edition of Cuvier (1818, p. 43).

p. 250   106. **Dr. MEADE**—The correct reference is: William Meade, *An experimental enquiry into the chemical properties and medicinal qualities of the principal mineral waters of Ballston and Saratoga . . .*: Philadelphia, 1817. Thomas corrected "Chimerical" to "Chemical" in the Errata sheet at the end of the volume.

p. 251   107. **CHARLES THOMPSON**—This is Charles Thomson (1729-1824), who was Secretary to the Continental Congress. The quotation is from Appendix I, Jefferson's *Notes on Virginia,* 3d. Amer. Ed., 1801, p. 297, 298.

p. 253   108. **M'KENZIE**—MacKenzie, Alexander: *Voyages from Montreal to the Frozen Pacific Oceans . . .*: Philadelphia, 1802, pp. 29, 46.

p. 258   109. **sandstone of this country**—The Lower Devonian Oriskany Sandstone; its outcrop on "Lot 69," about four and a half miles east of Cayuga, Cayuga Co., N.Y., is still one of the best exposures of this well-known formation.

p. 259   110. **a small bird**—Thomas's quite excusable paleontological naiveté occasionally startles one. These fossil "birds" were certainly not the remains of birds but probably outspread pairs of valves of bivalves such as *Pseudaviculopecten, Cornellites,* or *Panenka,* common in the Hamilton shales.

p. 260   111. **Dr. WITHERING**—William A. Withering: *A systematic account of British plants . . .*: 4th ed., 4 vols., London, 1801. Vol. 3, p. 747 (footnote): ". . . impressions of the leaves of *Osmunda* *regalis* are frequent in the nodules of ironstone found in Coalbrook Dale iron works . . . All the other impressions of Filices; which I have seen in iron-stone, seem to be those of American plants."

p. 260   112. **LA PLUCHE**—Antoine Noël, Abbé de la Pluche: *Spectacle de la Nature: or, Nature Displayed . . . Translated from the French . . . by Mr. Humphreys*: 6 vols., London, 1757. De Jussieu found in France a "figured stone" representing the foliage of the "arbre triste" (*Nictanthes arbor-tristis*), a tree not found in Europe, but only in the "Indies."

p. 262   113. **Ancient beach of Lake Ontario**—Others had earlier recognized this ridge as a beach formed at a higher level of Lake Erie. John Bartram and Lewis Evans in 1743 noted that Lake Ontario "is considerably diminished . . .," now fallen to its present lower level, possibly by "the removal of some great obstruction, which . . . might pen the waters up to a greater height than now." (Bartram, John, 1751, p. 53). Thomas had crossed the end moraines (Shepps and others, 1959, map) south of the beach ridges at Erie, Pennsylvania, and correctly realized that moraine ridges were not beaches. He did not distinguish between the beaches of the "Ridge Road," which he describes so accurately and the end moraine ridges. His observation that the [real] beach ridges do not "approach the outlets of these lakes" (p. 263) was accurate, but he did not realize that the higher lakes drained to other outlets than the present outlet of the lakes through the St. Lawrence.

p. 264   114. **gypsum operates as a manure**—Gypsum was sometimes called "land plaster." It is still controversial how beneficial it is and how it operates in those cases of apparent value. Perhaps it may have some value in adding trace elements, as Thomas implies.

p. 272   115. **NOTE**—This note actually refers to page 61.

p. 273   116. **. . . remarkable instance of sliding**—the Great Gardeau Slide in the gorge of the Genesee River, shown on E. N. Horsford's isometric map of the Genesee River, published by James Hall (1838).

p. 294   117. **BARTRAM**—William Bartram; 1791.

p. 294   118. **MEIGS**—Return Jonathan Meigs (1734-1823), Indian Agent for the Cherokees, 1801-1823.

p. 306   119. **Lime**—Thomas's knowledge of the chemistry of hardening of lime mortar is noteworthy, as is his recognition of sorting of sand from clay by rivers.

p. 307   120. **Topographical description**—Jervis Cutler (1812).

Bibliography

Works cited or referred to by Thomas are indicated by *

*ASHE, THOMAS, 1808, *Travels in America, performed in 1806, for the purpose of exploring the rivers Alleghany, Monongahela, Ohio and Mississippi*: London, R. Phillips, 3 vols.; American edition also 1808, Newburyport, W. Sawyer & Co., 366 pp. 1 vol.

*ATWATER, CALEB, 1818, Observations on the remains of civilization and population, extant on the vast plains situated south of the North-American Lakes; Aboriginal antiquities of the west . . . addressed to . . . James Monroe, President: *American Monthly Magazine and Critical Review*, vol. 2, pp. 332-336.

BAKEWELL, ROBERT, 1813, *Introduction to Geology*: London, J. Harding, 362 pp.

BARTRAM, JOHN, 1751, *Observations on the inhabitants, climate, soil, rivers, . . .*: London, J. Whiston and B. White, 94 pp.

*BARTRAM, WILLIAM, 1791, *Travels through North and South Carolina, Georgia, East & West Florida, the Cherokee Country. . . .*: Philadelphia, James & Johnson, 552 pp., 8 pl., map.

*BELKNAP, JEREMY, 1784, 1791, 1792, *The History of New Hampshire*: 3 vols., vol. 1, Philadelphia, 1784; vol. 2, Boston, 1791; vol. 3, Boston 1792; many later editions.

BERGER, A. M., REXROAD, C. B., SCHNEIDER, A. F. and SHAVER, R. H., 1966, Excursions in Indiana geology: Indiana Geol. Survey Guidebook 12, 71 pp.

*BIRKBECK, MORRIS, 1818, *Letters from Illinois*: Philadelphia, Carey & Son, 154 pp., 2 maps (also other American and English editions of the same year).

*BROWN, S. R., 1817, *The Western gazetteer; or Emigrant's directory . . .*: Auburn, H. C. Southwick, 360 pp.

*CARVER, JONATHAN, 1778, *Travels through the interior parts of North America in the years 1766, 1767, and 1768*: London, Printed for the Author, 542 pp. (many later editions, first American was 1784).

*CHAPTAL DE CHANTELOUP, J. A. C., 1796, *Elements of chemistry, translated from the French*: Philadelphia, 1796, 673 pp., (also later editions).

*————, *Chemistry applied to arts and manufactures*: London, 1807, 4 vols.

*CLARKE, E. D., 1810-1823, *Travels in various countries of Europe, Asia and Africa*: London, T. Cadell and W. Davies, 6 vols. (also later editions).

*COOK, JAMES, 1795, *Captain Cook's Third and last Voyage to the Pacific Ocean in the years 1776, '77, '78, '79, and '80 faithfully abridged from the quarto edition*: New York, Mott and Hurtin, 144 pp.

*CRAMER, ZADOCK, 1806, *The navigator: or the trader's useful guide. . . .*: Pittsburgh, Zadock Cramer, 156 pp. (many later editions).

CUTLER, JERVIS, 1812, *A topographical description of the State of Ohio, Indian Territory, and Louisiana, to which is added, an interesting journal of Mr. Chas. Le Raye . . .*: Boston. Charles Williams, 219 pp. 5 pl.

*CUVIER, GEORGES, 1818, *Essay on the theory of the earth. With mineralogical notes and an account of Cuvier's geological discoveries, by Professor Jameson, To which are now added, observations on the geology of North America . . . by Samuel L. Mitchill*: New York, Kirk & Mercein, 431 pp., 4 pl.

*DAVY, HUMPHRY, 1815, *Elements of agricultural chemistry . . .*: Philadelphia, John Conrad & Co., 332 pp. (first London edition was 1813).

*DRAKE, DANIEL, 1815, *Natural and statistical View, or picture of Cincinnati and the Miami Country*: Cincinnati, Looker and Wallace, 251 pp., 2 maps. [Not actually issued until 16 Feb., 1816, *teste* Stuckey, R. L., *Castanea,* vol. 34, pp. 185-187, 1969].

The Edinburgh Encyclopedia . . . conducted by David Brewster: First American edition, Philadelphia, 1812-1831.

FENNEMAN, N. M., 1938, *Physiography of the eastern United States*: New York McGraw-Hill Book Co., Inc. 534 pp.

HALL, JAMES, 1838, Second Annual Report of the Fourth Geological District of New York: [*New York*] *Assembly Document No. 200,* pp. 287-381.

————, 1843, *Geology of New York, Part IV, comprising the survey of the Fourth Geological District*: Albany, 683 pp.

HARPSTER, J. W. (ed.), 1938, *Pen pictures of early western Pennsylvania*: Pittsburgh, University of Pittsburgh Press, 337 pp.

HEDRICK, U. P., 1933, *A history of agriculture in the State of New York*: N. Y. State Agric. Soc., Albany, 462 pp.

HOWLAND, EMILY, 1882, Early history of Friends in Cayuga County, New York, 1795-1828: *Cayuga County (N. Y.) Historical Society, Collections,* No. 2, pp. 49-90.

*JEFFERSON, THOMAS, 1801, *Thomas Jefferson: Notes on the State of Virginia, with an Appendix*: Newark, 392 pp.

*KILBOURN, JOHN, 1816, *The Ohio gazetteer; or topographical dictionary [of the] State of Ohio*: Columbus, P. H. Olmstead & Co., 166 pp. (many later editions).

LAMBORN, R. E., 1930, Geology of Jefferson County, *Geological Survey of Ohio Bull. 35*, 304 pp. and map.

LINDLEY, HARLOW (ed.), 1916, *Indiana as seen by early travelers*: Indianapolis, Indiana Historical Commission, 596 pp.

*LE RAYE, CHARLES, 1812, *In*: Jervis Cutler; *A topographical description of the State of Ohio, Indian Territory, and Louisiana, to which is added, an interesting journal of Mr. Chas. Le Raye* . . .: Boston, Charles Williams, 219 pp. 5 pl.

LOGAN, W. H., 1922, Économic geology of Indiana: *Handbook of Indiana Geology*, Indiana Division of Geology, pp. 571-1058.

*LONG, S. H., 1818, A Description of the Hot Springs, near the river Washita . . .: *American Monthly Magazine and Critical Review*, vol. 3, pp. 85-87.

McFARLAND, R. W., 1903, The Chillicothes: *Ohio Archeological and Historical Publications*, vol. 11, pp. 230-231.

*MACKENZIE, ALEXANDER, 1802, *Voyages from Montreal . . . to the Frozen and Pacific Oceans* . . .: New York, G. F. Hopkins, 296 pp., map. (The first edition was London, 1801).

MALLOT, C. A., 1944, Significant features of the Indiana karst: *Indiana Acad. Sci., Proc.*, vol. 54, pp. 8-24

*MEADE, WILLIAM, 1817, *An experimental enquiry into the chemical properties and medicinal qualities of the principal mineral waters of Ballston and Saratoga*: Philadelphia, Harrison Hall, 15 + 195 pp.

*MELISH, JOHN, 1811, *Travels through the United States of America, in the years 1806 and 1807, and 1809, 1810, and 1811*: Philadelphia, J. Melish 2 vols., (also later editions).

*MITCHILL, S. L., 1819, To Alexander, Autocrat of the Russians; &c: *American Monthly Magazine and Critical Review*, vol. 4, pp. 221-222.

*————, 1819. Northern expedition: *American Monthly Magazine and Critical Review* vol. 4, pp. 232-235, on icebergs.

*MORSE, JEDIDIAH, 1797, *The American Gazetteer* . . .: Boston, S. Hall and Thomas and Andrews. (many later editions).

PATTON, J. B., 1956, *Geologic map of Indiana*: Indiana Geological Survey.

*PLUCHE, ANTOINE NOEL, ABBE DE LA PLUCHE, 1740-1748, *Spectacle de la Nature: or Nature Displayed . . . Translated from the French . . . by Mr. Humphreys*: London, R. Francklin, 7 vols., (also other editions).

*ROBERTSON, WILLIAM, 1777, *The History of America*: London, W. Strahan, 2 vols.; first American edition Philadelphia, 1812, 2 vols.; many later editions.

*RAFINESQUE, C. F., 1817, Description of seven new species of North American quadrupeds: *American Monthly Magazine and Critical Review*, vol. 2, pp. 44-46.

SHEPPS, V. C., WHITE, G. W., DROSTE, J. B., and SITLER, R. F., 1959, Glacial Geology of Northwestern Pennsylvania: *Pennsylvania Geological Survey Bulletin G-32*, 59 pp. and map.

*STEARNS, JOHN, M.D., 1819, Annual Address to the Medical Society of the State of New York: *American Monthly Magazine and Critical Review*, vol. 4, p. 463.

STOUT, WILBER, 1918, Geology of Muskingum County: *Geological Survey of Ohio Bull. 21*, 351 pp. and map.

STOUT, WILBER, and LAMB, G. F., 1938, Physiographic features of southeastern Ohio: *Ohio Jour. Science*, vol. 38, pp. 49-83.

*SUTCLIFF, ROBERT, 1812, *Travels in some parts of North America in 1804, 1805, and 1806*: Philadelphia, B & T. Kite, 287 pp. (also York, 1811; 1815).

THOMAS, DAVID, 1830, Geological facts: *Amer. Jour. Sci.*, vol. 18, pp. 375-376.

————, 1831, *Ulmus racemosa*, n. sp.: *Amer. Jour. Sci.*, vol. 19, p. 170.

THOMAS, J. J., 1888, Memoir of David Thomas: *Cayuga County (N. Y.) Historical Society, Collections*, No. 6, pp. 36-53.

*VOLNEY, C.-F., (CHASSEBOEUF, C-F, COMTE DE VOLNEY) 1803, *Tableau de climat et du sol des Etats-Unis*: Paris, Courcier, Dentu, 2 vols., 300, 532 pp., 2 maps, 2 plates. (English translations, Philadelphia, 1804, reprinted 1968; London, 1804; another French edition, 1822).

VON ENGELN, O. D., 1936, Early observation and attempted explanation of the glacial drift: *Science*, vol. 84, p. 134.

WAYNE, W. J., 1958, *Map of glacial geology of Indiana*: Indiana Geological Survey.

WELLS, J. W., 1958, *The Cayuga Bridge*: Ovid, N. Y., 14 pp. (Also Ithaca, 1961, 18 pp.), 2 figs.

————, 1963, Early Investigations of the Devonian System in New York, 1656-1836: *Geol. Soc. Amer. Special Paper 74*, 74 pp., 11 pl.

WHEELER, CYRENUS, 1882, The inventors and inventions of Cayuga County, New York: *Cayuga County (N. Y.) Historical Society, Collections*, No. 2, pp. 93-179.

*WILLIAMS, SAMUEL, 1794, *The Natural and Civil history of Vermont*: Walpole, N. H., Isaiah Thomas and David Carlisle, Jun., 416 pp., map.

*WITHERING, W. A., 1801, *A systematic arrangement of British plants . . .*: 4th ed., London, T. Cadell, Jun., 4 vols.